Surviving Napoleon
The Clockmaker's Tale

J J Baxter

Surviving Napoleon
- The Clockmaker's Tale -
J J Baxter

First published in Great Britain
in 2017 by Charonia Media

A catalogue record of this report is available from the British Library

ISBN 978 0 9560655 5 1

With special thanks to my family without whose encouragement and help this book would not have been published and particularly to my wife Elizabeth for her unwavering support.

Bioletti in Italy
- 1778 to 1798 -

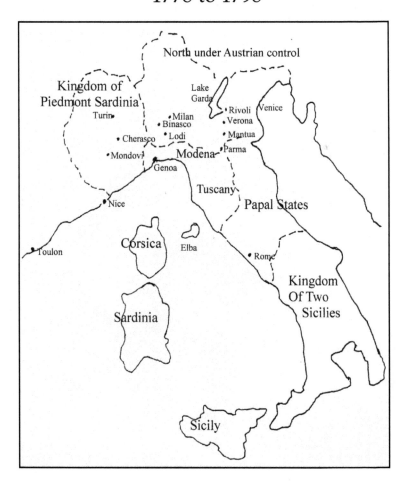

Chapter 1
Heretic

I am a survivor. Not rich or famous or a leader of men, but a survivor whose life has followed a path which I could never have thought possible. It is also a life that has been lived in the shadow of one man, Napoleon, and I have survived him too, travelling across continents and cultures to take part in his campaigns. This then is my story as I remember it based on the notes I have made.

I was born in 1778 in the proud and beautiful city of Turin. It is set in Northern Italy and crowned by its cathedral spire with the snow clad Alps shimmering in the distance. Italy for us then was an idea, not a country, the peninsula being a patchwork of more or less independent states: the Venetian Republic, Milan, Tuscany, Rome, the Papal States and Naples.

Turin was the capital of what was then called the Kingdom of Piedmont Sardinia, but it had for centuries been ruled by the grand and grasping Dukes of Savoy. I grew up often seeing Victor Amadeus III, our Duke and King, riding to Mass at the Basilica of Superga or attending a parade in his carriage surrounded by liveried footmen and grandly uniformed soldiers.

Turin had palaces, gardens and squares to rival those of Rome and Florence and the Dukes founded schools and a university. As a boy I felt proud to live in such a handsome, grand city. I also loved to go out into the countryside to the village of Pinerolo where my uncle and several of our family lived on their small-holdings, farming and tending vineyards. There in summer I would stay for weeks helping pick the harvest and tramp the grapes used to make some of the country's finest wine. I also took great pleasure in learning how to hunt wildfowl and deer for the table becoming quite a proficient shot.

An even earlier memory of Turin was of watching with my mother from an upstairs window while processions passed down our street. They wore strange garb and some passed chanting in Latin, others came in silence, masked and intimidating with high, pointed hoods, carrying candles. Many were beating their breasts, sobbing and tearstained. Yes, Turin has another claim to fame, the Shroud, the cloth claimed to be that in which Jesus was wrapped before his body was placed in his tomb. When put on display this attracted thousands of pilgrims.

My mother quietly told me as they came shuffling past, "They are praying that Jesus will forgive their sins. Yes. They hope Alberto that coming here on pilgrimage will save them from the fires of Hell." At that she smiled with pursed lips. She also pointed out that their custom greatly benefitted the cathedral and the city's businesses - and that of my father.

Our family however took no active part in all this piety beyond my father doing well selling his watches and clocks to rich pilgrims for he was a clockmaker. I was an inquisitive child and I wondered, "Mama why do we never dress up or take part in processions like our neighbours the draper family?"

Usually gentle, her reply was sharp. "I do not like walking about in the streets with strangers," she said, "And that is all I want to say about it." I was very surprised.

I had another question so I put this one to my father. "Papa," I said, "Why on some nights am I sent to bed early and then I hear you greeting a whole lot of visitors? Sometimes it sounds as if you are all saying prayers. It doesn't sound like a clockmakers meeting."

"I'm sorry Alberto." he replied, "But I'm afraid you are not old enough for me to explain why we don't take part in religious processions and what happens here at night. For your own safety I must now tell you one thing. Our family are Valois. The Church calls us heretics so we must keep what we are secret. When you get older I'll explain everything to you, but for now you must never talk about religion to anyone outside our family or terrible things could happen to us."

"Like what Papa?" I asked.

"Like us losing our home, my business or even your mother and I being taken away."

That really shocked me. "But what if my friends start asking me questions?" I asked.

"Just tell them you find talking about religion boring. Start talking about something you're interested in. I really mean it. It's very important you learn to do this."

He spoke so seriously it really frightened me. It also meant that from that day on I felt I was the bearer of a terrible secret. From the way people talked I knew "heretics" were evil people and in league with the Devil. I could not believe that of my parents, but what if the Church thought they were?

I had to wait until I was twelve when my father told me just what being Valois meant. He said, "I'm sure you've noticed we don't often go to Mass except on the "days of Obligation" when everyone's attendance is checked and then your mother and I do not take what they call "communion?" I nodded, feeling scared.

"Please Papa, is it true?" I blurted out, "I've heard it said that all heretics burn forever in Hell."

"Listen carefully Alberto." he said, "That's just nonsense. We are not heretics. We Vaudois stick to true Christianity while the Church has become corrupt and full of superstitions like this veneration for that Shroud. I'm sure it's just a forgery. I tell you God is not mocked."

He then listed many examples of what he saw as errors and superstition. I had never heard my father or anyone else talk like that and I found it frightening. More calmly he went on to teach me that real Christian faith should be based on the clear words of the Bible. He then brought out and showed me, wrapped in velvet and kept in a special case, the precious French translation of the Gospels he looked after for his Valois group.

My father then invited me to attend the meetings that took place in our home at night. There I heard him give long readings and lead discussions on the Gospels.

One night I found he had left a book for me on my bedside table. It was an account of our Valois history and it contained engravings showing Peter Waldo our founder and fearsome pictures of men and women being burnt at the stake. It absolutely terrified me and I started to wake up in the evenings screaming with nightmares and I remember both Mama and Papa sitting by my bed to calm me when this happened.

I was however proud to be invited to join these meetings and to see my father lead them and soon I was filled with fear and contempt for the oppressive rule of the Dukes and the superstitions of the Catholic Church.

This experience however did not in the end, make me want to join them, though I loved and respected my father dearly. For me the "plain words of scripture" seemed not so plain and raised more questions in my mind than answers. I also soon found raising my questions in their meetings was not appreciated.

Also, as a boy I found not all Catholics are bad. Some of our neighbours, like the draper family next door, knew or suspected we were not "good Catholics" and noticed how seldom we attended Mass and that we never seemed to receive communion when we did. They said nothing and were perfectly friendly for many of them also lived in some fear of the parish priest Father Bartholomew. His unctuous smile, prying questions and sudden unannounced visits terrified all of us, as did the famously pious Duke, his dangerous and brutal soldiers and his corrupt officials for we were living in unsettling times.

*****

My father Ernesto was well known and respected in the city for he, like his father before him, was a Master Clockmaker, recognised as the most skilled of all master craftsmen. His shop was near the centre of the city (for which he had to pay a high rent to the Duke's agent) and we lived above in a rather beautiful two story home with quite a large garden at the back complete with a trellis of vines.

His clocks were highly sought after for their beauty, wonderful complexity and accuracy. Members of the Duke's Court would appear at our door with their servants to inspect his work and to order special clocks for their grand houses, for only such people could afford them.

At that time clock makers were much more than the repairers and sellers of clocks many have become. In his studio at the back of his shop my father supervised three apprentices and it was hard, demanding work. They started from scratch with sheets of metal; brass, steel and copper. From these they crafted all the intricate parts; cogs, wheels, screws and springs, together with the tools they needed to fashion these things.

To work up from Apprentice to Master Clockmaker took years

and required not only practical, but computational skills. From an early age I found this work fascinating and started quite young to join the apprentices and help my father and watch what they were doing. He was wonderfully patient, both in the way he went about his work, methodical and thorough, and as a teacher in the way he explained what he was doing and why. It was taken for granted by both of us that at the right time I would be apprenticed to another workshop, then come to work for him, and finally become a Master Clockmaker myself and succeed him in running the business.

*****

I was an only child, being the second of four but the only one to survive infancy, and this had a sad effect on my mother Gina. I thought she was beautiful, but the loss of so many children weighed heavily on her. She had black periods of depression when she spoke little, placed our food on the table and retired to her room red-eyed. My father was always calm, quiet and solicitous when this happened, and I remember eating many meals with him in awkward silence.

There were times when she came out of these moods and was warm and vivacious, cooking me my favourite *tagliatelle* dishes, teasing my father for being too serious and singing excerpts from the operas around the house in her clear, pure soprano. In fact we all sang together, something I loved.

After the death of her last child she was much weaker and when the winter fever swept through the city - as it usually did - it was too much for her. It was just months after my father had told me about what being Vaudois meant. My father and I were devastated.

*****

While most ordinary people were illiterate both my parents loved reading. My father was obviously a clever man and he had built up a fascinating collection of his own books, and at first the two of them taught me to read at home. It was however taken for granted that I needed proper schooling. A potential master clockmaker needs to be educated and able to do careful calculations.

All formal education was of course under the strict control of the Catholic Church, still my father decided to enter me for a scholarship at the *Collegio della Province* founded and funded by the Duke "for 100 boys of low social extraction." His aim was to provide the city with more clerks, accountants, teachers and skilled craftsmen and so it was only a few months after my mother's death that I was sent off to attend a proper school.

Chapter 2
Collegio

The *Collegio* was housed in the impressive buildings of a former monastery and most of our lessons took place in what had been the Refectory where we sat on benches around our teachers. Our studies, which it was expected would lead to a place in the university, were of Latin, French, Italian, Law and Mathematics and of course Religion. Here some dissembling for a boy from a secret Vaudois family was necessary and I became quite skilled at learning how to parrot what the priests considered to be the right answer.

I enjoyed school, particularly Mathematics, learnt fast and was good at evading the cane. The other boys were divided between those whose families paid fees and the one hundred scholarship boys like me. We scholars were constantly reminded by the headmaster of our low social status. "Never forget" he told us, "That without the charity of the Duke you boys would be at home working, poor and illiterate and bound to do no better than your fathers. Thanks to our King you are getting an education that will change everything for you. Never forget this and be ready to repay him with loyalty and gratitude." We knew it was best to nod enthusiastically when such sentiments were expressed.

Besides the relatively poor scholarship boys like me, the boys at the school came from a wide range of backgrounds. A particular friend of mine, Peter Falconi, was the bright son of a banker. We both loved Mathematics, shared the same jokes and had a passion for chess.

As well as the sons of other Turin merchants and master craftsmen there were the sons of lawyers and bankers, humble shopkeepers, barbers and market traders. Two in our class

11

however, were the sons of aristocrats. One was a decent boy who mixed in well, but the other, Enrico Del Gardo, never let us forget his "superiority" and the importance of his venerable family.

Most of our teachers were priests, but our French teacher, Monsieur Clavell, was a young layman who had recently graduated from the Sorbonne. He was an excellent teacher and we responded with enthusiasm which left time at the end of lessons for informal discussion about what was happening in France. He brought in French newspapers and pamphlets for us to read. Not always a clever move.

This was a time of unprecedented upheaval in France whose border was very close and we all spoke French as much as Italian. My father kept saying that he thought France was bankrupt - something I did not understand, then on August 26th 1789 we heard a mob had laid siege to the Bastille in Paris. Soon after the shocking news came that the French king Louis XVI and his much caricatured queen Marie Antoinette, had been arrested and put in prison. Then came stories of a new means of execution, the guillotine. As ghoulish schoolboys it fascinated us to think of a great blade flashing down as we heard that a flood of aristocrats were being brought in tumbrels through the streets of Paris to be decapitated in a square now called the *Place de la Revolution*.

*****

Meanwhile life at home was not easy. Two years after my mother died my father remarried. His new wife, Damiana, was a Vaudois widow whose husband some said had died of drink. She was earnestly and fiercely religious. She introduced daily family Bible reading, prayers, and long graces before meals. She was also against us mixing socially with anyone outside the Vaudois circle such as my school friend Peter. I could see she was not unattractive and my father fell more and more under her influence. She also brought with her a son, a rather weak and submissive boy with a declared fascination for clocks. We loathed each other.

Every day the news got more extreme. We heard people appeared to be dying in their thousands as talk of Revolution swept across France. One morning Clavell brought in a paper to school which he said everyone in France was reading. It was written by a leading French politician, Maximilian Robespierre and it was headed *Liberty, Equality and Fraternity*. We wanted to know what it was all about and Clavell was happy to explain. After quite a rowdy class discussion I vividly remember how he summed things up.

"Well boys, by Liberty Robespierre is saying it consists of being able to do anything that does not harm others. That means we should all be free to do think and say what we wish - provided only that we respect equally the rights of others to do the same."

"And does that include freedom for the press to publish without censorship and freedom to follow any religion, or no religion at all?" one boy added.

"Even freedom for the Valois?" said Peter mischievously.

"Exactly." Clavell added enthusiastically. "And Equality goes with Liberty. The law must be the same for everyone. Also all citizens of a country should be equally eligible to take all high offices. Posts should be filled on the basis of ability, virtue and talent, not because of social status, family or inheritance. So this means the law should be recognised as fair for all, not something imposed by a despot."

"Monsieur, what do you mean by a despot?" asked Del Gardo. There was complete silence as everyone looked at each other and Clavell looked disconcerted.

"I suppose," he said, "A despot is a ruler who does not see himself as bound by the law and rules by decree. Would you agree?"

Del Gardo smiled and said, "And tell me Monsieur, do you think everyone should be eligible to hold high office regardless of rank and social position?"

Clavell stopped and looked thoughtful. "Del Gardo, as your teacher it is not my role to express personal opinions regarding politics. In this lesson I am simply explaining what this slogan is taken to mean, without agreeing or disagreeing with it."

"I see," said Del Gardo. "You are not denying that you think everyone should be eligible for high office."

Clavell said nothing, but went on to say how difficult it was to get agreement over what was meant by Fraternity. He pointed out that *Liberty, Equality and Fraternity unto Death* was being used as a battle cry and painted on banners by revolutionary groups. As he carried on in this vein I felt a deep sense of unease as I glanced at Del Gardo.   *****

13

During this time Peter and I read everything we could get our hands on about the Revolution, collecting newspapers and pamphlets and, discussing them for hours and Monsieur Clavell became our hero. The revolutionaries we learnt were out to overthrow absolutist monarchies and rule by hereditary privilege. This was what France and most of Europe had been suffering from and it was still the case for us in Piedmont. They were also totally against the Catholic Church and its hold over education, and its attempts to stifle science and critical thinking.

Such ideas reminded me of the Valois protests against church and pope and the way my father criticised the rich and powerful who he said got their wealth from oppressing the poor. I also was inspired to read that the revolutionaries were in favour of human rights, democracy, free speech, the rule of law and the abolition of slavery.

It was also at this time – 1791 – that we heard the slaves in France's most wealthy colony in the West Indies, Saint Domingue, the French half of the island of Hispaniola, had staged an insurrection in the name of the Revolution. The National Assembly in Paris had called for the abolition of slavery and they demanded that this should apply to the half a million slaves on the island. Were they leading the way to a new and fairer world? I never imagined I would ever see Saint Domingue.

Inspired by such news and filled with zeal I went home and on several occasions expounded my new found faith in the Revolution with all the arrogance of youth at the dinner table. My father tried to listen in a tolerant way nodding and smiling for he had always encouraged me to speak freely. Damiana however looked pinched and kept silent. Finally after one of my little tirades she burst out, "All this godless revolutionary nonsense has got nothing to do with our Bible based faith. Next you will be expecting us to join them! Can't you see what you are demanding will simply bring about more persecution for us and anyone seen as a threat to the Pope and our rulers? The end of all this is just going to be war and more war."

My father said nothing. He seemed to agree and I felt betrayed.

*****

When news of Louis 16th's execution reached Turin in January 1793 the bells of the city were tolled in mourning and a special

Requiem Mass was celebrated in the Cathedral. The whole school had to attend. Victor Amadeus and his family were present dressed in black and the Bishop preached a sermon warning us against the godless teachings of the Revolution.

As we left the Cathedral men in the Duke's livery were waiting for Monsieur Clavell. They took him away looking terrified and we never saw him again. He was immediately replaced by a zealous young priest without a word of explanation. While the rest of us were shocked and upset, I noticed Del Gardo had a quiet, smug smile. The time for lively discussions and expressing opinions in the class-room was past. If Damiana was right and the future was war, I knew which side I was going to be on.

Chapter 3
Insurrection

It was some months later, when I was seventeen, that the Turin University students came around to our school to hand out a leaflet as we left for home. "Join us tomorrow at noon," it read. "Support the just demands of the students and apprentices of Turin for Democracy and the Rule of Law."

I went home and said nothing. I knew I would go. Next morning before class we met by the school gate. We all agreed we would join the students at noon.

"We will just get up and walk out of that jackdaw's class at five minutes to noon." said Peter and with little discussion everyone agreed with him. "There's nothing they can do to stop us if we move together and keep silent." he said.

It worked and as we arose from our desks in unison the young priest glared at us and said the head master would soon know all about it. As we left the class together he added, "Remember we know where all of you live." I had never ever done such a thing and that comment made me scared. Could I now expect a knock on the door of our home from the Duke's sinister men?

In the square we joined a crowd of about three hundred. Not huge. The student leader who addressed us we were told had been elected by his peers – how democratic. He jumped up on a packing case and started to speak. In a highly emotional and flamboyant address interrupted by much cheering, he said, "Even as I speak the first units of the French Revolutionary Army are moving into Turin. They will overthrow the House of Savoy and break the Church and now is the time for us to get ready to join them, and do this not as Frenchmen, but as Italians, ready to take what is rightfully ours. We should get to the Duke first and demand he resign. We should follow the example of the Paris crowd and arrest him. Then perhaps we will see the guillotine come to Turin."

Everyone cheered wildly for it was stirring stuff, but it also sounded like madness to me. Did they really think Victor Emmanuel would let such things happen and wait for the arrival of the guillotine? I shared my misgivings with Peter and we fell back towards the end of the procession. We then set off for the ducal palace with everyone chanting over and over the revolutionary "Liberty! Equality! Fraternity unto Death."

On coming around a bend in the road we found ourselves faced by the Duke's troops. They were drawn up across the street in line at the end of which stood an officer with a drawn sword. When our leaders were about fifty yards in front of them he raised his sword and we could hear him order them to take aim.

As his sword flashed down he called, "Fire!" and the muskets crashed. I had never experienced the flash and plume of black smoke of a musket volley before. I had never heard the terrible screaming emitted by some of those around me as blood splashed into my face and Peter went down like a rag doll beside me. He was dead before he hit the ground. A musket ball had smashed into his eye going deep into his skull. I screamed and held him, but it was obvious. He was dead.

Dropping onto one knee the soldiers calmly proceeded to reload their muskets which is quite slow and complicated. Terrified I scrambled to my feet and started to run. I had just ducked down a side-street before I heard the second volley crash out, followed by more screams and moans.

I rushed straight home and pounding on the shop door distressed and weeping, told my father the whole story and that my friend Peter was dead. He remained remarkably calm and took me upstairs. Damiana could not of course restrain herself from laying into me, "Well you cannot say I didn't warn you. As for now we must get you out of here as soon as possible for it will not be long before the Duke's men come for you."

"Get packed for Pinerolo where you can stay with your uncle as quick as you can." my father added. "I'll go straightaway to give Falconi this terrible news about his son."

"Of course you realise," said Damiana, "We will have to say

we had a great row with you last night because of your dreadful revolutionary ideas which we as loyal subjects of the Duke reject completely. Your behaviour has put us all in real danger and we will be lucky if your father and my son are not arrested. To explain why you are not here we shall have to say you sneaked in, told us nothing, stole some money and have run away. I hope they will believe us."

*****

It was the first time I had thought about what the consequences could be, not just for me, but for the whole family. Penitent and nervous I set off for Pinerolo looking as ordinary and inconspicuous as possible and speaking to no-one. I thought I had behaved very badly and had been nothing short of a coward running away and leaving Peter when he fell. On reaching Pinarolo my uncle was none too sympathetic to my story and quickly had me hard at work on the farm. At least I felt relatively safe.

It was the start of a terrible time as Turin descended into a drawn out civil war. Undisciplined French troops, members of what they called the French Revolutionary Army poured into Turin. They came marching down the streets behind their banner of Liberty, Equality and Fraternity unto Death singing the *Marseillaise*. Dressed in a motley collection of old clothes with a tricolour in their hats their look and behaviour was more gangster than soldier. Sporadic fighting took place between them and what was quite a well-equipped Piedmontese army under the leadership of Victor Emmanuel. Neither side, however, was able to overcome the other and the conflict dragged on.

On my uncles farm it was not long before we were paid a visit by a smiling corporal in a grubby French uniform and two scruffy looking men with cockades in their hats. They were armed and had a horse-drawn cart and announced that they were a foraging party for the Revolutionary Army.

"You understand monsieur," the corporal said to my uncle, "That we are fighting for you. We are here to free you from the wicked, unjust rule of the Duke, but to do that an army must eat, so to help us we invite you to let us have some of your surplus food."

As he spoke the two with him had started to prowl around the farmyard. Suddenly we heard the screech of a pig getting its throat cut, and sure enough one of them emerged carrying a dead pig that had been destined for market. They then proceeded to load their cart with everything they could find, wine, meat, fruit, vegetables, eggs and a couple of chickens all the time thanking my uncle for his kindness and generosity as if he were giving them freely. "Such services to the Revolution will not be forgotten and will surely bring you glory!" declared the corporal and they smiled as they climbed on their cart and drove away with a wave. I had never seen my uncle so angry.

"And those are the lot you support," he growled, once they had gone. "And they are supposed to be better than the Duke's tax gatherers? No Alberto, I just can't see it."

A month later we had a similar visit from a different team of foragers who went through the same routine leaving my uncle with very little except his rage which he directed towards me. Feeling distinctly unwelcome I went hunting for as much wildfowl as I could find for them before returning to Turin to visit my father.

*****

I discovered Damiata had left Papa straight after I left for Pinerolo, taking her son with her. He told me she said she feared her son would be associated with me and my republican ways and he might be taken away by the Duke's men. My father said now she was gone he was pleased for he did not miss her and her overdone religion and could not stand her son. Also he agreed with me. He had no love for the Duke.

Business for him, however, had become slow and the Duke had increased his rent and he had to lay off his apprentices. A clock is an expensive investment even now, but then they were much more valuable. At the same time even the rich were not buying and coins were being hoarded. This meant his collection of clocks in the shop built up and was bigger than I had ever seen it.

My father told me that my student riot had resulted in the closing of the *Collegio* and that the Duke's men had come around to ask about me just after Damiata had left. Now he thought things were so disorganised and with the fighting going on no-one would be interested in chasing after me. Perhaps it was now safe and I should come home. I agreed and moved gratefully back into my room.

Civil war is a terrible thing. No one really trusts anyone and for the next eighteen months that was what we had to endure. A sort of stalemate existed with areas of the city and of the villages round about falling under the control of one side or the other. Many shops closed, food and even water was in short supply. Beggars, starving children and pick pockets wandered the streets in numbers never seen before.

I spent my days keeping a low profile in my father's workshop building and repairing the accumulating stock of clocks. I learnt a lot and my father was very pleased with me.

"Keep at it Alberto." He said "You have been working well and when this awful war is over I'm sure these clocks will be worth a fortune ad you will be a fine clockmaker."

Surviving Napoleon

Chapter 4
No Way Back

By night I often slipped out to meet some of my former schoolmates to drink and talk politics. I took care where I went because gangs purporting to support both sides now roamed the streets and the inns became drinking spots for one side or the other, or the scene of drink fuelled fights. I could see why people joined gangs for they gave the only protection anyone could get. The problem, as the civil war dragged on, was many of these gangs became more and more criminal using their politics to justify theft, robbery, violence and on occasion rape. Certainly there were rich pickings available for anyone who was organised.

Politically the fight was between "law and order" Monarchists and "revolutionary" Republicans. Those who supported the traditional ways of the Duke, mainly the rich, well-established and religiously pious, said they feared "chaos and mob rule". The Republicans who followed the French felt they were "oppressed, cheated and unfairly treated" by the aristocracy, grasping landlords, extortionate employers and of course by the Church. My sympathies were with them.

Since the execution of Louis XVI the Duke and the surviving monarchies I read had allied themselves into what was called the First Coalition and were intent on overthrowing republican France and re-establishing the Bourbon monarchy. The Duke was trying to drive the Revolutionary Army out of Turin and out of his kingdom but neither his forces nor the French seemed strong enough to win control.

At the same time the news coming out of France was hardly encouraging. In fact it was frightening. Starting in 1793 stories were printed in the papers and rumours spread that the Revolution

23

had gone mad. It seemed that under the leadership of a small group called the Committee for Public Safety led by that same Maximillian Robespierre who had written so eloquently about democracy, something called "The Terror" had been unleashed. It went on for over a year and during this time the tumbrels to the guillotine were again rumbling through Paris and the leading cities of France. The news we got was that tens of thousands were being executed as "enemies of the Revolution." It sounded so bad my father and I wondered if we had chosen the right side.

*****

One evening when I was drinking in an inn with some friends the door opened and in came a smartly uniformed French sergeant accompanied by two privates. They sat down quietly and ordered drinks, but within the hour (no doubt spent listening carefully to what we were saying) they invited us all to have a drink on them.

"Alright," said the sergeant, "My name is Sergeant Diderot. Why are we here? We are a recruiting party for the French Army. We gather from your conversation that there is no love here for the Duke and his court and some sympathy with the cause of Revolution." People nodded warily. "Well, this is your chance to become a part of it."

Obviously quite an educated man he spoke well and the wine flowed. He did not promise an easy life, but a chance to have a part in changing history, of building a new Europe led by a new France which would bring liberty and freedom to all and give people opportunities they had never had under the old system of king, class and church. He ended by saying he would be back the next night to sign up those who were interested or we could present ourselves at their camp, giving his name.

"This Revolutionary Army," he said, "Is not just for Frenchmen. You Italians are welcome too. In fact it is open to all men who share our ideals and are ready to fight for a better future." Yes, as I walked home that night I felt quite inspired.

On approaching my father's house I sensed something was wrong. No light came from the windows and oddly a large laundry basket stood abandoned by the front door, empty, save for a blanket. I tried the door and found it was unlocked. I rushed inside and tripped over a body lying on the floor. By the dim light coming in from the street I could see it was my father and from the amount of blood it was clear he had been stabbed. I fell to the floor and tried to pick him up but I could see he was dead. Around him I could make out broken glass and smashed cabinets.

I screamed, "Murder! Help!" as I rushed out into the street, but the surrounding houses stayed silent, dark and shuttered. I pounded on the door of an elderly neighbour, someone I had known since childhood.

"Mr Faraldo! It's me, Alberto. Papa has been murdered!"

Finally I could hear bolts being drawn back and locks opened and old Faraldo stood there with a lighted lamp. He beckoned me in and relocked the door. He had been seated in his study upstairs and had seen a coach and a cart arrive about an hour after he had seen me leave. Eight men had got out with a laundry basket and with some tool had forced open the door. Two stayed outside, clearly armed with swords and pistols. Who could take them on? Then they had started carrying out clocks wrapped in blankets from the basket. These they carefully loaded onto the cart and into the coach. Finally they had driven off. No one had done anything to stop them. We agreed there was now no-one to turn to, no authority to report to. In a city in a state of anarchy like ours, law and order is lost.

I asked him to come with me into the house and to bring another lamp for I had been able to see almost nothing. The sight that met us was utter devastation. Everything had been trashed and my poor father lay in a pool of blood. A note had been placed next to him. It read, "The Vaudois heretic with the Republican son." Devastated and with a heavy heart I found a jug of water and washed the blood from his face and laid him out on a table.

Old Feraldo looked on anxiously with his lantern.

"This is a dark day Alberto, but you cannot stay here. In fact we should leave now. If you had not gone out I think you would be lying here with your father. They, whoever they are, may send people back to watch out for you at any minute. I can offer you a bed for the night for they won't know you are with me, but perhaps it would be better if you were gone from here as soon as possible."

I had to agree. We discussed that there was no way of knowing who had carried out this murder. Clearly well-organised and confidently carried out, it was either the work of a criminal gang or of henchmen of the Duke. Either way they had good intelligence so I certainly should not hang about. We went back to his house and sat for a bit in his kitchen.

"Sir, I think you are right. The quicker I get away from here the better." I said. " I think I know where I should go. Perhaps you could give me a bag, a blanket and some food."

"Certainly Alberto," he replied, "I am so sorry. I have known and admired your father since before you were born. I know you are a secret Vaudois family and respected your father as a generous, honest man. He once lent me money when I was going through a tough patch and charged me no interest. And, of course, he was a brilliant maker of clocks. Tomorrow I shall contact some of his Vaudois friends to arrange his funeral, but I do not think you should try to be there. It would be the obvious place to catch you. His friends may tidy up his shop. I don't know. He rented it from the Duke's estate did he not? We could leave that to them. The main point is you have got to get away and get away fast, for you are not safe here. Those clocks are worth a lot of money and whoever has them does not want you turning up to claim them."

I felt stunned and devastated. It was such a sad and horrible end for my father and it had all happened so quickly and without warning. Here I was, almost eighteen, alone in the world and with no money, and no-one to turn to. The wreckage of the house also meant something else. The career as a Turin clockmaker my father and I had imagined could now never come about.

Faraldo helped pack up a few things and again asked if I knew where I should go

"Yes sir, I do." I replied, "But it is best I do not tell you."

"I understand," he said, "I will also give you some cash to tide you over. No, please, accept it in memory of your father and of his past generosity to me."

Chapter 5
Culottes
and Sans-Culottes

As we packed up the bag I thought about my father opening his door to be confronted by men who would kill for clocks, and who also wanted me dead. The thought of coming across them terrified me. It also made the path ahead for me clear. I should try and join the French Revolutionary Army and fight for a cause I could believe in.

Old man Faraldo also found some bread, cheese and a bottle of wine. "For your journey." He said. Thanking him I slipped out quietly into the street. I spent the rest of the night in woods I had known since childhood. There I stayed keeping out of sight all the next day as all that had happened to me sank in. I wept a lot for it was terrible leaving my father's body unattended in our smashed up home, but Faraldo was right, I was lucky to be alive, if lucky was the right word for someone who had lost a father he loved and a future career with him which despite the war had looked so good.

When darkness fell I saw Sergeant Diderot enter the inn with his men. I waited outside – now not trusting any of the group in the inn. Finally they came out and set off to walk back to their camp. They were alone. Perhaps their mission to recruit had not been too successful.

It was only then I approached him. "Sergeant I have been waiting for you because I want to join the Army. Can I come with you and do so immediately?

"You know what you are doing?" he said,

"Yes Sergeant. I have thought about doing this for a long time. And hearing you last night made up my mind."

"So you can tell me why?" He said.

"Certainly. I believe in this Revolution, not just for France but for all of us here, in Europe or even beyond. I believe in freedom. I want to live in a democracy. We must never let the Duke or the Bourbons get back in power."

"So why our Army?" he asked.

"Because the old powers are out to destroy us, destroy the new France and stop the Revolution spreading. To stop them means being ready to fight."

"Oh very noble," he replied, "Don't get me wrong, perhaps I agree with you, but I don't suppose you are running away from something you might have done.? You wouldn't have anything to hide would you, creeping up on us like this late at night?"

"I'm sorry Sergeant, but yes, in a way I have," I replied and with that I told him about what I had found when I got home the night before and how I was certain I was now in danger.

"I think you are right. I've heard stories like yours before." he said, "And you do well to join us. Certainly you can come with us now. We need young men like you who can see what we are fighting for."

*****

The French Revolutionary Army had set up camp in a park on the edge of the city and entering it came as a bit of a shock. It seemed such a mess. There were tents and men standing around smoky braziers drinking. At the entry gate we were waved through by two cockaded soldiers in scruffy baggy trousers. They too had obviously been drinking and the sergeant reprimanded them sharply. Other guards were to be seen surrounding the whole site and by the braziers an array of muskets, pistols and short swords were stacked ready for use.

There was a distinct smell of smoke and sweat and most of those inside the camp looked as if they had not washed for weeks. Only a few, like the sergeant and his men, were in uniform, wearing blue jackets and the traditional white knee breeches - *culottes*. Most were in ragged civilian dress with trousers. So these were the *sans-culottes*, those without breeches, the breeches which the Jacobins said were "un-republican." All wore hats with a tricolour cockade.

Sergeant Diderot ordered his men to get me blankets and a cockade for my hat and sat me down at a table while he filled in my enlistment form.

"I'm afraid we have no uniforms to issue recruits with here and we have been waiting almost three months to get paid. Glad to see you have good strong boots on. You will need them."

He went on to explain that he and his two men had been members of the French National Guard whose uniform they wore. They had now been merged with the Revolutionary Army and mixed up with the *sans-culottes* who were mainly enthusiastic volunteers with no military training. "We and regular soldiers of the old army are mixed in to show how things are done and we wear our old National Guard uniforms." he said. "When it comes to training this lot and any volunteers like you we have a long way to go."

He was interested to know that I had been a scholar at the *Collegio* and so was not illiterate. "I am afraid you will find quite a few are," he said. He was even more interested to hear that I had experience hunting and handling a gun. All these details were entered on his form.

"So you say you are eighteen. You look quite tough and fit to me even if you are not so tall. I will put you down for sharp shooter and skirmisher training."

"And what is skirmisher training Sergeant?"

"You will find out soon enough if the drill sergeant agrees with me and thinks you are suitable. I am sending you down with a group of other recruits to our main training barracks in Nice. The march there should get you fit. They are leaving tomorrow."

"Thank you Sergeant."

"Yes, Private, you have joined at an interesting time. Joining you at Nice will be our new Commanding Officer. He has just been appointed by the new Directorate. Have you heard of them?"

"No Sergeant,"

"Well they have taken over running France since all the members of the Committee for Public Safety and their leader, Citizen Robespierre, have been deprived of their heads. Yes, all of them!"

Surprised, but certainly not sorry to hear this news, I was glad to notice that Sergeant Diderot was clearly pleased. I waited for him to finish.

"The papers say this Directorate declare they are going to turn France into a proper democracy with votes for all and fair laws. Well, we shall see. Yes. And arriving straight after his marriage in Paris after having been appointed by them, comes our new Commander of the Army of Italy, General Napoleon Bonaparte!"

And that was the first time I heard his name.

*****

Next day I was drafted into a section of twenty recruits under the command of another National Guard member, a very terse young man. The time for polite chat was over. We were told that the 200 mile march to Nice should take us ten days and should get us up to full military fitness. Anyone who could not keep up would have to be left behind to fend for themselves. We carried ammunition, a musket, a short sword, a blanket and if we had one, a coat.

Looking after one's feet became the top priority on that march and I was lucky to have brought strong boots. Many of the others were soon in great pain with blisters. At the end of each day or when we passed a likely farm or village, those of us who could still walk well had to set off as a foraging party. This was because we carried almost no food with us. Having been on the receiving end I sympathised with the anger and resentment our "donors" showed but now I could see an army like ours had little choice but to rob people. They could do this politely and with some consideration or violently with none.

The sense of achievement on reaching Nice and marching into the large army barracks there was terrific. Now we really felt like soldiers.

The army we were joining consisted of many thousands of men freshly conscripted and drawn from right across France, something that had never been done before. This meant they came from every social class. Their condition in Nice however had been little better than that of the camp in Turin until a couple of weeks previously.

We were put under the authority of a drill sergeant, an experienced old soldier. He told us, "You lads from Turin have been lucky. Our officers have been able to extort millions of livres from the banks in nearby Genoa. They are terrified of being occupied. As a result we are all getting paid for the first time in months. We also have good strong shoes for you all. By the look of you most of you need them."

"And what about uniforms Sergeant?" someone piped up.

"You must be joking." He replied. "Not top priority, but I can tell you the Army has acquired large numbers of mules for carrying goods and a great store of wheat." That was certainly encouraging.

*****

Drill and marching continued apace and for the first time I was armed with the 1777 Charlesville musket. The drill sergeant described it as "a product of perfection." Muzzle loaded and smooth bore it fired a single shot triggered by a flintlock. It was five foot long and could carry a fearsome looking bayonet. Without the bayonet the wooden stock could be used as an effective club.

Reloading was tricky and slow, though our instructors set out to get us able to reload and fire three volleys in a minute. This was not easy but we could all see speed in re-loading could be decisive or a rank could be overrun. A good shot like me could hit a target the size of a man's head at thirty yards. Beyond that it became inaccurate even though the shot remained potentially lethal and very damaging as I had seen so sadly to my poor friend Peter in Turin.

For the next three weeks the entire army based in Nice were put through a relentless drilling and training programme devised by and under the direction of General Bonaparte. We were told this had two aims. The first was to build up all our fitness and basic skills as artillerymen, infantrymen and cavalry. The second was to take part in mobile exercises based on developing flexible and co-ordinated actions together.

I was drafted into a demi-brigade (later renamed regiment) under the command of General Massena. An impressive and unusual man he embodied the ideal of the Revolution in that his father was a Nice shopkeeper. He was as much Italian as French, and unusually he had risen through the ranks having joined the Army as a private. This was based on his bravery, tactical skills and ability to inspire those he commanded as I was to learn.

In line with Sergeant Diderot's recommendation I was very pleased to be selected for skirmisher and sharp shooter training (years later provided by Napoleon with a distinctive uniform and named *voltiguers*.) Chosen as we were told for our physical fitness, intelligence – because we were literate - and marksmanship, we regarded ourselves and were regarded by others as something of an elite.

We were trained to take initiative in gathering intelligence and reconnaissance, in taking cover, and in firing individually at approaching enemy lines, to work in pairs covering for each other and to take up positions as snipers. Our job we were told was often to work with the cavalry, go ahead and gather intelligence and then to harass and disorganise troops in the enemy line before retreating behind our own lines of light or heavy infantry. These formed lines or squares from which they fired volleys under tight discipline.

In all this training I certainly found my hunting and shooting experience helped me develop a sometimes arrogant self-confidence. Certainly compared with the new infantry regulars who had never used a gun in their lives, let alone stalk prey in the countryside, I was quite proficient.

We were also schooled in hand to hand combat, the use of the bayonet, our short swords and the use of the musket as a club. Again this was training I enjoyed.

*****

On the day before our planned invasion of Italy a grand parade of the whole army took place in the *Place de Revolution* of Nice. If the uniforms remained a strange mixture, our marching and drill was transformed and impressive. Taking the salute as we all marched past, was Napoleon, a small slight man with no wig but his own dark hair visible under his cockaded hat. He climbed up on a platform and addressed us.

He spoke clearly with passion, an easy wit, complete self-confidence and a strong Corsican accent. This went down well as it marked him as being no stuck-up "aristo".

He described how his aim was to overthrow the coalition of old rulers who had declared war against the French Republic. This meant Victor Emmanuel of Piedmont, the rulers of Milan,

Parma, Modena and the Pope with his several states, The Doge of Venice and the Emperor of Austria who controlled a great swathe of Northern Italy.

"I will then liberate all their people from rule by hereditary aristocrats and replace them with republics based on the principles of the Revolution!" he declared. We all cheered wildly.

He concluded his speech saying, "The patience and courage you have shown so far are admirable, but they have brought you no glory, no brilliant feats. I want to lead you into the most fertile plains on earth. Rich lands and great towns will be in your power, there you will find honour, glory and riches." The cheering that greeted this just went on and on. I wondered what he meant and what some of those around me understood him to mean. Was it an invitation to take what we wanted?

This was the first time I had actually seen Napoleon, but already word of him as quite a phenomenon was spreading. He was only twenty-eight. At first some said he was just a young artillery officer with little experience, a much over-promoted political appointee who would not last. Already however, the word was filtering down that all who met him and dealt with him found him formidable. It was being said that he was brilliantly clever, with detailed knowledge about everyone and everything that was going on. Certainly the training programme we were undergoing had been devised by him and seemed excellent.

Already I thought we looked and felt quite different from the undisciplined ruffians I had seen in Turin, ineffectively led and on the edge of mutiny over pay. Napoleon had transformed us in Nice into a disciplined, motivated force, all fired up, self-confident and ready for battle.

Chapter 6
Lodi

Battle was not long in coming. The next day we started moving out, marching in columns into the lands he had spoken of. Our first target was the hill-top town of Mondovi which we had passed on our journey from Turin to Nice. This time we faced the Piedmontese army.

As skirmishers we were sent out first to gather intelligence and we saw the Piedmontese troops had been marched out of the little hilltop town to take up position at the top of a large sloping field in a broad line three deep. This was ideal for us skirmishers as we were able to get remarkably close while still hidden around and behind trees and hillocks, firing off individually at the men in their line. We could see individual soldiers going down. They were held back by the shouts of their officers from using volleys against us, for they were rightly expecting our lines of infantry to appear.

Behind us our infantry approached rapidly at a quick march and in a broad column about fifteen wide. Then with remarkable speed, as they had been trained to do, they spread out into a line three deep facing the Piedmontese line. This was the time for us to fall in behind them. The first volley our line fired was devastating and enough for us to see the Piedmontese break ranks and flee. Our artillery then opened up wreaking havoc. With that they went into full retreat leaving their bodies on the field and the little town of Mondovi to our mercy.

I found what happened next an unexpected horror. Laughing and screaming a wave of *sans culottes* broke ranks and set about looting and smashing up the town and decent young women were dragged off and raped, several taking one girl. I had never imagined anything so dreadful and I can never forget what I saw. Some officers and sergeants attempted to stop this, only to be laughed at and ignored as for a whole day the pillage went on. After that a decree from Napoleon that anyone caught looting would be shot on sight was put up everywhere. Rather too late I thought.

I also heard several soldiers saying, "He did say great towns would be in our power with their riches. Armies have always done this and look at us, no uniforms, poor boots, very little pay. We deserve our pleasures."

*****

Still the forces of Piedmont were clearly on the run and had no stomach for a serious fight. We were quickly formed up and marched north towards Turin. At Cherasco we were met by a delegation sent by Victor Amadeus and an armistice was signed giving Napoleon the right to pass through Piedmontese territory and so focus on the main enemy that was coming down from the North, Austria.

It was soon after this that the old duke "had a fit of apoplexy" and died. His son, Charles Emmanuel also ratified the treaty allowing the French Army freedom to pass through what was now only in name his territory. The campaign against Piedmont had taken ten days with few casualties on our side. We were jubilant.

The rapid collapse of Piedmont was probably due to the general unpopularity of the old Duke and because the Piedmontese troops were already war weary as a result of the indecisive Revolutionary Army attacks I had seen in Turin. Fighting Austrian troops was expected to be a very different matter. We would be facing experienced, trained, professional soldiers.

So I had my first taste of active fighting, had seen troops drawn up in battle formations and had used my training and my musket to good effect. Certainly, despite what I had witnessed, I felt I was a real soldier and was ready for more action and Napoleon saw to it we had more. Immediately we were sent off into the Duchy of Milan on a forced march (that is almost double time) going north to engage the Austrians before they could expect us to reach them.

*****

On the 10th of May 1796 we skirmishers and sharp shooters were part of the advance guard that reached Lodi, a small and rather beautiful city south of Milan. I was ordered to take a team of six into the town and find out what we could. This was a situation where not wearing a uniform and being Italian was useful for I quickly found locals all too ready to talk to me. The German speaking Austrians were none too popular and I learnt many in the city would welcome us once we drove the Austrians out. We also learnt that the town was lightly defended. A vigorous and swift attack seemed just what was needed and we returned and reported this to headquarters.

The light infantry were then sent into the town and we joined them in the fighting that followed. Here the training we had just been through and the self-belief we had showed. Very quickly the Austrians deserted the centre and fell back to the river bank on the far side of the town by way of a rather small wooden bridge.

Napoleon and his generals then entered the town and took up position in the campanile of the Church of San Francesco which gave them an excellent view of the bridge and surrounding terrain.

The Austrian army were lined up on the opposite bank facing us with about a dozen cannon. This looked quite formidable, except our numbers were soon far greater. Napoleon placed a single small cannon at the end of our side of the bridge which proceeded to fire grape shot, grape being a bag of small metal balls. A powerful deterrent, this stopped anyone on their side damaging the bridge.

As sharp shooters we skirmishers were ordered to keep up a barrage of fire against anyone on the Austrian side who went near the bridge. We did this by entering the high buildings alongside the river and shooting down from their upper windows. From these we could see more and more of our cannon being put in place, so by mid-afternoon I counted thirty blasting away at the Austrians, while they attempted to do the same with far fewer guns aimed at us.

We, and no doubt the Austrians, could see that Napoleon had deployed detachments of cavalry both to the north and the south of the bridge to try and find a shallow crossing place.

By six o'clock the whole of our army were in the town and had been given a break after the forced march they had all completed. Napoleon decided that this was now the time to deploy his Grenadiers. These, reputedly the biggest and toughest of the French troops, were all over six foot tall and all gallantly moustachioed, a detail that amused us skirmishers.

We heard cheers coming from them when suddenly they appeared from behind one of the buildings facing the bridge. We later heard this was because they had been given a rousing speech by Napoleon. With bayonets fixed they proceeded to charge the bridge. As they reached the half-way point there was a single boom of a gun. This time it was Austrian grape shot. It stopped the grenadiers in their tracks as they fell dead or wounded. It was truly horrible to see.

With that six of our senior officers, including our general Massena together with Generals Berthier and Dupas rushed onto the bridge and rallied the Grenadiers. Together they all showed great bravery in pressing forward in a new assault before the cannon could reload, something our sniper fire made very difficult for the Austrians manning their cannon. On reaching the other side our troops found if they left the bridge and went down into the river it was shallow and from there they could provide covering fire for the others who came pouring across after them.

At the same time the cavalry on the north side discovered shallows where they could take their horses across and so were able to attack the Austrians from the rear. The Austrians retreated, but re-grouped in tolerably good order and were able to re-join their main army some few miles away at Cremona. This however meant they had lost Milan and the whole of the surrounding duchy.

There followed for us the sad business of collecting and burying the dead. This was something I had never done before. There were over 300 bodies from each side. In addition there were many wounded. A terrible reality which I had not thought about before, came home to me as I saw what happens after a battle. So many soldiers who are wounded can expect to die from their wounds. This happens either quickly or slowly and usually very painfully for there is little the surgeons or doctors can do or seem to understand about infection or pain relief. The stench of gangrene around the wounded soon became familiar.

*****

Compared with later battles, Lodi was a small affair, but for us and for Napoleon it proved crucial. The Revolutionary Army had often been seen as ineffective and shambolic. Now as the French Army our reputation was transformed and our enemies feared us. Napoleon we soon learnt was a master at reporting what we had done. He wrote letters that were sent to Paris to be published in the papers there. He was also a master at showing his own behaviour in the best possible light.

Within a month we saw reports where-ever we went about the great General Bonaparte and his fantastic victory at Lodi who against heavy odds had imposed a defeat on the Army of Austria.

He also soon saw to it that there was a special newspaper produced for us soldiers to read and pass around recounting our deeds of heroism and his brilliance in strategy. These were illustrated by dramatic engravings which also inspired the many in the ranks who could not read. This was something new and the result was to boost morale amongst us. We could see ourselves as driven both by love for the New France and the Revolution. We were not just mercenaries or professional soldiers like our enemies, we were the future, an army of citizen soldiers, crusaders for Liberty, led by a great leader.

Chapter 7
Milan "Liberated"

May 1796

A gain there was little time to rest for us sharp shooters and skirmishers for we were ordered to prepare to march straight away to Milan and get the city ready for the triumphal arrival of our Army. At this point Sergeant Diderot joined us from Turin. To have such an able, intelligent man leading gave us confidence. I liked him and soon found he had a clever way of picking up on the latest political and military gossip and was ready to share it with us.

"Good to see you Bioletti." He said on meeting me, "So you have made it into the skirmishers."

"Yes Sergeant, and may I thank you for recommending me." I replied.

"It's the best place to be for an intelligent soldier who is a good shot and able to take some initiative. You saw what happened to those gallant Grenadiers on the bridge?" We both nodded sadly. There was no need to say more. Still the Grenadiers saw themselves as the elite of the Army and would do so even more when the time came for them to be kitted out in splendid uniforms with imposing bearskins. The fact remains as Lodi had demonstrated, compared to skirmishers the gallant Grenadiers were cannon fodder. We lost no-one at Lodi and had taken a very active part. On that bridge they had lost many. Our company of around eighty set off for Milan the next day as the advance party. It is a distance of some 25 miles so we spent the night in the grounds of a country inn before entering the city the next morning.

Arriving with us at the head of a party of cavalry was our commander, General Massena. He told us that when we got into the city and he had decided on a suitable square, we were to make contact with friendly locals and set about erecting with their help, a triumphal arch of branches and flowers, and an artificial Tree of Liberty. He told us that Archduke Ferdinand, ruler of Milan, had fled and it was General Bonaparte's intention to celebrate the overthrow of the duchy with a grand triumphal entry in the style of the classical Roman Army. This we set about doing.

We soon discovered there was quite strong support for us among the middle-class in the city who were glad to see the Archduke and his men go and dreamt of Milan becoming a self-governing democracy, and part of a future Italian Republic. So keen were they that they had formed a local National Guard with green uniforms and cockades of green white and red and wished to be used as a guard of honour when Napoleon arrived. This they duly did when on the 15th of May 1796, a Sunday, he arrived with 500 cavalry and 1,000 foot soldiers. We skirmishers, more unobtrusively, were lining the way.

Mounted on his funny little horse Bijou, he passed through the ancient *Porta Romana* and led the way into the city with his generals in a line behind him. In front of him morosely walked a group of disarmed Austrian prisoners in the style of a Roman Triumph!

The middle-class it seemed turned out in some numbers to see this young general, though the crowds were no-where as big or as enthusiastic as those portrayed in the many engravings of the event different artists made to celebrate it later. We also heard people in the crowd around us commenting in amazement at the sad state of our troops proudly marching by without uniforms, with broken shoes, and many in ragged and dirty clothes. Many wore outlandish headgear with their cockades. I saw fox, sheepskin, rabbit and even cat! How had such an army been able to defeat the Austrians they wondered?

That night saw the leaders of Milanese society entertaining Napoleon and his officers to a sumptuous banquet at the *Palazzo Real* with a full orchestra in attendance playing suitable revolutionary music including *La Marseillaise*.

Napoleon however surprised everyone by excusing himself at the start of it all and going off to bed. The gossip was he was worried about his new wife Josephine who he had left behind in Paris and who was known for her "sociable" ways.

A few days later the good citizens of Milan heard what the price of their "liberation from tyranny" would be. Sergeant Diderot heard from a local banker that the city had to pay twenty million francs, deliver a huge consignment of clothing and shoes and provide the Army with six thousand horses!

In addition after a couple of days we were ordered to visit the homes of the wealthy and respectable and demand from them whatever cash they had. Doing this made me feel very uncomfortable for being terrified they all just obeyed. We heard millions were raised by doing this and as a result we were all paid our wages in cash. Again Diderot said the word was this was done because the Army had run up huge debts in France which had to be paid. He also pointed out that by paying us in cash "raised on campaign" Napoleon was moving Army loyalty from France and the Directory to himself – like that of a Roman general.

It was not just cash that we were taking. All around me I was aware soldiers, including senior officers like our General Massena, were simply robbing Italian families of anything they wanted while at the same time the policy of foraging for food from local farmers continued without let up. Not surprisingly it did not take long for revolts against us "liberators" to break out together with stories some of us found amusing for they involved accounts that statues of the Virgin were moving, changing colour or weeping in the face of the depredations of the godless French. The Tree of Liberty we had so carefully erected in Milan was surreptitiously torn down and the unrest there reached the point of holding up Napoleon's planned offensive against Austria in the north. This he dealt with by having a city councillor and a priest executed as ringleaders.

This was followed by a revolt led by the local clergy and nobility in the village of Binasco which resulted in several of our soldiers being killed. Napoleon's response was to remove the women and children from the village, execute all the men he could find and burn the village to the ground. He then used Binasco as an example to threaten the people of Lombardy that if they rose against our French Army that would be their fate.

As an enthusiastic young revolutionary soldier I did my best to justify such actions to myself and those around me as being a necessary response to the forces of tyranny, reaction and superstition and that in the face of revolt and non-cooperation we needed to be feared. At the same time on reflection I was not so sure. Looking at the wider picture however, it still seemed to me that we needed to defeat Austria and its Holy Roman Empire if the forces of Revolution and Enlightenment were to prosper and the New France stay free.

Chapter 8
Spoils of War

Soon however I was off from Milan with our company of skirmishers under Napoleon's direct command on quite another type of mission. Napoleon announced that the attack on Austria was to be postponed and attention given to the Revolution's enemies in the South, that is the Pope and the Dukes of Parma and Modena. None of them had armies to field against us so I asked Sergeant Diderot if he knew what was going on.

"It's quite simple Bioletti. France is in a bad way economically, and this is a way of raising cash."

"For France?" I replied.

"Yes. The Directory in Paris has woken up to the fact that in Napoleon they have a general whose wars are costing the French state nothing, which is rare."

"Yes, I suppose so."

"What is more they seemed to have in Napoleon a general who could, through the treaties he makes and the requisitions he takes from our enemies, end up making war highly profitable for France.

"How? I don't see it."

"Again quite simple. If instead of attacking and destroying all those who have signed up in their Coalition to fight us, after an initial and well publicised victory like Lodi, he says that he is ready to sign an armistice agreement, he can get all three to hand over huge sums in gold coin to pay for this Army with the balance going to France.

"I see." I said amazed.

"But that's not all. Those three have much else besides money that is valuable. Art and ancient manuscripts."

To this end the Directory sent out to Napoleon in Italy - Diderot said he heard it was at Napoleon's bidding - a body with this long-winded title: *The Government Commission for the Search of Scientific and Artistic Objects in Countries Conquered by the Armies of the French Republic.* This commission was made up of distinguished French artists and scientists. They travelled to Italy immediately and had the task of selecting work to be "requisitioned" and sent back to France.

Our role as soldiers was to accompany and back up the Commissioners when they went "requisitioning" and help pack up the works which were destined for the National Museum in Paris.

They were very thorough and knowledgeable and we packed up just under two hundred paintings and one hundred sculptures, together with some five hundred rare manuscripts. Never having been exposed to fine paintings before, except a few I had seen in Turin, this was a task I found really interesting. I wondered however if this "requisitioning" simply amounted to theft.

One of the Commissioners was an artist named Jean Simon Barthelemy. We seemed to get on well and he was always keen to tell me about the importance of the works we were packing up so one day I asked him about this.

"Young man I am only too ready to explain." he said. "Art can only thrive in a free country, not under the domination of monarchs or of the Church. Do you get that?"

"I suppose so. Artists might be censored by the Church or have their work turned down on some whim by a rich aristo." I said.

"Exactly. And the country which provides such freedom for talent is France. What is more France, as leader of the Enlightenment in its Politics, Philosophy and Art, is the legitimate successor of Greece and Rome. We are thus preserving the best Art in the best place where visitors to France may come to our museums to appreciate it and our artists can come to see it, study it and be motivated by it. I believe our Revolution will inspire great Art now and in the future!"

Yes, he got quite carried away. I still had a nagging feeling that great Italian Art should stay in Italy as part of our special heritage.

Chapter 9
How we Fought

Soon however the Commissioners were gone and we were back with the Army as skirmishers and sharp shooters in General Massena's demi-brigade. Ranged against us now and in huge numbers was the proud and professional Austrian Army. It was the start of the most dangerous, relentless, punishing and exhausting campaign we could imagine.

Mantua, with a huge Austrian garrison was under siege by our Army for months and the Austrians were determined to relieve them. In the freezing winter of January 1797 they counter attacked by coming from the North down both sides of Lake Garda in huge numbers. In response Napoleon sent Massena to led us on a series of forced marches and pitched battles to stop them. These encounters were terrifying and it seemed never ending. Somehow we were able to inflict heavy losses and retreat in good order.

Rather than describe all these battles which it is frankly difficult to remember for they took place relentlessly one after the other and usually after we had carried out an exhausting forced march, I will say more about how we fought. Both we and our European enemies had similar arms and used similar tactics. Napoleon's edge was that he was a master tactician in reading the lie of the land and deciding where to place his mobile artillery. To do this as he had first done from Mondovi to Lodi, he ordered us to go on a forced march. By travelling across country almost at a jog we arrived over and over at the next potential battlefield before the other side was ready to engage.

Basically the demi-brigade (later renamed a regiment) in which I fought under General Massena consisted of a majority of light and heavy infantry – which included grenadiers. This was backed up by our company of skirmishers, together with cavalry and artillery.

Both light and heavy infantry basically fought in the same way as we had at Mondovi. That is they approached a battle-field in columns, on open ground about seventeen men wide but much deeper. When close to our enemy the infantry would rapidly spread out into a line as wide as possible. This was always three deep in order to present a wide field of fire with the cavalry and artillery on either side of them. When they spread out we skirmishers who as I will describe had preceded them, fell back behind them.

At all stages the infantry were tightly disciplined and drilled for the key to their effectiveness was their ability to fire volleys at quite close range. They were trained to reload as fast as possible and to fire only when ordered, rank after rank. To do this in the face of an enemy about sixty to one hundred yards in front of you doing the same thing was terrifying, so officers and sergeants with drawn swords besides and behind were ready to drive you back if you broke ranks, for breaking ranks could result in your whole line being routed.

Volleys on the battlefield from muskets spewed out clouds of black smoke, smoke so thick that it was hard to see the troops who had just fired. In this atmosphere, and if a melee developed, brightly coloured uniforms made it easier to identify which side you were on.

The heavy infantry, as I mentioned describing the Grenadiers at Lodi, were tall and intimidating and after firing their volleys, if it was judged the enemy was about to break ranks, they would be ordered to fix bayonets and charge, screaming. This was a terrifying sight and often resulted in the enemy breaking rank and being routed.

We skirmishers and cavalry were both used to gather intelligence and take a look at the lie of the land before an engagement started and be ready to drop behind the infantry once the volleys began. The cavalry would then be ordered in to charge at the enemy as required. A cavalry charge was a truly fearsome thing to witness. If the enemy broke ranks or remained in line they could quickly be cut to pieces by cavalry and routed from front or back.

If as happened in some battles enemy cavalry charged us, the infantry were formed into three ranked squares, the front rank holding their muskets with the butt on the ground and with a fixed bayonet for no horse would run into that. We skirmishers would slip in behind them. Those second and third ranks could then direct their volleys in all four directions. This use of squares could decimate cavalry. Squares however could be decimated by artillery.

Basically we skirmishers could expect to be deployed in small groups working in pairs and in sections of twelve, led by a corporal and with each three sections led by a sergeant. We were used to advance with our cavalry and gather intelligence and then to set ourselves up using any cover to take pot shots individually at the advancing enemy infantry in their lines. Our aim was to take out enough of them to demoralise them and slow their rate of re-loading and thin out their ranks. They could seldom return fire in a volley at us, for they needed to be ready for the infantry ranks approaching them.

Once our infantry was close enough to start volleying, we fell back behind them to fire from the side or from behind, again not in volleys, but individually as quickly as we could re-load which we were skilled at doing really fast.

We were also deployed to defend the artillery. Battles usually involved the use of horse drawn mobile artillery, something Napoleon had always specialised in and he was brilliant, knowing just where to place his guns. Setting up canon and reloading after firing was hazardous. This was because the gunners could be vulnerable from skirmishers and sharp shooters from the other side coming over to neutralise our canon. Their aim would be to over-run our battery and then use nails to "spike" the guns so even if they were driven back the guns could not be fired again.

When defending artillery batteries we needed to get into positions where we could direct sharp-shooting at any who would attack our guns and be ready for hand-to-hand combat and I can assure you I had a great deal of experience of doing both.

The artillery of course could impose devastating carnage with their bouncing cannon balls, or close-up shots of grape.

Many battles ended with men on both sides finding themselves in situations where there was no time to go through the slow process of re-loading a single shot musket. This was when you either attacked with the short sword, or used the musket as a club.

I preferred wielding the musket or using a knife.

In addition as skirmishers we had to deal with the skirmishers from the other side who would come at us before their infantrymen engaged ours with volleys.

These situations all resulted in us skirmishers often being involved in hand-to-hand one-on-one fighting. I was very fit, had grown strong and quick and knew that speed and ferocity was essential if one was not to end up dead or badly wounded. So many on both sides just never got this, lacked the speed and ferocity needed, did not train and as a result, did not survive. Somehow I did. Looking back I am amazed.

Did we hate our enemies? Not really. The Austrians were professional soldiers trained much as we were but lacking the élan, motivation and confidence we had in our brilliant Napoleon. Fighting had nothing to do with personal hatred or emotion directed at the enemy, but in having and using the right fighting skills. It seems I was rather good at this. Those around me certainly recognised this in me and I got a bit of a reputation and was treated with some respect, even if I was Italian.

Yes, we were inspired. The more we fought, the better we got at doing so and we were brilliantly led. Both Messana and Napoleon radiated confidence. They seemed to know what they were doing and as commanders knew what they wanted and how to place us and they both laughed and joked with us as they went past and made us feel special.

At five in the afternoon of the 13th of January 1797, Napoleon ordered Massena to send us on a forced march from Verona to Rivoli, 20 miles. We marched all night over snow covered roads, arriving at 6.a.m. There we were set up in a gorge outside the village by Napoleon himself commanding fifteen guns of his mobile artillery. Our role as skirmishers was to protect the guns from any sniper fire. We knew we were facing a huge Austrian army of thousands and were seriously outnumbered, but the night before, Napoleon - as later reported in our newspaper – had climbed up to a point where he could see where the five Austrian columns were camped. From there he had worked out what in his judgement they were going to do, and he guessed right.

The Austrians planned to launch what they thought would be a surprise cavalry charge through the gorge using their finest dragoon guards. Instead they found our artillery was ready for them and they were met by a devastating point blank cannonade of grape shot. This brought about a rout as men and horses panicked in terror and rode back onto their own troops. The scene that followed was slaughter as the brigade of General Charles Leclerc and the French cavalry Chasseurs attacked, sabres swinging and we left the guns and joined in. This was quickly followed by the mass surrender of the Austrians. Never had I seen so many dead and wounded men.

Chapter 10
Glory and the
Price of Victory

Time for a break? Not a bit of it. General Massena rallied all of us who were not wounded and set us off on another forced march south for Mantua, forty-five miles away. There we took on the Austrians who were trying to relieve the siege and help those holed up inside. Again our speed of arrival took them all by surprise. Both their troops outside and inside were finally and decisively beaten totalling, so our paper told us, sixty four thousand dead or surrendered. I do not know how accurate those enormous figures are. I do know that once inside Mantua we discovered the bodies of thousands who had died of starvation and it was pitiful to see the state of those who were left alive when they stumbled out to surrender.

So Napoleon had won a great victory, a victory which demonstrated his brilliance as a commander. He and his generals, including our Massena, had driven us on a series of forced marches which had given him greater mobility in moving around men, cavalry and artillery than I think had ever been achieved by any military leader before. Time and again Napoleon had correctly predicted what his enemies would try and do. For them this was deeply demoralising as fear that they were facing a military genius with a highly motivated army grew.

In all this Italian campaign Napoleon and his generals had not spared themselves or removed themselves from danger. We heard Napoleon had ridden many of his horses to death. We saw him ride past us from column to column and we saw him seeking out strategic vantage points and it was obvious he hardly slept.

When he had appeared to command the artillery and us at Rivoli he had looked pale and utterly exhausted, but his presence among us inspired enormous confidence.

As for us soldiers, you either developed the grit, stamina and strength of a long distance athlete or you were finished, and many were. What is more even a small wound could finish you if it became infected and all the surgeons could do it seemed was amputate.

What was amazing is that our officers and non-commissioned officers were able to inspire us so effectively, particularly when we were so poorly equipped, cold and badly clothed, under fed and only paid occasionally. Certainly they led from the front and were not averse to facing danger themselves, many being killed or wounded.

And what kept us going? Love of *Patria*, France or Italy or hope for a better future where Liberty, Equality and Fraternity would be realised? In fact Napoleon never mentioned Liberty, Equality and Fraternity, though they had certainly inspired me. He spoke only of "Glory," the glory of victory. Once victory was achieved, he said, other things were possible. Without victory there could only be defeat.

And what of Private Bioletti? Apart from sore feet I had somehow come through it all in one piece. Mentally it was another matter. Several in our section were now gone, dead, wounded, or in a mental state that made them useless or dangerous. We were all young men and I had got to know many well sharing the privations, terrors and the strange exhilaration of combat. Why had I been so lucky I wondered for I had been through a most dangerous, exhausting and testing series of battles?

What I had done and experienced, particularly at Rivoli with the cannonade and cavalry charge and seeing the corpses of the starved at Mantua could not be forgotten. Such experiences I know destroy many who remain haunted for years, often it seems in a miasma of rage and alcohol.

So how did I handle it all as a young man of nineteen? I suppose as soldiers so often have, by seeking solace in alcohol and loose women. Getting dead drunk with the men I had fought with seemed good and necessary at first despite the hang-over the next day. Being led to explore the pleasures of passion by a sympathetic and apparently eager young woman keen to provide value for money seemed even better. I had never had a woman before, and since joining the Army life had consisted of marching, fighting little sleep and not much else. Only when based in the attractive old city of Parma where we were attached to the French *Taro Departement* for a few months did the frenetic pace of our lives slow down for the first time.

It was in Parma that at last we were all properly fitted out with uniforms. We were issued with calf-high black boots, white breeches and waist-coats, blue jackets with red cuffs and crossed white leather belts to carry our short swords on one side and ammunition pouches on the other. In addition we had dashing high hats and elaborate helmets with cockades and grey overcoats for cold weather. It seemed typical of our Army that we only received all this flashy kit after the fighting was over.

Setting off for a night out on the town in our new found finery felt great and certainly attracted the attention of the young women. They were however of the type who expected to be paid for their company as "respectable" girls would certainly not be seen accompanied or unaccompanied in the sort of taverns and inns soldiers frequented. However I did dally upstairs in the rooms the inn-keepers so thoughtfully provided on several occasions until I had a nasty shock. One of us who liked to talk about his exploits of the night started to urinate blood, crying and screaming as he did so. I also saw that the faces and bodies of others I knew, were erupting in sores. Not good. In fact I found these revelations as terrifying as grape shot. Having survived so long through so many battles I decided I would give up behaviour like paying to be pleasured which appeared to be almost as dangerous. Again my luck held out for when I made this decision I seemed to have avoided infection by any dreaded pox.

If I sound as if I was bit priggish and detached about all this, it is because that was how I was. I think keeping detached was how I dealt with the mad mayhem and sufferings of war. As for avoiding risky sexual situations I was not simply motivated by fear of sickness and disease. I now found I was more deeply influenced by my father and the Valois way of life than I had realised. I often thought about him and wished he was there to speak to or at least to write to. Drunkenness was always condemned by him and the other Valois men and promiscuous behaviour even more so. Self-control and responsible behaviour were what they valued and promoted. When I contrasted that with the way many of my fellow soldiers behaved when off duty, I rather felt that the Valois way in these respects was right. If some of them thought me odd for not following them in continuing to get totally drunk and finding girls who were ready to please for cash, "Well," I thought, "They are the stupid ones."

Chapter 11
Italy and Paris at Napoleon's Feet

The overwhelming defeat of Austria in Northern Italy left the unconquered Sicily and the Papal States highly vulnerable. As our paper told us Revolutionary France and Pope Pius VI were implacably opposed to each other, the Pope having condemned *The Rights of Man and the Citizen* as undermining *the One True Church* and denying what he considered to be *the One True Faith.* The Directory members simply saw the Pope as their greatest enemy in his denial of freedom in religion or thought.

The Pope's Swiss Guard of a few hundred men offered only token resistance to Napoleon. Rather than enter and sack Rome and smash the papacy as some revolutionaries would have liked and we expected he might do, Napoleon used his well-tried technique of signing a treaty which left the Pope still in control of Rome. In return France gained Bologna, Ferrara, the Romagna and an indemnity of thirty million francs. In addition he received another cache of one hundred selected paintings and sculptures and five hundred ancient manuscripts, all acquired again without firing a shot. Diderot and I discussed Napoleon's treatment of the Pope and found it baffled us. In the next few years he would surprise us even more.

Again the Commissioners arrived from France to select these artistic prizes and again those of us who had survived were selected to work with the Commissioners. So off we went into the grand palaces in and around Rome where the best art works were held to help pack them up safely for their trip back to France.

This time, not having been to Rome before, I was amazed and disgusted by the incredible wealth and ostentation on show in the palaces of some of the cardinals. At least the works taken back to Paris would be on public display instead of being seen only by nobility and "princes of the Church."

I recognised that the one man I knew who quietly seemed to conduct himself in a way I respected was Sergeant Diderot. He would join our section at the start of an evening's drinking to see how we were, and then after a drink or two, excuse himself. He was some seven or eight years older than us and was generally appreciated and liked. As sergeant for our section he had been with us through all our battles, leading and supporting and ordering us what to do next. Somehow, he like me, had got through all our actions unscathed.

Now Napoleon had "liberated" Italy we and many others wondered if he and the Directory that ruled France would accede to the desires of those of us who wanted to see an Italian Republic set up.

"What do you think about that Bioletti," Diderot asked me as we sat quietly having a drink in the corner of an inn.

"You really want to know Sergeant?" I replied. "I think there is very little chance that will happen. It's just a case of divide and rule. Napoleon keeps on setting up these funny little "sister republics" that are just the puppets of our Army

"I think you're right." He said. "When I'm with the officers I hear the way many of them think and talk about Italians. It is quite ridiculous. So many of them think they are superior and Italians are cowardly and untrustworthy."

"I'm afraid what they forget is why they have become unpopular." I replied.

"I fear so," he said and we went over what we had both thought and seen. We found we had both become increasingly aware, starting from the time we had first entered Piedmont from Nice, that the behaviour of the French Army in tolerating or encouraging looting and pillaging and denuding the countryside of produce was a really bad mistake. I knew we had quickly alienated most Italians of all social classes and Diderot had noticed the same thing.

"Instead of being seen as an army of liberation, we have become and have been behaving like an army of occupation, increasingly loathed and hated." he said.

"I am afraid you are right," I replied.

I really appreciated him talking to me like this for one thing I had learnt I had to live with was the almost unthinking prejudice I had to deal with from the others in my section because I was Italian and not French. It was not that they were unpleasant to me, it was rather that they took French superiority - in anything you cared to mention – from food to fighting - for granted. It also meant I had not made any close friends amongst them, though we got on well enough.

The comparatively small Italian uprisings we had seen outside and around Milan were now being repeated in other areas such as Verona and Venice. The disturbance in Verona was swiftly and violently put down by force. This was followed by the execution of rebel leaders found or captured and the levying of a huge cash fine and a huge order for the supply of more boots and clothes. Again the opportunity was taken to requisition their works of art and old manuscripts.

Venice had seen an attack on a French ship and as a result lost its ancient aristocratic republic and its best art works, including the bronze horses that surmounted the loggia of St Mark's Cathedral. Quietly helping the Commissioners around Rome I was glad not to have been called out to put down these rather understandable revolts against the French Army.

*****

Diderot was then away from Parma for a week, accompanying General Massena on a visit to Napoleon's holiday base, Mombello, a magnificent chateau he had chosen to take over outside Milan. What he had to tell me on his return was amazing. Our General Massena who had fought with conspicuous bravery and success supporting Napoleon against the Austrians, found himself clearly out of favour and relegated to places away from Napoleon at the dinner table. Instead of being run as a military headquarters with senior officers all sharing a table, he discovered meals were now excessively formal with Napoleon behaving like a Bourbon monarch running a court.

He was also accompanied by his wife Josephine, his brothers and sisters and his youngest sister Pauline, then aged sixteen. While there Massena attended her marriage to General Leclerc who we had seen in action at Rivoli. He was twenty-four and the gossip was that the marriage was pretty much forced upon them both, by Napoleon after they were caught *in flagrante delicto*.

What struck Diderot and Massena most however, was the grand and formal way Napoleon behaved. After what they had all gone through together on the field of battle, they were not impressed. Next we heard that after ten weeks at Mombello, Napoleon had returned to Paris. I imagined after what I had just heard about Mombello that we and much of the Army of Italy would be summoned to Paris and there we would all take part in a triumphal march as he had done in Milan, only on a much grander scale. I imagined us all being cheered by great crowds and him playing the conquering hero returning to his capital. I must admit I was quite excited by the idea. I was wrong and I underestimated him.

What he actually did was leave us all behind in Italy except for a few generals, (not including Massena) and once in France he proceeded to be seen everywhere in civilian dress behaving as the papers reported "with great modesty and humility." The effect was that the public went wild with enthusiasm about him, turning out in huge crowds to see the conqueror and liberator of Italy play the modest gentleman. As a result he made a much bigger impression than if he had played the general in a triumphal procession.

Some thought his aim in acting like this was crudely political, that he wished to be appointed to the five man Directory. Diderot however explained to me there was a problem there. The law stated Directors had to be forty and Napoleon was only twenty-eight. Diderot then suggested that joining them might not have been Napoleon's aim. Perhaps he saw himself some-day supplanting them. I did not forget that comment.

In October 1797 it was announced that the Directory had appointed Napoleon Commander of the Army of England. This made sense. With Austria and the Coalition defeated, England stood alone as our enemy. If anyone could do it, he was the man to lead an invasion. We waited, expecting a call to come ordering us all to return to France and invasion training camps in Normandy, but no call came.

Finally in March 1798 the strange news came through that Napoleon had a new appointment, Commander of the Army of the Orient. A week later our demi-brigade was ordered to return to France and report to Toulon, the naval port in the South near Nice. That certainly was a surprise. Where were we going and what was meant by "the Orient"?

Chapter 12
Toulon

18th May, 1798

Toulon was chaotic. Thousands of troops marching into the town and setting up camp – far too many for the naval barracks, so we spread tented into the fields and on the edge of the town. Toulon had been the proud home of the French Navy for centuries before the Revolution, having a huge natural harbour which a sailor boasted to me provided "one of the best anchorages in the Mediterranean."

I had never seen so many ships. The largest were the majestic ships of the line carrying around 76 guns, but grandest of all was the navy flagship, the huge and beautiful *Orient* – 100 guns. It was the largest ship of the line ever built, and again I was told it was the most advanced in design and superior to anything the Royal Navy had. There were also a large number of smaller and faster frigates and schooners and a great many troop ships which looked vulnerable with only a few small guns.

Manning them were sailors, conscripts like the Army who when ashore seemed a cocky, undisciplined lot and mostly very young. They missed no opportunity to make rude remarks about us soldiers as "land lubbers." No doubt they were envious of the varied and very splendid uniforms we now all wore. I also soon discovered if you asked any of them how much ocean sailing they had done, their answers got vague and seemed to refer mainly to in-harbour drills.

Huge quantities of food, and various provisions were being loaded onto these ships and I saw thousands of horses being stabled prior to embarkation.

Rumours were rife for no-one could tell us where we were going. Some said Portugal, others Turkey, others Syria or the Levant. Our normally well-informed Sergeant Diderot said, after carefully scanning the newspapers, that he thought it was Egypt. We would just have to wait and see.

After a few days he was summoned to see General Massena to be told that he was to be made an officer and promoted immediately to major. My reaction was that this was about time. Diderot seemed far more astute and capable than most officers I had served under.

That promotions were being announced at this juncture was no surprise. Many officers and men had died or been invalided out by the Italian Campaign and now there was also a new cadre who had proved themselves in battle and in administration. What is more Napoleon had made it clear that promotion should be made on the basis of performance, not family background or wealth and many, including Messena, had risen through the ranks from humble background to General of Division.

Prior to taking up his new role as an officer Diderot joined us all for a last celebratory drink and I had a chance to talk to him. After congratulating him he said to me.

"Well, Bioletti, I suppose you are wondering if you are being considered for promotion."

"Well yes sir, the thought has crossed my mind."

"I shall miss our conversations and drinks together," he went on. "Of course with my promotion I shall be relocated into a different demi-brigade where I have not been known as a sergeant."

"Yes, sir, Of course I guessed that would happen. I have really appreciated the way you have treated me, going right back to when you recruited me in Turin." I said.

"It is a little less than two years, but it feels like a lifetime ago." He continued, "By now you must be twenty and we certainly have seen some action. Few skirmishers have distinguished themselves in the field as bravely and as competently as you have."

"That is very good of you to say sir," I replied.

"I'm telling you this for a reason Bioletti, because I remember how when I recruited you I said the Army was for all ready to fight for the Revolution, and not just for Frenchmen."

"I remember," I replied.

"Sadly, I have discovered that is not quite true." he said, "Some officers, I am not mentioning any names, are dead against promoting any Italians to sergeant or above. (I guessed he meant

Messena whose views about Italians were well known despite his own background) They say Frenchmen will not put up with being ordered around by an Italian sergeant and that anyway Italians are untrustworthy and liable to revolt or desert."

"I see," I said feeling rather sick.

"But I have been thinking, and I have come up with something which might be just what you need. In fact it could work out to be far better for you than promotion to sergeant now."

With that he introduced me to the idea of becoming an *ordonnance*. General Messena had one and on several occasions he had arrived on horseback to deliver the general's orders. In fact I had never seen the general without his *ordonnance* in attendance, though I had little idea what the man actually did.

He explained that while in peace time the job could become little more than that of a valet or butler to a general, when the army was in the field on active service the role of *ordonnance* was transformed into something very different. He then went on to spell out the expected duties.

"The first is to act as a messenger, passing on written and sometimes verbal orders to subordinates. That can be both dangerous and difficult under fire. The second is to look after the general's weapons, uniform, boots and clothing and see he is properly kitted out at all times. Can't have a general looking anything but immaculate. The third is to cover the general's transport needs, to supervise the care of the general's saddle horses, coach horses or other transport and be ready to ride with him whenever needed. Fourth, at all times to act as the general's bodyguard and to take charge of his security, which again can be tricky, and fifth, do anything else the general asks for!

I was quite taken aback for it was a far cry from being a skirmisher, but the more I thought about it, the more it attracted me.

"Think Bioletti. You are still very young and at the end of this campaign if you prove yourself as I know you will, there may be new opportunities for promotion, possibly higher than sergeant, also, though you can expect almost no time off – and who has that on campaign anyway - you will have all the advantages of being in headquarters. Imagine, eating what the generals eat. What's more you certainly would have a much better chance of coming out of this campaign alive and in one piece, for who knows what this trip to the Orient will bring." I nodded.

"And there is another thing. An *ordonnance* on active service has to be intelligent and able to pick up on just what is going on if he is to help his general. He has to be reliable and totally trustworthy, not to gossip, but good at picking up gossip, in short all your qualities. Yes, I think you will find it fascinating to be in the presence of generals and to hear just what they are saying and how the campaign is going." When I heard that my interest certainly was whetted.

"What I have done is given your name to the sergeant major. He's tearing his hair out trying to find suitable men for there are several newly promoted generals, and several who for one reason or another need to appoint an *ordonnance* before this weird Orient campaign gets launched. I hope you will be chosen by someone you will enjoy working with, for you will be seeing an awful lot of him."

I thanked him and he told me that he would still be serving under Messena who had been moved to a new command on the Swiss border, looking after French interests and the ever dangerous Austrians while we were away. That evening I also asked Diderot if he knew what had happened to the planned invasion of England.

"Quite simple really," he replied. "As soon as Napoleon looked carefully at the success of the Royal Naval blockade of France and at the poor state of the French Navy in comparison, he concluded he could never get a French invasion force embarked to cross the Channel without it getting sunk."

That evening was the last time I ever saw Diderot. Despite our differences in rank and age I felt he had been a real friend and I had learnt so much from him. Now I needed to wait and see what his last intervention would bring me.

Everywhere plans for the invasion of the mysterious somewhere oriental were going ahead as men and material poured into the port. We guessed the secrecy was an attempt to thwart and confuse England's spies. The uncertainty about our destination however caused much general discontent and consternation on our side. What was the point of it? How would we fight in some quite different and foreign terrain? Why should we be sailing off anyway, if it was not to invade England? What did some exotic Eastern people have to do with France and our Revolution? These were the comments everyone was making.

Soon enough however Napoleon arrived with his wife, the much talked about Josephine. He was taken out to sea to inspect all the battleships. Each greeted him with a two gun salute which echoed around the hills of the harbour stirring up general excitement. Then the order was published. General Bonaparte would address us tomorrow, the 10th of May at noon.

We were marched onto the main parade ground in front of the grand arsenal entrance and formed up in tight formation to fit in as many as possible. Together we made up by far the largest number on parade I had ever seen. Napoleon arrived in an open carriage and was cheered lustily as he climbed up to a balcony. There he spoke clearly and self-confidently, but this time with a certain pomposity I thought.

He compared us to the Romans taking on Carthage and himself to the Roman general, a point lost to most of us, particularly the uneducated. He then expounded about us taking liberty to a people ruled by cruel oppressors. Apparently we were going to this nameless place, not so much to conquer it, as to liberate it and bring it civilisation. Everyone cheered at that.

He then reminded us of the spoils and booty we had been able to take for ourselves in Italy, and repatriate as ours back to France. (Not something I had benefitted from) He promised that this expedition would provide us with even richer pickings. This seemed a pretty direct invitation to loot and plunder yet again. Finally he made a promise that every man who returned would be able to claim the equivalent of six acres of land. This promise was greeted with wild enthusiasm and by the end of his speech it seemed that he had everyone behind him, raring to embark and go. Even then I wondered if that promise of land would ever be heard of again. It wasn't.

The next day the full text of his address was published in our Army paper and it was claimed that he was greater than the Roman generals who had taken on Carthage for he had already won such great victories while only being twenty-eight. The paper also gave our numbers. Forty thousand soldiers, ten thousand sailors, thirteen ships of the line, nine frigates, twenty-three corvettes, sloops and smaller armed vessels and one hundred and thirty-five transport vessels. We were about to take part in the biggest foreign military campaign in the history of France.

Bioletti in Egypt and Syria
- 1798 to 1801 -

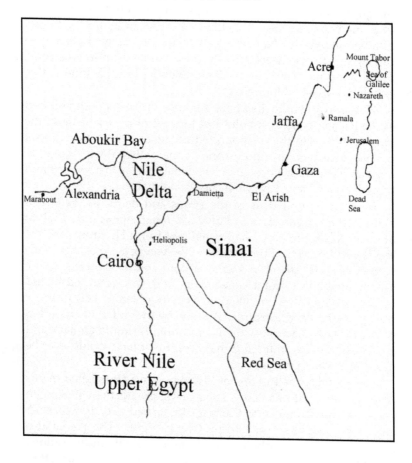

Chapter 13
Ordonnance to General Kleber

Next I was summoned by the sergeant-major to appear at Army headquarters. There were ten of us who had been called for *ordonnance* selection and we were lined up in uniform looking our best and standing at attention in the middle of a large room. The generals then came in chatting among themselves and the sergeant-major handed each of them background notes about us. They then read these and started throwing questions at us. It was most disconcerting and unpleasant and from the way several of them spoke it made me think that this must be what it is like to be the subject of a slave auction. Certainly some of them behaved as though picking an *ordonnance* was simply a case of picking a personal servant to do their beck and call.

One general, a tall, large, bluff man with a mane of naturally greying hair, (no powder) seemed very different. He immediately struck one as having real presence. He read his notes deliberately and spoke in a direct, straightforward manner, asking me a string of sensible questions. In no time he addressed the sergeant-major.

"Thank you Sergeant Major. I will be taking this one, Private Bioletti. And Bioletti, I am General of Division Jean Baptiste Kleber. Come, follow me." And with that we marched out to his office and the start for me of a dramatically new life.

At that stage I had not seen or heard of General Kleber before. I soon learnt that early in the Revolution he had served in France putting down a royalist rebellion in the Vandee. He had then proved himself to be a very brave and successful commander in the Army of the Rhine fighting Austria and the German states. Surprisingly he had then turned down offers of overall command of the French army. I later learnt that his victories in those areas had been as spectacularly successful as those of Napoleon, but that he had made political enemies for his refusal to execute four thousand French prisoners after the Vandee revolt against the Jacobin Terror.

On returning to his office to my surprise he waved me to sit down in a chair opposite him. "Right Bioletti," he said, "As my *ordonnance* we are going to be seeing a good deal of each other, so it is very important you know just what I expect of you as my right hand man."

"Yes sir."

"Your Sergeant Diderot has written a glowing report of your service as a skirmisher in the Army of Italy. You have survived and it seems have earned a reputation as a formidable fighter. He also lists personal qualities. I can assure you they will all be sorely needed and fully tested."

"Sir." I replied.

"One of the most important aspects of this job will be the need for tact and total trustworthiness. You will see and hear much that is confidential. I must be certain there will never be any leaks or gossip spread to others by you."

"Of course sir, I fully understand that." I replied.

"So, I will start by telling you what is known only by members of the Directory, General Bonaparte, myself and the other generals taking part in this campaign. Tell me Bioletti, where do you think we are going?

"I don't know sir, but Sergeant Diderot thought it might be Egypt." I said.

"Bright man. He was right. But we need keep that fact secret for as long as possible so that Admiral Nelson and his merry men don't turn up to create havoc among us when we are at sea."

"Yes sir. That could be catastrophic."

"Indeed. A few words about myself. Born in Strasbourg, my father was a stone mason. As a lad I went to sea for two years. I then joined a Bavarian dragoon regiment and through a fluke event received officer training in Munich. I then found promotion in that army was blocked at a low level on account of my low social origin. I left, came back to France, gained access to university and trained as an architect.

Come the Revolution I joined the French Revolutionary Army to fight for Liberty and Equality. Oh yes! I fought hard and rose fast to the rank I hold today, but for political reasons I retired over a year ago. A month ago I received a visit from General Bonaparte. He asked me to come out of retirement despite being forty-five years old and to join him. Yes, he said he really needed me and prevailed on me to join this Egyptian campaign as his second in command."

"I see sir" I said rather amazed."

"And I can tell you now even without Nelson we will be facing the toughest, most difficult and complicated campaign the French Army has ever attempted. The opportunities for disaster are legion and it will be my job to constantly warn General Bonaparte of the dangers facing us whenever I see them coming."

"Yes sir."

"And Bioletti, another thing."

"Yes sir?"

"Can you cook?"

"Only basic army stuff sir."

"What and you an Italian! Still, better than nothing. Get some cookery books. The point is in Egypt to keep healthy we need to eat only good, clean, fresh food properly cooked. Forget that for a moment and we can be down with dysentery and other diseases puking and shitting. This is where Egypt gets really difficult. At each step on our way we will be facing surprises, like being poisoned by the locals."

"But sir," I said, "I thought we were going to liberate them."

"Good to see you have a sense of humour Bioletti." he replied.

Providing me with writing materials to take notes, he then went through a careful list of what he expected me to do. It certainly was going to be a challenge to keep on top of everything. Listening to him talk I felt that I was in the presence of someone really remarkable who combined exceptional intelligence and ability with a rare sensitivity. Compared to Napoleon, on that first meeting, he struck me as the better man, an opinion I was not to change.

At the end of that session he turned to me and said, "Bioletti, did you train for anything before you joined the Army?"

"My father was a master clock-maker sir, and I hoped to follow him." I replied.

"An excellent, skilful and demanding trade, just what you'll need when your soldiering days are done." he said, and with that he dismissed me.

Chapter 14
On Board the *Orient*

After a frenetic day spent rushing around familiarising myself with all his kit and getting it packed up, the Admiral's long-boat arrived to pick us up at the quay side and row us out to the *Orient*. The sea was choppy and there was a rising wind. The *Orient* I learnt had in fact just received that name, almost certainly at Napoleon's bidding. Formerly it had been called the *Sans Culottes*, a name no longer in political favour. Sailors however said changing names on a ship brought bad luck.

The ship towered above us with its guns on three decks, an incredible, majestic sight. Sadly, I was having difficulty not throwing up as we pitched about, but Kleber looked comfortably at ease. We were piped on board with a small guard of honour and greeted by a rather anxious seeming admiral. He accompanied us to the general's cabin on the quarterdeck which seemed a decent size.

When I had unpacked Kleber's kit I was escorted to my quarters on the upper gun deck, provided with a small locker and introduced to my hammock in what looked like a very crowded space. By this time the weather had deteriorated into a full scale storm, the chilling Mistral. This continued to howl down the mountains with driving wind and rain for the next seven days, seven of the most uncomfortable and sick making of my life. As for the hammock, slung in very close proximity to the hammocks of others I had no wish to know, I just hated it and hardly slept. We and all the fleet then rode it out at anchor, rocking and pitching about, unable to set sail.

Little did we know until weeks later that in fact that storm saved us. Nelson and his squadron had been waiting for us, riding at anchor out of site just below the horizon. Believing we were out to invade England they were determined to wreak devastation on our flotilla of small, slow troop ships loaded with men and horses, not to mention our ships of the line, but the storm hit the English also, dispersing them all over the southern Mediterranean and taking them a long way from us.

In the early hours of the 19th the storm abated and the order was given for all the ships to set sail. A military band was set up on the poop deck and Napoleon watched as each ship lowered its colours in salute as it passed the *Orient* on its way out to sea. A stirring moment. I stood by Kleber on the quarter-deck and he said he was glad to see I seemed to have found my sea legs.

"It is a few years now since I was on a ship, doing the Atlantic run to America. Eventually the body adapts." he said. After that pleasantry there was a long pause and he turned to me and said, "Have you thought Bioletti, what these past seven days and nights must have been like for those poor devils crammed into those miserable little troop ships?" To my chagrin I had not, being far too concerned with my miserable retching self.

We then spent three weeks at sea. The weather was fair and we were joined by other smaller fleets loaded with troops coming from Genoa, Marseilles and Sicily, making every ship more and more crowded. Napoleon also sent a frigate to collect Josephine from Naples, but she did not show up resulting in black looks from him and much surreptitious sniggering.

He had a bedroom, a dining room and a salon to himself and he spent much of his time seeing his senior officers and several of the savants, the young scholars, mostly scientists and mathematicians, also some historians, who he had recruited for the campaign. No-one quite understood why. There were one hundred and twenty-seven of them, and most were with us on the *Orient.*

Here for the first time I experienced being in Napoleon's presence. Access was strictly controlled and very formal. Only those invited to do so ate with him or spent time with him as I heard it said had been the case at Mombello. If Kleber was invited to have a meal with him, then I would be present to wait upon them and pour the wine. Napoleon had made it clear that he preferred such services to be performed by Army *ordonnances* rather than Navy stewards who he clearly did not trust to keep their mouths shut. I had to agree with him there. So many of them came across as green, undisciplined and pretty useless.

Some of these sessions went on for many hours and they were a revelation. Both Napoleon and Kleber were prodigiously well read and fascinated by the culture and military history of the Roman Empire. They were both also keen to discuss both politics and religion. While Kleber showed himself to be knowledgeable but non-committal on both, Napoleon made it clear that as far as religion was concerned, he was completely cynical but that it was politics and the exercise of power that drove him.

While I never heard him describe himself as an atheist, he often said that all religions are made by men. He had also clearly spent time studying the religion of Muhammad and considered it to be better than Christianity because it did not rely so much on miracles – which he rejected. He also repeated such witticisms as "religion is excellent stuff for keeping the common people quiet." and "religion is what keeps the poor from murdering the rich." These shed light on his policy in dealing with the Pope. He saw religion as something to be used by government to encourage compliance with the will of those in power and to attempt to destroy it as the first Jacobin revolutionaries had, would simply turn out to be counter-productive if you wanted power. We would see how he would deal with religion again soon enough.

After sessions like this on our voyage I was very lucky that on several occasions Kleber, knowing I had heard what had been discussed and aware that I had found it all interesting, was ready to continue the discussion and explain things to me walking up and down the quarter-deck. To have such a man as a mentor was certainly an unexpected privilege.

On the 9th of June we awoke to see the island of Malta before us. Kleber told me it had been ruled for hundreds of years since the Crusades by the Knights of St. John. It was he said, "A conquest ripe for the taking."

The knights were generally known to be elderly, corrupt and cruel, and Napoleon's spy-led intelligence was that they were weak and despite their huge fortress, militarily incompetent. Also many were French and not prepared to fight France. The Maltese apparently loathed their rule and were ready to revolt against them and be "liberated" by the French. With a mixture of bribery and a show of overwhelming force the knights were encouraged to surrender, accept pensions and leave the island.

This French take-over was almost bloodless and only took two days, then almost everyone disembarked to explore the island.

Napoleon took up residence in the castle in Valetta and set to work relentlessly working all hours, while Kleber organised the military side and I scuttled around delivering orders to military and civil departments. Within seven days Napoleon issued a huge number of reports and dispatches abolishing feudal privileges, taking over monasteries and guaranteeing equal rights to Jews, Christians and Muslims.

The knights had run galleys, rowed by Turkish and Moorish slaves who worked under the lash and the most brutal conditions. He freed them all, calling them "the disgusting galleys." He reformed the schools, freeing them from Church control and set up a scholarship scheme to send sixty pupils to France for a free education. All very liberating.

What came next followed the Italian model of "liberation." Among his savants were two of the commissioners who had been so active and efficient, dealing with Italian art. They were set to work doing the same thing there. Off they went to the churches, monasteries and homes of the knights. The overall haul of gold bullion, jewels, silver coin and valuable art was enormous, giving Napoleon the much needed cash to fund the whole Egyptian enterprise. I heard from Kleber, to my amazement, that the Directory in France had provided no money to fund the expedition, but as with the Italian campaign they expected Napoleon to see to it that it paid for itself and that he would also be able to send back cash and art to France. Very liberating.

Meanwhile the good people of Malta who had welcomed us with open arms and many of them I heard with open legs, were subjected to theft, looting and pillage until we all embarked again on the 19th of June, taking with us the freed galley slaves. Some nine hundred of them chose to come with us rowing in two galleys and some of the knights volunteered to join us on this "crusade". Four thousand men were left to administer the new dispensation. What a lot can be achieved in a week.

Conditions back on board continued to deteriorate. The usual complement for the *Orient* was one thousand. We were carrying twice that number and we were the flagship. Conditions on the troop ships were as Kleber had noted, filthy, putrid and disease ridden and sea-sickness continued. Relations between soldiers and sailors were at breaking point, each blaming the other for making things worse. It was not a good time.

It was at this time however that I came to understand two questions that had bothered me. The first was why Egypt, the second was why bring savants, the young scientists and intellectual experts on the campaign.

The answer to the first as dished out to us in the paper for the troops printed from a press we had upon the *Orient* was that we were going to "liberate" the Egyptians. They being Muslim Arabs were being ruled by the Turkish Ottoman Empire headed by the Ottoman Caliph in Istanbul. He it seemed had almost handed over Egypt to be ruled by the cruel and oppressive Mamelukes, Muslim "slave warriors" whatever that meant. Once they were defeated Egypt could become a rich French colony. This would provide France with wealth and the Egyptians with "civilisation" and "enlightenment."

Such talk however seemed a little different from what another of Napoleon's proclamations said. This read, "Soldiers! You are about to embark upon a conquest which will change the world. Its effect upon civilisation and world trade will be incalculable. You are about to inflict upon England the most certain and telling blow that she can suffer until the day comes when you can deliver the blow that finishes her off."

So the real reason for invading Egypt was to have a go at the old enemy, England. After subduing Egypt I heard Napoleon and Kleber discuss how they planned to invade Britain's richest colony, India. This was to be done by working with rebellious Indian princes to drive the English out. They talked about doing this either by a naval invasion via the Red Sea, or a land invasion via Syria and Afghanistan. To do either of these things however, they first needed to invade and take over Egypt.

And the savants, the wise young men? Napoleon had become fascinated by what he had heard about ancient Egypt, and Egypt at the time of Cleopatra and her affairs with Roman generals. He wanted to know and understand as much as he could about this mysterious and powerful ancient culture and to take back to France as booty and as objects for further study as much as possible. He hoped to enhance his own reputation as a man of the arts and sciences and that of France as the leader of European culture.

There was no doubting his genuine fascination for the whole subject of Ancient Egypt. He spent many hours deep in conversation with the savants interspersed with many hours discussing plans for the invasion with his generals.

As regards Egypt and its Arab Muslims we also received leaflets about how we were to treat the Egyptians and particularly their religion. Their sheiks, muftis and Imams were to be treated with respect and we needed to recognise that their customs as regards women were very different. Rape though was always "monstrous" and there should be no pillaging for personal gain. In other words we were told to do as we had in Italy, respect the religion of the locals .

As an active soldier I had never before seen or thought about the amount of time and research that goes into planning a military campaign and I saw Napoleon certainly did not spare himself and expected equal effort from others.

Thus after we had spent ten miserable days at sea after leaving Malta on the 29th of June the leading French frigate *La Junon* caught its first sight of the coast of Africa. The Invasion of Egypt was about to begin.

Chapter 15
Alexandria Invaded

July 1ˢᵗ 1798

*L*a *Junon* sailed straight into Alexandria's harbour and picked up the French consul Magallon who was stationed there. It then sailed straight out again hove to next to us and despatched him to the *Orient* in a long-boat. He brought dramatic news. Nelson had been prowling outside Alexandria only two days earlier, but on finding us not there he had set sail north; probably for Syria and possibly then Turkey. We knew that if he found we were not there either, he would probably come straight back. If he were to catch us before our troops disembarked from their vulnerable little transports, his battleships would easily be able to destroy them and put an end to our whole campaign. Napoleon calculated he might have no more than three days to get us landed before he could expect Nelson to return.

Magallon also reported that the Mameluke in charge of Alexandria, the bey El Karaim, had refused the French fleet permission to enter the harbour which seemed quite well defended with artillery, though he understood El Karaim only had a very small Mameluke force to head his local Egyptian Arab troops. Napoleon decided to make a beach landing a few kilometres west of the city by the fishing village of Marabout. Long-boats to do this were in short supply, the sea rough and at midday on the 1ˢᵗ of July our men had to jump from their ships into the pitching long-boats. Not fun.

Vice-Admiral Brueys would not let his fleet come in closer than five kilometres from the shore for fear of being grounded on the rocks and shoals and because he considered preparing to face Nelson to be his most urgent priority.

The cause of the pitching was a strong wind from the land which whipped up the sea and made the task of the sailors rowing the soldiers in very difficult. The soldiers of course were weighed down with their muskets and all their kit.

Napoleon on the *Orient* wished to observe the landing and encourage the men so he transferred to a Maltese galley. This amazing craft was a warship from a bygone age. It had a very shallow draft and was powered by some two hundred oarsmen and was able to go in really close to the beach. Kleber and I took to a long-boat filled with men from the division under his command. We had a truly horrific and terrifying trip for it took us several retching hours to reach the beach. Being far too fully laden we nearly capsized several times when waves hit us and we saw two long-boats near us go under, each with around thirty men on board. None of them could swim and we simply watched them drown. Being ourselves already so crowded it was quite impossible to pick any of them up ourselves.

Finally by nightfall our sailors landed us on the beach and we scrambled off through the surf. At least our arrival was un-opposed by any of the few Arab fishermen some saw lurking around.

By one in the morning after doing repeated trips, the sailors were able to see us all landed. Kleber, escorted by me, rushed around getting all our men together in ranks on the beach, encouraging them and seeing to it that they had something to eat and that sentries were set in place. I discovered all the water we had was one small personal flask each. Kleber then encouraged us to lie down on the sand and take some sleep while we could.

Napoleon's landing plan had been decided on the *Orient* so we knew what was expected of us. The initial invasion force would take Alexandria from the land which we understood was protected by a walled fort and a wider encircling wall. Kleber's task was to storm the central section of that wall with a force of a thousand infantry. The whole assault would have to be done without artillery or cavalry support for they were still confined to the ships. Similar tasks had been assigned to generals Menou and Bon, for the left and right sections, but Bon's men were not yet ashore. Menou's were.

*****

The scene on the beach was illuminated by a brilliant half-moon casting an eerily bright light. By it we could see, surrounded by his aids, Napoleon lying asleep on the sand. Not for long though. At three a.m. the bugle called us to get on parade and we all formed up. Bon's men had now been landed and there was a warm dusty wind blowing in from the desert. The men carried little more than dry biscuit for food and sixty cartridges of ammunition. Most had already drunk all their water. We then set off through the sand in marching column, Napoleon in the lead. In the distance we could make out the walls and minarets of Alexandria blinking mysteriously.

By five in the morning the sun was up and the temperature was climbing to what was soon an insufferable level, something which we were quite unused to and unprepared for. At this point the remains of a scouting party sent out by Napoleon under the leadership of a young captain returned. They had been discovered and attacked by El-Koraim and twenty mounted Mamelukes who had cut off the captain's head and born it away on a pike, presumably to parade with it through the city. Kleber told me this was El-Koraim's answer to a letter from Napoleon asking him to surrender so the French could make a peaceful occupation.

Soon after we found ourselves under attack. Some five hundred Bedouin of the Henady tribe, mounted on horseback and armed with lances suddenly appeared. They were almost naked, black and scrawny, with wild hair and flashing eyes. They charged us with terrible screams, but somehow we did not break ranks. Seeing us load our muskets and prepare to fire a volley, they withdrew rapidly, but grabbed some dozen stragglers at the back of our column and rode off with them screaming in terror. If they had been trained Mameluke cavalry we could have been badly mauled or even defeated.

We marched on through the heat for over an hour until we reached an imposing classical column which we were told was named Pompey's Pillar. Here we had a brief break as we prepared for our assault and Napoleon gave us a rousing address about how we were following in the steps of Alexander the Great, the city's founder. From this vantage point we could see it all stretched out before us. On coming closer however, it looked less impressive than it had from a distance with many poor, dilapidated buildings of mud brick leaning against ancient buildings made of stone.

The city walls we could see were lined with what looked like the whole population, men women and children, all staring down on us, but we could also see that the walls were in bad repair and some had broken down. That was encouraging as we formed up ready for the attack.

Thirst consumed us all and I remember passing Kleber a couple of oranges I had saved from Malta. He in turn offered one to Napoleon who ravenously sucked it of every drop of juice without saying a word.

*****

No sooner had this happened than the population on the ramparts let out the most terrible scream, firing their muskets and what canon they had despite being effectively out of range. Immediately Napoleon gave the order to begin the attack and with that our bugles rang out and the three brigades each charged our designated section of the wall. Our task was to scale what was straight ahead of us. Kleber took the lead going in with his grenadiers with me right behind him. We simply clambered up the rough and crumbling stonework while the Arabs on the wall shouted and shot at us. If ferocity was needed our men certainly had it though as I heard some say the next day, "We were as much driven by thirst as we were by courage and determination."

And then it happened. An Arab raised his musket and fired from the top of the wall and down went Kleber, blood flowing from his forehead. I grabbed him and called one of the grenadiers to help me. He was out for the count with a deep gash. Clearly however, the ball had not entered his skull and I could see he was still breathing. His second in command, Adjutant General Pierre Boyer immediately took over leading the men and soon after the Arab defenders fled back into the city leaving many dead behind them.

We followed after them with another grenadier helping to carry him as gently as we could to the door of the nearest house. A veiled and terrified young woman with kohl blackened eyes and two naked small children let us in and brought us water from a large jar which we gulped down. Outside we could hear the sound of sporadic gunfire which soon seemed further away. Our troops were moving on down to the harbour area.

At first we lay Kleber on our coats and I examined his bleeding wound. To my surprise I found the woman had brought a bowl of clean water and a cloth without us needing to gesture for it. I sought to wipe the blood away and see how clean the wound was. I was worried for I knew wounds caused by musket balls could flare up red and oozing after a few days bringing with them a high fever which often led to death. At this point Kleber came round groaning and insisting he had to sit up.

"My head feels terrible." he said, "Aching, but that will take care of itself. I'll need rest. More worried about this slash on my forehead. Listen Bioletti, the wound needs to be washed with fresh sea water or it could turn nasty."

"Yes sir," I replied.

"But you don't understand." he said, "I've often seen seamen's wounds heal better and quicker where sea water is used, than what happens to wounded men on the battlefield whose wounds so often go bad."

With that he ordered the first grenadier to go down to the harbour and get the biggest jug he could find and fill it from the sea. I hoped he was right but knew he had had experiences I had not. The second grenadier, an eager, keen young man of about eighteen, was sent off to find headquarters and see to it that Napoleon was informed of what had happened to General Kleber. He set off with alacrity, recognising his big chance to be noticed.

To our surprise, the woman then brought in some small cakes which she offered us silently and with dignity, despite her hands shaking with fear. I wondered if she thought such courtesy to the invader might reduce the chance of her and her children being misused or killed. I was impressed.

Kleber then groaned and rather worryingly lapsed into unconsciousness and did not respond to attempts to get him to wake up. I removed his bloodied jacket and boots and laid him out on rugs and a blanket the woman brought. Soon he was snoring loudly. This was un-nerving. The first grenadier then returned with salt water and I bathed his wound in it. He still did not wake up.

The second grenadier then returned with a party of four to say that Napoleon had taken over the house of the French consul Magallon as his headquarters and that accommodation was being prepared there for Kleber and I. They brought with them the local version of a sedan chair and Kleber was placed in it, still not conscious, but clearly breathing.

I handed some coins to the woman and thanked her by gesture. I also wrote a note which I pinned to her door which said in French that the occupants had given us help and should not be disturbed by order of General Kleber. I remembered what had happened after we had taken Lodi in Italy and as we left the house I heard some cries and screams coming from nearby houses and feared what they might mean despite the orders we had been given. Later I heard my fears were fully justified. In the first few hours our men had indulged in slaughter and rape on quite a scale killing all who had taken shelter in a mosque where someone had fired from its roof. It appeared Boyer had given the order for this.

*****

When we got to the consul's house medical orderlies helped me set up the bedroom for Kleber. They said such loss of consciousness sometime after a severe blow to the head was common, but that it was a good sign that he had stopped bleeding and had briefly come round and given orders about the sea water. They were not sure he was right about that, but thought it could do no harm. They thought there was a good chance he might recover well, provided the wound did not go bad, but there was no certainty about this.

I stayed with him and an hour later there was a knock on the door and in came Napoleon looking grave. He asked me to describe all that had happened from the time we had gone into action. He listened intently, thanked me and told me to let his staff know as soon as there was any change in General Kleber's condition. It was the first and last time he ever spoke directly to me.

The consul's house, quite a large and impressive building, was on the seafront overlooking the harbour. It looked across the bay to the fort on Pharos Island, site of the classical lighthouse, known as one of the seven wonders of the ancient world. When we arrived there were sounds of gunfire coming from it and we were told that El Koraim and his Mamelukes were holding out there, the rest of the town having surrendered.

That night I slept by Kleber's bed and saw to his needs after a medical orderly came in and did an impressive job bandaging his head after washing it first with the sea water. The bleeding had stopped. He woke up a couple of times and seemed quite rational, which was a huge relief. After the initial shouts, shots and screams the city fell strangely silent except for the comings and goings I could hear in the building. Napoleon was clearly working late.

In the morning Kleber insisted on getting up declaring that he was quite well enough to attend Napoleon's staff meetings. Napoleon agreed and Kleber was provided with a chair and I stood behind him in case he suddenly felt dizzy or lost consciousness. Napoleon, seated at a desk with his officers coming and going was working flat out. Magallon was also present with a resident Greek trader who acted as interpreter as needed. He spoke both Arabic, Turkish and French.

Officers were questioned searchingly, listened to carefully and orders then rapidly given. Napoleon seemed completely in control and to know exactly what he wanted to do. I heard that between thirty and forty of our men had been killed and around eighty-five wounded. Instructions were given to find and take over a suitable building to be used as a military hospital. We also learnt that between seven and eight hundred Egyptians had been killed. This seemed a lot for the population was estimated as only about four thousand. I wondered how many had been women and children.

*****

Alexandria has both an old and a new harbour, one on each side of the peninsula that stretches out to the Pharos Island fort and already both harbours were filled with the smaller ships and the troop ships. They were unloading everyone and everything as fast as they could. As well as the troops it was vital to get the guns and horses landed. The horses looked a sorry sight and the senior cavalry officer reported that there was little fodder to be procured for them locally. Rather worrying.

Napoleon was particularly keen to see two printing presses brought ashore and installed in the house with us. He was very proud that one was set up to print in the Arabic script. It turned out to be the first Arabic printing press ever to be see in Egypt. The other of course was to print notices and leaflets in French for us. Both were set to work immediately printing documents which Napoleon had already prepared.

By mid-morning the news came in that El Koraim had finally accepted the inevitable. He had surrendered. Napoleon then discussed with Magallon just what he thought of El Koraim who of course he knew quite well. Meanwhile El Koraim marched out of the fort with his Mamelukes and was escorted by a guard of French soldiers to the consul's house.

On coming into Napoleon's presence he dramatically prostrated himself on the floor in front of us and declared that he was now Napoleon's slave. Napoleon bid him get up and gave him a chair. A tall, impressive looking man in his turban and flowing robes, he came across as intelligent and dignified. Coffee was brought in and offered around ceremoniously. That done Napoleon said he would like El Koraim to take charge of security, to see to it that the population was disarmed and that the French Army was provided with everything that it required.

He went on to emphasise that the French came as allies of the Sultan and as friends and admirers of Islam. In particular there would be no restrictions on Muslim worship or customs and most importantly El Koraim was charged with responsibility for seeing that Muslim law was upheld as applied to locals. As regards French soldiers, any cases of theft or violence carried out by them from now on should be reported. This turn of events must have come as much of a surprise to El Koraim as it did to the other officers present for no mention had been made of the unfortunate captain who had lost his head. El Koraim however was quick to understand what was on offer and agreed. Napoleon then suggested he bring a party of all the leading local people to meet him in a few days' time and with a low bow El Koraim took his leave and withdrew.

Napoleon then looked around at his rather stunned officers and said quietly, "Anarchy is the greatest enemy a conqueror has to dread, above all in a country so different in language, customs and religion."

*****

Soon after Vice-Admiral Brueys arrived from the *Orient*. Maps were laid out and the naval situation discussed. With Nelson's arrival expected any day the question was where best to place the French fleet to take him on. The harbour was considered by Brueys to be too small and too shallow. Napoleon at first disagreed but finally decided upon Aboukir Bay, fourteen miles to the West of Alexandria and close to the mouth of the Nile.

The secret of Napoleon's success in Italy had been the speed of his campaigns and his ability to get his army in place for a battle before his enemy was ready and clearly this was what he wished to do here. Alexandria was actually something of a backwater, much reduced from its former glory as we could see. Rosetta and Cairo were Egypt's big cities and Cairo the capital, so plans were drawn up for the rapid advance on Cairo and his first division of soldiers were sent off the next day. I wondered if Kleber was up to such a physical challenge and my doubts were evidently shared by Napoleon.

Over lunch as I stood behind Kleber's chair, Napoleon announced, "Well old friend I have been thinking and for the next stage in our campaign I have the perfect post for you. Governor of Alexandria."

Immediately Kleber stiffened and was about to speak when Napoleon continued, "Yes I know you would like another front-line campaigning role and you may have one before we are finished here, but not yet. At the same time I think in El Koraim we have someone who will keep the locals compliant and accepting of our presence. He could turn out to be very useful in getting things done here and keeping the atmosphere peaceful. At the same time he will need to be watched like a hawk by someone who will not let him get away with anything, will see to it he does what he is told and that he delivers what he promises. Frankly, I can think of no-one who could do that better than you, and to back you up I will be leaving you in charge of a garrison of six thousand men – yes more than the population here."

So it was decided. Later that day when alone Kleber grumbled about having been given a desk job, but I was relieved for he still needed time to recover.

The printing presses could be heard working flat out and soon we saw why. A sheet in Arabic appeared repeated in French and Turkish which went on to describe how the French were bringing liberation from corrupt and grasping Mameluke rule and how the French would see to it that when the Mamelukes were overthrown public jobs would be open to all for "all men are equal before God, wisdom, talent and virtue are the only things that distinguish them." It also claimed that in a sense

Revolutionary France and Napoleon were true Muslims and that the French invasion would bring all in Egypt untold benefits. I wondered how believable educated Egyptians would find this strange mixture of revolutionary French and Islamic rhetoric.

These sheets were being enthusiastically pasted up on all buildings and Napoleon pointed out that we could be certain copies would make their way back to the Mamelukes who ruled Cairo and their leader Murad Bey.

On the 5th of July, El Koraim appeared with his leading locals dressed in their finest. Among them it turned out were the sheiks who had led the Henady Bedouin raid on our column and who had captured the twelve stragglers. They agreed to sell Napoleon hundreds of horses and camels and provide guides and spies for the invasion. This was because they considered the Mamelukes had stolen much of their land and Napoleon promised he would return it. The Bedouin then revealed that they were holding the dozen captured stragglers. A sum for releasing them was then agreed.

Later that day the twelve appeared and were taken before Napoleon who wanted to hear what had happened to them and anything they might know of military value about the Bedouin. The men however simply broke down and wept. The Bedouin they said had been fascinated by their white skins, had stripped them naked and had then abused them in the most shameful and upsetting way. Napoleon was not very sympathetic. He said they were lucky to be alive and otherwise unharmed. They should be aware what could have been done to them.

News of their treatment quickly got about however and was generally considered to be shocking. One of the generals said, "We are up against an enemy whose way of making war is just savage and disgusting." All those around him nodded and I did too.

The next day an Arab elder came in complaining that one of his family who had been going about his peaceful business had been waylaid by a French soldier and his fine ornamental dagger stolen. Orders were given to find the man, he was brought in, confessed and Napoleon ordered he be taken out and shot because he had broken the published rules forbidding looting. Napoleon was never to my knowledge sadistic, seeking pleasure from the infliction of pain, but he certainly could be brutal and use terror when he thought it was needed. Here he wanted to get the message across to both sides, that disregarding orders would not be tolerated and could have fatal consequences.

*****

Much was then made by Napoleon over the seven hundred former galley slaves who after being freed by him on Malta had chosen to join our campaign. These Muslim sailors had joined the fleet in their galleys and had been properly clothed and fed after their harsh treatment by the Knights of St. John. They came from all over Egypt and other parts of the Turkish Empire. Those who needed it were given travel grants to get home. Their generous treatment by Napoleon was widely advertised as an example of how the campaign was bringing liberty to the people while showing Arab Muslims they had nothing to fear from a French invasion.

Preparations for the invasion of the Delta, Rosetta and Cairo continued apace. Napoleon decided on using two different routes sending off General Dugua and his division almost immediately for Rosetta at the mouth of the Nile. He continued to work frenetically, organising everything in sight. As well as hospitals, prisons, barracks, arsenals and workshops were all set up. He decreed that the leading Muslims, the imams, muftis and sheikhs as designated by El Koraim could continue to carry arms, but they should wear a tricolour sash and all men on the street were to wear the tricolour cockade. Finally he handed over control of Alexandria to Kleber and marched off on the 9th of July for Cairo, using the canal route which he thought joined Alexandria to the Nile. We had only been in Egypt for a week.

I was present with Kleber for almost all of these staff meetings, keeping in the background, but also delivering messages to officers at work around the town. It certainly meant Kleber was fully informed, and though he remained weak, his head-wound did not turn nasty so by the time Napoleon left he certainly was ready to take over.

Chapter 16
Nelson in Aboukir Bay

One piece of bad news was delivered to us by El Koraim the day before Napoleon left. The Bedouin sheiks on returning to their tribes had received word from Cairo where Napoleon's leaflets and letters had been examined not only by the Mameluke leaders, but by the leading Arab cleric, the Grand Mufti. He declared that Napoleon and the French were infidels and issued a fatwa that all true Muslims should take up arms against them. At a stroke this meant there would be no horses, camels or spies coming from the Bedouin. It also meant that all of Napoleon's forces found themselves under attack from sudden raids by the Bedouin.

While we waited uneasily for the British fleet to appear Kleber and our garrison had plenty to do, in particular putting in place artillery to prevent a British invasion from the sea. At the same time sailors from the fleet in Aboukir Bay were given shore leave, but their behaviour towards the local people was deplorable, drunken and insulting to say the least. They considered the rules imposed on the army did not apply to them so Kleber simply banned them from coming into Alexandria except in work parties. Our soldiers tried hard not to offend the locals even as they found their behaviour often baffling.

For his part El Koraim kept his side of the bargain and maintained peace. At the same time it was quite clear that all of Napoleon's talk about being pro-Muslim if not an incarnation of the Prophet himself, counted for nothing with the locals. We were simply hated infidels who had invaded their land and who for the moment they had to accept.

The day after Napoleon left Kleber called a staff meeting for all his officers and addressed them. "Gentlemen, we are all well aware that the greatest threat facing us is the British Navy and this Horatio Nelson. They could be here tomorrow, or in a week's time. One thing is pretty certain, they are coming. But I do not think an attack on Alexandria will be their main target. I think they will be going after our fleet in Aboukir Bay." everyone nodded. "This could be a huge and terrible battle." he continued, "And the consequences extremely far reaching. If we destroy Nelson then our chances of holding Egypt and getting to India will be greatly enhanced. If our navy is defeated this whole campaign will be threatened. Either way large numbers of prisoners and wounded may need to be dealt with, either ours or theirs. We must be prepared for that."

He then decided to give us all a talk about naval warfare that I will never forget. He explained that it is similar to war on land in that it is about lines and columns. Naval battles are carried out by ships of the line, these are basically great water-borne gun platforms capable of firing broadside volleys from their canon, like infantrymen fire volleys when in line. Opposing fleets line up against each other and blast away. The longer the line of ships, the more damage it can inflict on the enemy's line of ships. The bigger the ship, the more and the heavier the guns it carries. Seventy six is a common number, but the *Orient* had one hundred canon of different sizes (thirty six and twenty-four pounders) on three decks. These could fire a devastating barrage. The problem is these ships of the line are often slow and always difficult to manoeuvre. To handle them well takes great skill by their commanders and high levels of training in the crew. Both qualities perhaps a bit lacking in our navy.

To play the role of skirmishers, he continued, the navy has frigates. These are much smaller, faster, and more manoeuvrable and are used to scout, gather intelligence, pass on signals and enter waters too shallow for ships of the line. They are however easily sunk and outgunned by a ship of the line – if they get too close, but they are the eyes and ears of the fleet.

As with infantry, ships approaching an enemy in a column can do very little for they have few guns at the bows. This is when they are most vulnerable to a salvo or volley fired by ships in line.

He continued pointing out that when Vice-Admiral Brueys was here with Napoleon he was ordered to take his ships of the line into Aboukir Bay as close to the coast as was safe from rocks and shoals and moor them at anchor. This would give him thirteen ships of the line with a combined fire-power of over five hundred guns mounted to starboard. They should then be ideally placed to concentrate all their fire seaward. They would not have to worry about sailing their ships, or of being attacked from the landward side. If Nelson were then to appear, our navy would have nothing else to do but load and fire their guns.

"So you all see," he concluded, "Our navy, despite the many untried ruffians it has in its ranks, has been brilliantly placed, by our young commander. This means it should be capable of driving them off, if they are cautious, or of inflicting upon them a terrible defeat if they choose to engage our full line of ships." At this everyone applauded.

*****

We then waited and waited while nothing happened and there was no sign of the British fleet. The navy sent in frigates from Aboukir Bay to collect rigging, water and fresh food, and we heard that parties of sailors were given some shore leave on the beach and that attempts were made to dig wells for water, but these trips needed to be defended because hostile Bedouin were about.

It was almost three weeks after Napoleon had left when on the morning of August 1st two English frigates were sighted on the horizon by the lookout on Pharos Island. "Bioletti," said Kleber, "As we have discussed I want you now to be my eyes and ears."

As planned I was to take a good horse and two cavalrymen and ride to Aboukir Bay and watch the battle.

"You know what to do. When it becomes clear what the outcome is, ride straight back here to let me know." said Kleber.

It took no more than an hour and a half of riding to get in position at the top of the dunes with both muskets and telescopes. Alarm flags were being run up on the French ships which meant the approaching British fleet had been sighted, though we could not see them because of the headland that stretched into the bay. Sailors in small craft who had been on the beach could be seen rowing back to their ships. The *Orient* rode majestic at anchor and we could make out Vice Admiral Brueys on the quarter-deck with a telescope.

By 5 p.m. the British fleet came into view. They were not in line or in any particular order. Our first guess was that they would get together and anchor for the night and attack in line the next morning, but no, as it darkened they kept on coming. That looked like a mad move to me. How could they attack if they were not in a proper line and how could they recognise friend or foe in the dark?

Suddenly I noticed the leading British ship cut across the first French ship and slip in on the landward side of the French line, risking running aground on shoals and rocks, but using space left by the French for their ships to swing when at anchor. This skilful and risky example of seamanship was followed by three other ships. This meant the leading French ships of the line now had British ships on both sides of them which they were unprepared for. Then the canons started roaring, devastating the French ships. It was also obvious that the British were reloading and firing again extremely quickly, so outgunning the French.

The remaining British ships had now formed a line and they dropped anchors and started firing as they came alongside the French ships. One, which I later learnt was the *Bellerephon,* came right alongside the *Orient* whose three decks of guns wreaked havoc upon it, taking down its masts and clearly doing much damage. Soon it could be seen drifting away, unable to take any further part in the battle. However two late arrivals on the British side now moved in with pounding broadsides, one on each side of the *Orient* which started to burn. Later I heard the firing from the *Bellerephon* had taken the legs off Admiral Brueys who bravely then sat in a chair on his quarterdeck directing his fire-fighters until another cannon ball finished him.

At this point the wind cleared the clouds of smoke and we could see both lines illuminated by the moon. The *Orient* was now seriously on fire with masts, sails and rigging blazing. Men could be seen jumping from it into the sea. This was followed by the most enormous explosion as the fire reached the magazine. The flash and the roar was awesome, the sound carrying and the flash visible in Alexandria and in Rosetta as it carried masts, rigging ,guns and human bodies far up into the night sky.

There followed a strange silence as every gun on both sides

stopped firing. Everyone on deck who could we then saw scrambling to get below before a great shower of all that had gone up, including human body parts and burning debris, came crashing down on the ships. This in turn set off fires so those below were soon up on deck fighting these. Of the *Orient*, literally nothing was left. The pride of the French navy and almost all her crew were obviously gone. To our surprise we noted an English longboat being launched. Evidently it was picking up the few French survivors it could find.

*****

The battle however was not over and the canon opened up again. Later in the early hours as the firing continued a second French ship exploded. By morning it was clear. Not a single British ship was lost but two French ships were destroyed and six had struck their colours while four others were beached. The beach itself was the most ghastly melange of bodies, body parts and wreckage of all kinds.

We rode off to Alexandria and reported it all to Kleber. He listened intently and said sadly, "I think we will soon be receiving some English visitors."

He was right. Within an hour a thirty-eight gun English frigate appeared at the entrance to the harbour, signalling permission to land. Its captain brought a letter from Admiral Nelson saying that bearing in mind the many wounded on both sides and the large number of French prisoners who had been taken, an urgent meeting was needed with the French governor of Alexandria. The English captain, speaking good French and behaving very civilly, invited Kleber to come with him with appropriate staff to meet Admiral Nelson on board the Vanguard. Kleber brought Boyer and me and without further ado we boarded the English frigate.

The frigate had not taken part in the battle itself as could be expected and so was quite undamaged. Half the size of a ship of the line it was all the same very impressive. It was spotlessly clean with scrubbed decks and shining brass, everything "shipshape" and neatly in place. Orders were given quietly and carried out with near silent efficiency by jack tars who clearly knew just what they were doing as they climbed rigging and set sails. We remained standing on the quarterdeck for the two hour voyage to Aboukir Bay.

Rounding the headland the scene that met us was a truly sorry sight of floundering and damaged ships, bodies and wreckage. On the beach we could make out a large number of French prisoners sitting under guard by red-coated marines. Half naked and despondent in the heat, most of them also looked extremely young. Most turned out to be seventeen or eighteen.

*****

Coming into the bay on the frigate gave us quite a different view from what we had been able to make out from the dunes the night before. Here the bodies and limbs of the dead were floating right past us and the devastation and damage all the ships had suffered was clear to see. Still while almost all the British ships we passed showed signs of damage, that was nothing to what the French fleet had undergone. Clearly we had suffered a catastrophic defeat.

The ships we passed were full of activity as carpenters hammered, and broken spars and ripped sails were thrown overboard. To clean all this up would take some time. Transferred in a long-boat we were politely received aboard HMS Vanguard and taken to the quarter-deck. Much of the rigging and both masts were shattered. Several gaping holes were visible in the hull.

Kleber, who still wore a dressing on his head-wound was greeted by Nelson who also had a bandage around his head. As they compared stories about their injuries I noticed, for I had not known about it, that Nelson had already lost an arm and an eye. They sat down and got straight to business, speaking French.

Nelson reported that he had over one thousand wounded French prisoners. "I am prepared to return your wounded officers on our ships to France. There are two hundred of them. As regards the rest I will deliver them to your care in Alexandria. I have around seven hundred of my men wounded and we will of course be taking them home. It is a dreadful business seeing so many men on both sides die painfully after they have given their country valiant service." Kleber agreed saying that since taking Alexandria they had prepared a hospital, but this number would really stretch the care he could provide.

"Then there is the question of what to do with all of your men that we have captured." Nelson continued, "At a pinch we could cram them all into the French ships we have taken. They have all been badly damaged so the men could endure a very slow and frankly dangerous journey home for as you can see those ships are now hardly seaworthy. Certainly I have no wish to take them back to England. Perhaps we could agree on an alternative."

"And what would that be?" asked Kleber. "It seems your victory here has been pretty overwhelming."

"Well, perhaps. If this succeeds in finishing off your General Bonaparte's dreams of invading India it may be worth what is a heavy price. Did you notice those poor wretches of yours on the beach as you came here?"

"Certainly, "said Kleber.

"My captain of marines tells me they have just completed a headcount. There are three thousand two hundred fair youths of France out on that sand. What I propose is this. I have prepared a document here for you to sign which states that we are releasing these men to you on parole, on condition that they do not in future take up maritime arms against His Britannic Majesty in this conflict."

"You mean you expect General Bonaparte to send them back to France?"

"Yes," said Nelson.

"I see," said Kleber. "I cannot of course commit General Bonaparte to doing this, but it seems a reasonable suggestion. I am prepared to put it to him and I am prepared to sign your paper."

"Excellent." said Nelson. "I am sure that will make my masters in the Admiralty very happy."

So concluded the business part of our visit. Both sides were under no illusion that Napoleon would incorporate these poor young men into his army at the first opportunity, but the British certainly had no wish to be saddled with looking after them either. They also expected, based on this agreement, to be able to come into Alexandria and load up with fresh water and provisions.

This was agreed while we were taken to visit the wounded French officers they had on board. We found them surprisingly appreciative of the way they had been treated by the enemy and several told how they had been rescued by English long-boats. The Vanguard itself they said had lost thirty men and carried seventy-six of its own wounded. There was no way they or we could be certain of the overall number of French dead. Some estimated it must have been in the region of fifteen hundred.

The officers had already been visited by Nelson who asked how they were being treated and indulged in wit and repartee. Still it was clear from the wounds of many of them that however much kindness they received, they would not be seeing France again.

The frigate returned us to Alexandria and Kleber sent a company of soldiers to bring back the sailors on the beach from Aboukir Bay. He then had much to do and kept me on the run delivering messages and orders in preparation for their arrival and the visit for provisions by the English. That went off surprisingly smoothly. Sometimes it was hard to believe we were all still at war.

Chapter 17
Cairo

1798 - 1801

Getting news of the defeat of French Navy at Aboukir Bay (that became known as the Battle of the Nile) to Napoleon was not easy. It took the messenger Kleber sent eleven days to deliver the news. He arrived in Cairo on the day before Napoleon's twenty-ninth birthday with Napoleon receiving the news phlegmatically, playing it down and declaring the French still controlled the land.

We also learnt when the seamen and the wounded arrived from Aboukir Bay that two of our ships of the line, one commanded by Admiral Villeneuve, and two frigates had escaped - without engaging in the battle. When Napoleon heard that he was very angry and blamed the whole defeat on Villeneuve.

The destruction of the *Orient* also had a serious consequence beyond the loss of the ship and its crew. All the treasure and money acquired in Malta had gone up in smoke in the explosion and was meant to finance the whole invasion. I learnt from Kleber this amounted to six hundred thousand livres in gold and diamonds, money to bribe the beys, (the leading Turks) pay the army and coin a new currency for Egypt.

As for Napoleon's choice of route to Cairo it turned out the "canal" he had chosen was completely dried up and it took them three days to reach the Nile walking through extreme heat and driving sandstorms. They also had left in such haste that they were desperately short of water and rations. Dying of heat and thirst many committed suicide. Boyer reported that some upon reaching the Nile threw themselves in it in order to drown. All the way we heard they were attacked by Bedouin and they hit back by massacring whole villages as they passed, looting with impunity as morale and discipline broke down.

On reaching the Nile however where they could get food and water, they recovered. There the Mamelukes, who were by all accounts brilliant cavalrymen, were taken on by Napoleon when they finally attacked outside Cairo near the pyramids. After several unsuccessful charges on the French they withdrew baffled by the French use of infantry in squares which they could not break. This left Napoleon and his army free to march into Cairo on the 24th of July.

*****

Back in Alexandria we then heard that conditions in Cairo and the Delta were deteriorating. On hearing of the French invasion of Egypt and their defeat at the Battle of the Nile the Turkish Sultan Selim III signed a treaty with Britain and Russia and declared war on France. He also as Caliph sent a *firman* or royal decree which was read out in every mosque in Cairo denouncing the French as infidels.

A copy of this was sent to Kleber by Napoleon who could not believe the Turks could ally themselves with the British and the Russians (their traditional enemies) against the French (their traditional allies). As a result he sent us two representatives to take ships from Alexandria out to the blockading British to parley. They were received with diplomatic politeness, but found a senior Turk was on board and were assured that Britain and Turkey were now allies in their war with France. Napoleon however just refused to believe this and saw it as a British trick to mislead him. He was wrong.

A portion of the *firman* read, "they (the French) mock all religions, they reject belief in another life, as well as its rewards and torture, they do not believe in the resurrection of the body, nor in the last judgement and they think that a blind chance presides over their life and death, that they owe their existence to pure matter, and that after this life their body returns to the earth. Their aim is to incite subjects to revolt."

My reading then of this *firman,* which said much else, was that the Caliphate had understood us quite accurately.

Napoleon wrote frequently to Kleber, sometimes twice a day, and it was clear things were not going according to plan in Cairo despite his attempts to celebrate the Prophet's birthday in style, have firework displays and repeatedly tell the Egyptians that the French were "friends of Islam."

Here in Alexandria things were not easy either. Daily I accompanied Kleber as he visited the large number of wounded sailors who needed hospital care. Equally sad and worrying, plague broke out, both among the locals and among us. Ninety-three Frenchmen died of this horrible condition covered in great puss filled swellings or buboes. We were all ordered to strip off and wash ourselves in the sea and concentrate on keeping clean. Strict regulations were introduced to place anyone who made contact with a victim in quarantine despite our having no real understanding of contagion or of what was causing it. Quarantine however seemed to work in containing the spread.

Add to that the behaviour of the three thousand young sailors we now had to contend with. They were wandering around the town pilfering, drinking heavily, assaulting local women and insulting the men. On hearing this from Kleber Napoleon ordered they be formed into a "naval brigade" and sent out to man the fort at Aboukir Bay and there wait to be assigned to French ships. Kleber was not happy with this, pointing out that their parole explicitly excluded sending them to sea and to do so would be regarded by the British as a crime.

Sure enough when two were assigned to the crew of a corvette that tried unsuccessfully to get through the British blockade, when captured and identified, they were shot on the order of Captain Cook. Napoleon however continued to over-ride Kleber with this policy to his great annoyance.

*****

Then there was El Koraim. Kleber quickly suspected our tamed Mameluke might be up to something and by some careful intelligence work we were able to intercept a letter he was attempting to smuggle out of the city. It was to Murad Bey, commander of the Mamelukes who since his defeat by the Pyramids was now in Upper Egypt beyond French reach. In it he promised the bey that if he attacked Alexandria he would deliver the city over to him.

Kleber placed him under arrest in a French warship in the harbour and then despatched him to Cairo under armed guard to stand trial. There he was convicted of treason and sentenced to death, but as appeared customary in Egypt he was given the option of death or of paying a heavy fine. Possibly as a result of a misunderstanding over the fine, he chose death and was shot on the 6th of September. His head was removed and paraded around the city with an inscription describing his crime. No doubt this did not improve relations with the locals and Kleber was not happy when he heard what had happened and how the case had been handled.

Relations between Kleber and Napoleon did not get better. Kleber hated being an administrator and being responsible for the accounts and Napoleon accused him of spending far too much. He wanted to be back commanding his brigade. He was also very critical of Napoleon. I remember him saying, "Never a fixed plan. Everything goes in fits and starts. Each day influenced only by the events of that day. He claims to believe in fate. Is he loved? How could he be? He loves nobody." At the same time I heard him admit to Boyer that Napoleon was always daring and was an extraordinary man. I found Boyer a brutal, arrogant and ambitious officer who spoke of the locals with complete contempt. I did not trust him and kept as low a profile in his presence as I could.

Finally the tensions between Kleber and Napoleon reached the point where he offered his resignation and asked to be sent home to France, but somehow Napoleon cajoled him into staying saying how much he admired and valued him. He was then summoned to join Napoleon in Cairo, so off we went and on the 22nd of October 1798 we arrived with a suitable armed convoy.

*****

Something we could see had gone terribly wrong. The gates of the city were open and unguarded. Beyond them the streets were in turmoil. Everywhere there was riot and disorder. Much shouting was coming from the minarets and yelling from the men in the streets and above that we could hear the boom of gunfire. Howitzers on the walls of the Citadel were pouring volley after volley in the direction of what we were to learn was the ancient mosque and university of Al Azhar. This artillery fire continued for hours.

What had happened was an unplanned and spontaneous uprising of the stallholders and bazaar people triggered by fear of a new French property tax and anti-French preaching by young students of Islam from Al Azhar in the mosques. No-one, French or Egyptian had predicted it. It was however put down with summary and efficient brutality which involved the invasion and despoiling of the Al Azhar mosque. The artillery barrage flattened all the properties surrounding this ancient centre of Islamic learning, though care was taken not to destroy it or its most sacred and ancient manuscripts which Napoleon's savants were sent in to remove.

Napoleon played his cards cleverly by calling meetings and issuing soothing words and peace was quickly restored. We were set up in a very comfortable house formerly owned by a leading Mameluke which came complete with obsequious servants. Kleber was treated as Napoleon's best friend and kept right by him as he rushed around the city while he indulged yet again in a flat-out period of organising things, saying that he would teach Kleber good administration as he intended to transform Cairo into a modern city with broad boulevards. Kleber was not impressed sounding off to me after these sessions when I was getting him ready for dinner, that he thought Napoleon was very bad at administration because he was far too hands on and did not think things through properly, leaving chaos, waste and destitution behind him.

Cairo was however a large and well supplied city with extreme wealth and poverty side by side. We rested and I was able with visits to the markets to make sure we ate well and safely and we were all provided with freshly tailored uniforms made of linen suitable for the heat.

One of the Mameluke bey's grandest palaces was taken over and renamed *Le Tivoli*. It was set up like a gentlemen's club for the officers with bar, lounge, library and billiard room. The high point of its opening, attended by Napoleon and Kleber, was a grand ball at which I and other *ordonnances* were expected to act as waiters and footmen. A military band played while some fifteen European ladies dressed in their best finery were entertained. Kleber again was not impressed. The problem was there were simply far too few women given the large number of men. There were of course no Egyptian women present.

*****

Everyone at headquarters knew that Napoleon's wife Josephine had taken a lover, (His identity was intercepted and then leaked by Nelson. He was a hussar with the wonderful name of Hippolyte Charles) so it was not the greatest surprise when he became enamoured of the very beautiful twenty year old Pauline Foure, new wife of a young chasseur officer who had smuggled her into Egypt fetchingly dressed in the uniform of his division. This young man, after an attempt by Napoleon to despatch him to France failed, (The British picked him up and returned him to Alexandria) had to put up with his commander in chief carrying on a very public affair with his wife. She divorced him and took to riding around Cairo in a coach with Napoleon dressed as a general! She also appeared looking beautiful in gowns and was referred to as Napoleon's Cleopatra and as "The General." Everyone wondered if this was partly for Josephine's benefit.

Such fun and games were interrupted when Napoleon went on a trip to Gaza. There he intercepted a message prepared for Murad Bey who was still holed up in Upper Egypt. It was from Ibrahim Bey the joint leader of the Mamelukes and Pasha Ahmed Djezzar, Turkish governor of Damascus in Syria and a very powerful figure. The message said that Djezzar and Ibrahim Bey were building up an army in Syria to invade Egypt and defeat the French. Immediately Napoleon knew he would have to lead an army against them.

Chapter 18
From Egypt to Syria

On returning to Cairo Napoleon had a careful planning session with his four best generals and set out his general plan in a document which I saw. His intention was to lead his army out of Egypt and along the Syrian (Palestinian) coast taking first El Arish then Gaza, then Jaffa and finally taking on and defeating Djezzar in his coastal fortress at Acre. If he succeeded in doing this Turkey would be confined to its Anatolian heartland and France, with allies in the local Christians, Druze, and Jews, would be able to control a substantial Oriental Empire from which an invasion of India could be launched.

Kleber was put in command of his old division and was delighted and it was heartening to see how glad the men were to have him as their commander when he set off to inspect them. I was glad to be back doing what I felt was a proper military job sorting out horses for him and myself and getting all his and my kit ready for what would be a long and difficult campaign.

*****

At the start of February 1799 Kleber's division with General Reynier's division were the first to set off and attack El Arish. In all our army consisted of four divisions of nearly ten thousand infantry. There were also 1,400 artillery, 800 cavalry and a new unit of 100 men in a camel corps able to handle the desert and transport the sick and wounded. The baggage train consisted of 3,000 package camels and 3,000 mules laden with provisions. It was planned the heavy artillery would be placed in small boats to sail for the coast near Acre where they would be needed to bombard the walls when the siege was launched there.

We thought El Arish would be a push-over. It was not. To our surprise it contained a garrison of 1,800 Turks and Mamelukes and had just been re-enforced by 1,500 Albanians and Moroccans sent by Djezzar from Acre. After an initial success surprising their outer garrison in which we killed 400 and took 800 prisoners, the men in the inner fort resisted with determination. They also had been well supplied by sea with food and water while we, after our trip from Cairo marching across desert, were short of both. After nearly a week of the siege our men were sufficiently desperate to start eating our horses. Finally, accepting the rules of war that state a defender in a siege should surrender once the walls are breached or face massacre, the Turks and Arabs surrendered after an action which still cost many French lives.

Inside along with their wounded, there was a chamber stuffed with dead and nearly dead plague victims. The stench was unbelievable and the implication ominous. What was to be done with these hundreds of prisoners and the wounded? It was decided that the prisoners be made to swear on the Koran that they would not take up arms against the French for a year and then, instead of being let go to return to Egypt, which happened to the small number of Mamelukes among them, they were forced to enlist into our army – from which hardly surprisingly - they quickly deserted.

*****

Our division was then placed in the lead and on we went having fallen behind Napoleon's planned time-table by eleven days. Kleber was keen to keep us moving for the desert heat was unbearable. We had an Arab guide but Kleber became increasingly suspicious of him. Finally the man professed to be lost. Kleber did not believe him and deciding he had deliberately led us around in the desert, had him shot. After several wasted and exhausting days we finally arrived in Gaza which had fallen to Napoleon without a fight providing us with water and provisions, a surprising amount of ammunition and an unexpected stock of cannon balls.

Now we were out of the desert and we found the Mediterranean climate was like a French winter, extremely cold and with rain lashing down. This did not suit the camels which sickened in large numbers. It did not suit us either. Our new linen uniforms were far too thin and many fell sick and a hospital for seven hundred had to be set up. Worryingly more than thirty men developed symptoms of the plague from which very few survived.

*****

On March 3rd we reached the ancient city of Jaffa with its imposing crusader castle and harbour. It was surrounded by a strong outer wall with a high inner fort. Our division was set in place on the North of the city so we could repulse any attack that Djezzar might launch from Acre or Nablus. Our light guns then pounded this outer wall and our sappers put in place explosives which brought part of it down. It was then breached on the 7th with the loss of many French lives, for breaching walls always results in heavy casualty rates. Because of this as at Al Arish the accepted rules of war were that once walls are breached in a siege, the besieged should be given the choice of surrender or expect to be slaughtered within to the last person. Napoleon duly sent in an emissary with a letter for the governor reminding him that his choice was surrender or death. The response was to decapitate the emissary and display his head on a pike above the gate.

To prepare for this dangerous second assault the troops were issued with a second stiff dose of spirits. The effect of the decapitation and of the spirits on the troops not unnaturally was an alcohol fuelled rage and loss of inhibitions and they stormed the walls with ferocity, suffering many more casualties. Within three hours however they had broken through.

Our division remained on the North side as directed and my primary duty while we were in and around Jaffa was to keep close to Kleber at all times as his bodyguard. The other divisions then poured into the city.

What followed was as shameful and horrific as can be imagined as everyone, old and young male and female suffered murder and rape as French soldiers screaming hate massacred everyone they could find. The cries and howls went on right through the night during which time we think some two thousand Turkish soldiers were killed though several thousand more managed to barricade themselves into the inner fort or citadel.

The next morning Napoleon sent in two of his aides. His choice was peculiar, two seventeen year olds. These were Beauharnais, son of Josephine who often accompanied him, and his young companion, Crozier. Issued with a ceremonial sash which denoted they had Napoleon's authority, they were told to go in and tell the rampaging troops to desist from further rape and pillage.

As you can imagine this provoked laughter, but Crozier bravely pushed forward and ordered the men to do as he said in the name of their commander, General Bonaparte. This time they fell silent and stopped. At that the bey commanding the Turkish troops, shouted down from the citadel to Crozier asking him to accept their surrender on condition his men would not be killed. Crozier, with no real authority to do so, agreed. With that the Turkish soldiers came filing out silently, laying down their arms as they did so. The more sober French soldiers then formed a guard and marched them down the street past Napoleon's headquarters directing them into two camp areas. Their numbers totalled just on four thousand. Napoleon standing by Kleber watched them go by his face ashen and incredulous and I heard him exclaim, "What am I going to do with them?" He then took the two young men aside and I could hear him berating them.

The prisoners were all sat down on the ground and their hands tied behind their backs after being given some biscuit and water. This provoked anger from our soldiers who were short of both and there was an ugly, almost mutinous atmosphere.

Napoleon then called a meeting in his tent for all the senior officers. I was in there with Kleber when Napoleon asked them first what was known about the prisoners and then for their opinions as to what he should do. He was told that nearly a thousand of the men were among those we had captured at El Arish and had released on parole and had then been drafted into our army.

The point was then argued by several officers that this made those men guilty of breaking parole and of desertion. As for the others, it was argued that according to the generally accepted rules of war, since the Turkish commander had rejected the offer of surrender by cutting off our emissary's head, they had all forfeited the right to live and Crozier's act of offering the bey safe conduct did not change that for he had no authority to do so. No-one was ready to say what should now be done, so Napoleon closed the meeting and announced he would be calling a second meeting the following day.

*****

On coming out of that meeting, Kleber suggested we go for a bit of a walk and after a long silence he said, "Bioletti as an ordinary soldier I am interested to see what you think we should do with these prisoners for I think we are faced with a terrible dilemma."

"Yes sir, we are." I replied. "I doubt any of them know or understand anything about these rules of war I heard mentioned. Perhaps we should just send them back under guard to Egypt?"

"I am glad," said Kleber, "That you have not suggested we just let them all go for we know they would then simply rush up to Acre and join Djezzar."

"I can see that sir."

"The problem with sending them back to Egypt is the large number of men it would take to supervise and guard such a large number of prisoners. I think that would weaken our already barely adequate forces greatly."

"Yes sir, particularly as we have so many now sick and I heard the senior surgeon reporting that we have a growing problem with plague."

"So you think the parole rules should be applied?" he said.

"I don't know sir. It seemed harsh but not unreasonable when the English Captain Cook shot the two sailors who tried to escape with the corvette for breaking a parole agreement they had signed, but to shoot nearly a thousand defenceless men for doing so – surely that cannot be right?"

"I am not sure the number makes any difference Bioletti. A thousand extra defenders of this castle I am certain cost many more French lives than if they had not been here."

"So we soldiers will just have to be formed up into firing squads to finish them off?" I asked.

"Rather that than us being defeated." He replied.

"And what about the three thousand others who thought they had been able to surrender to Crozier and handed in their weapons? They and the bey who commanded them could not know he did not have full authority could they?" I asked.

"His action in accepting their surrender, no doubt done out of a sense of humanity, has placed General Bonaparte in a terrible predicament.

I think it may boil down to us either going forward to attack Djezzar in Acre where victory could result in the establishment of a real French Oriental Empire, or retreating back to Egypt with four thousand prisoners to await a Turkish invasion led by Djezzar."

"But before we "go forward to attack Acre" what will need to be done here?" I asked.

"I think you know." he replied, "And I hate to think what it will do to our men." After that we both just kept silent.

The next day Napoleon had his meeting. This time I was not present having much to sort out concerning our horses and kit. The meeting went on for several hours for Napoleon insisted all his senior officers were in agreement with his decision before they went ahead. This was that if the campaign was to continue all four thousand prisoners would have to be killed.

I was I suppose lucky in that my role and duties meant I was not directly involved as on the 8th, 9th and 10th of March firing parties and then bayonet parties systematically slaughtered all of them by the sea shore. Kleber supervised his grenadiers to see that the executions were carried out as quickly and cleanly as possible. He found the whole thing sickening. How Kleber's adjutant General Boyer went about his duties I would rather not know.

Even while this was happening the plague was spreading. Desgennetes the chief medical officer was sure many soldiers had caught it when carrying out their initial pillage of Jaffa and he set up isolation wards for the sick and buried the bodies of the dead in lime pits. Napoleon thought susceptibility to the plague was a matter of will-power. Those who were afraid of it got it. Still he backed Desgennetes' isolation policies and on the day after the prisoner slaughter was concluded, he spent an hour and a half visiting the wards and talking to the sufferers, an act of courage and humanity that was subsequently much celebrated by those who wished to forget what had happened on the days before. Those of us who were there could not.

Chapter 19
Acre and
Sir Sidney Smith

Soon it was time for our four divisions to press on. Acre was another large walled coastal Crusader fortress and town some sixty miles on up the coast and we proceeded to march there mostly through driving rain, halting on Mount Tabor on the 17th of March. There we could look down and see it and what we saw came as an unexpected surprise. There in front of us were two Royal Navy ships of the line, several British gunboats and a flotilla of Turkish ships. They had all arrived to support Acre from the sea and were under the command of a most unusual man who I was to learn was wily, brave and humane, Sir Sidney Smith.

Ahmed Pasha el-Jezzar "the Butcher "as I also learnt, was the Sultan's governor of Acre, and was a man in his late sixties with a fearsome reputation. He was known for sadistic cruelty, political cunning and considerable ability. He was a self-made man who had started out as a Mameluke slave who had fought, schemed and murdered his way to the top ranks of the Ottoman Empire. Now backed with all the food, guns, supplies and ammunition he could want by the British and their Turkish allies he and Smith made for a formidable partnership.

Our first assault on Acre failed, This turned out to be because Smith had cleverly toughened their fortifications. Jezzar's response to our attack was to have all the Christians in Acre slaughtered and all the French prisoners he held strangled. At first Napoleon and his generals, including Kleber, thought we would soon win and in the next assault Kleber sent in his grenadiers. He went in with them, against Napoleon's orders, his sabre flashing as he bellowed encouragement. "Sorry Bioletti, but you're too small for this. Wait for your chance to fight as a skirmisher." he told me.

They were repulsed but somehow Kleber came through unscathed. It was then decided they would take more time before their next assault on the walls. The local Druze arrived and at inflated prices provided us with everything we could need as regards food, so we could rest a bit after the forced march from Jaffa and our assault. Not for long though.

*****

At the start of April intelligence came through that the Turks were putting together a huge and disparate army heading out from Damascus and Napoleon decided to send off 4,000 of us to face it. This included Kleber's brigade and I soon had my chance to support him in active combat. It was however a close run thing.

Kleber led us on a forced march around Mount Tabor hoping to surprise the enemy on the other side before daybreak, but it was further and tougher than he thought and when we came around the mount at 6.a.m. it was light and Mameluke cavalry and Turkish infantry were waiting for us. We immediately formed squares and fought off a relentless attack from the huge numbers surrounding us. This went on for hours of close fighting in the full heat of the day. Disciplined and experienced our infantry did not break ranks, but we were close to doing so.

In the end Kleber decided that all he could do was to get us into a column and attempt to break through the surrounding force, clearly a last desperate move, but just before he gave the order Napoleon arrived heading quite a small force. When he had heard what Kleber was planning from a letter Kleber had left him, he had guessed it could go wrong and had followed to give us support. On sizing up the situation instead of going straight for our attackers, however, he sent in his skirmishers to burn their camp and baggage train. This upset the Turks no end and many broke off their attack. Kleber then ordered his grenadiers to form a line, fix bayonets and charge. The enemy broke and ran. It was a route despite their ten to one advantage in numbers. Everyone agreed it was a brilliant example of Napoleon's tactical skill and it certainly saved our lives turning defeat into victory. Again somehow both Kleber and I came through it unhurt.

We then returned to Acre to attempt to besiege the town for what turned out to be the last time thinking we had the upper hand. The wily Smith however now sent Napoleon letters which enraged and upset him, for Smith wrote and saw himself as Napoleon's equal. In his last letter (which Napoleon showed Kleber) he suggested that Napoleon would do better to withdraw and return to Egypt as he could assure him that a huge allied fleet was on its way to drive him out of Syria, adding he only suggested this in order to save both sides from unnecessary bloodshed.

He also had leaflets dropped in large numbers from the walls of the castle purporting to come from the Sultan for the French troops. These repeated the claim that massive fleets would soon arrive, adding that if they gave themselves up they would be given passports to go home. Of course if you could believe that you could believe anything, but the claim that a huge fleet was on its way certainly sapped morale. (In fact as we realised later, there were no massive fleets. It was just Smith's plausible propaganda.)

Kleber thought all this un-nerved Napoleon for after a final and very bloody attempt on the walls, on the 21st of May he decided to call off the siege and return to Cairo. Smith it seemed had foiled his destiny.

Chapter 20
Retreat to Cairo

The retreat back to Cairo was a nightmare. Of course Napoleon never accepted it was a retreat or that we had suffered defeat. Instead he issued a proclamation that claimed the expedition had been a succession of glorious victories! The reality was we were faced with transporting 2,300 sick and wounded 500 miles back to Egypt.

Kleber was of the opinion that things could have been greatly improved if Napoleon had been prepared to ask Smith for the safe passage of French ships to carry the wounded back to Cairo. Smith had already behaved well over prisoner exchanges and he had taken two hundred of Kleber's grenadiers who had broken through into Acre only to find themselves surrounded. He had offered them the chance of surrendering to his marines to prevent them being slaughtered by the Turks who took no prisoners, so that is what they did.

Napoleon however had been so annoyed by Smith's clever and "impertinent" comments that he refused to have anything more to do with him.

At Jaffa however when there was a chance to put twelve hundred sick onto small boats to proceed to Damietta on the Egyptian coast, they immediately ran into Smith's blockade. His response was not to sink them but escort them and provide the sick with food, water and all the help his men could give. With his ships observing our journey south he could see the dire condition we were in. Quite the considerate enemy, but as I was to learn there was method in this policy of "being nice to the French" too.

*****

115

Desgenettes did an admirable job with his medics and Napoleon saw to it that the whole army, including officers, walked, and that all horses, donkeys, mules and camels were used to transport the sick. Inevitably though, many of them died.

No-one could be left behind for Turkish practice was to kill enemy wounded and often to torture them first, something that could be expected after what we had done at Jaffa. The plague cases though posed a real problem. Most who contracted this horrible illness died, but a small minority recovered. When ill they were very difficult to transport and care for so Napoleon suggested to Desgenettes that he administer a fatal dose of opium to the worst cases. Desgenettes however was adamant that he would stand by his Hippocratic Oath to "do no harm." Kleber and I discussed this and found it hard to decide who was right. We saw terrible suffering, but the medical team though they could give little relief or hope, could often provide gentle care and were trusted to be doing their best. In the end a Turkish apothecary agreed to mix opium in with the food of those most ill who we would have to leave behind. Between thirty and fifty died in this way.

*****

Outside Cairo we were housed in a village while they provided all of us who were still able bodied with new uniforms and General Dugua who had been left in charge of Cairo was ordered to prepare a triumphal procession for our glorious victorious army. We marched into Cairo on the 14th of June through the Bab-el-Nasr Victory Gate escorted by military bands and were greeted by curious crowds. We were then given a bounty payment and three days leave for the fleshpots of Cairo.

For me this meant returning with Kleber to our fine Cairo house where there was time for some comparative rest and relaxation after such a demanding campaign. I really enjoyed the chance to visit the markets and stock up with the best food I could find for our table. Kleber was quick to visit the sick and wounded of his division and I often accompanied him when he did so.

He also did some calculations which he showed me. He thought it very difficult to be certain of numbers, but his estimate was that we had lost a third of our men, almost as many from disease as killed in action with as many wounded or ill.

So here I had a short period of respite after the relentless pressures of being out on campaign. I was not wounded or ill, but, like many of us, I had other reactions to deal with, in particular the dreams and nightmares that plagued me. Dreams and nightmares that went all the way back to being with Peter Falconi when he had dropped dead at my side in Turin, through Lodi, and the siege of Mantua. Now I had El Arish and Acre to add. I had seen not just death and pain in battle, horrible as that can be, but so much cruelty and violence, so many occasions when the perpetrators derived a deliberate and positive pleasure from inflicting pain and suffering on others with impunity, freed from the constraints of any sense of right or wrong.

*****

What we did not know, but later heard from Smith, was that Napoleon was planning a secret departure for France in two frigates he had specially prepared. Smith correctly guessed this would happen and encouraged it by providing Napoleon with up to date newspapers. These showed what the political situation was in France and in Europe which for the French was dire.

He then tactfully took his ship the *Tigre* and the other ship of the line that kept the British blockade effective, out of commission for nearly a month while he "put in for supplies" to Rhodes. This was noticed by the French admiral in the Mediterranean who put in to Alexandria in order to send Napoleon a message that the blockade was not in operation. Immediately, on the 17th of August, Napoleon set sail for France.

Smith's thinking was that with Napoleon back in France it would be much easier to negotiate a treaty with the French which would see us all leave Egypt without further loss of life or threat to India.

Kleber (and I) only heard all this later when he dealt with Smith. At the time Kleber was furious when he learned that Napoleon had left without telling him of his intention or even saying goodbye – probably because he did not wish to face Kleber's anger for he really could lose it when provoked. Napoleon had however appointed Kleber to be his successor, leaving him fully in charge.

Why had Napoleon gone? Though the first reaction of many of us including Kleber was that we had been left in the lurch because of his overall failure, it also became clear that he had concluded that France was in a terrible political, military and economic mess and only he could save it, and as things turned out many in France agreed.

The Directory, government by five often competing lawyers, was as the papers said, a corrupt disaster and militarily the Austrians were again in the ascendant and everything achieved by us in the Italian Campaign had been lost. Napoleon on his return quickly overturned the Directory, became First Consul and in fact imposed a military dictatorship on France.

Kleber discovered that organisationally and financially he had been left with a bankrupt and half-strength army with no funds to pay for it and a city and a country in a complete mess. He had long decided, as I had heard him say back in Alexandria, that he felt the whole campaign had been over-optimistic and misguided. He concluded that its driving force was the aggrandisement of Napoleon and he wrote a damning report on these lines to the Directory.

*****

Someone else who had been deserted by Napoleon without a word, despite walking with him dressed very prettily in her smart, specially made chasseur uniform the day before he left, was the beautiful Pauline Foures. Rather to my surprise she and Kleber were soon consoling each other despite their difference in age. Tall, good-looking, with enormous presence and a deep, rich voice, not to mention his reputation as a brave, very clever and dashing soldier and commander, Kleber had more than enough to attract many women I thought. His life though had been such that he had never had much chance of marrying and certainly in these past two years since I had joined his staff there had been little opportunity for any social life. Frankly I was glad for him. To see them together was to see a quite different side in him from the military man I had been serving.

As for me as in Italy I had no intention of paying for sex with the available Egyptian or the French women "camp followers". They really were not very attractive and it certainly did not look as if many of them were free from infections. Kleber had another interest. Not only was his father a stone-mason but he was a prominent Freemason and was instrumental in bringing freemasonry to Egypt. In 1800, Kleber opened a masonic temple in Cairo and thus created the Isis lodge (*La Loge Isis*), serving as its first Master. Promoting Liberty, Equality and Fraternity especially to brother masons and describing God as the Grand Architect of the Universe the free-masons also promoted religious toleration. I soon discovered many French officers and for that matter many English officers were masons. It was and remains an international brotherhood and though I was not asked to join while in Egypt it impressed me and I was impressed that some well-educated and travelled Egyptians were encouraged to join. Finally I heard that Smith was a mason.

*****

It then did not take long for Smith and Kleber to get together with the Turks. They met on the *Tigre* which was moored off El Arish and worked out a peace treaty between them.

It certainly was fascinating to see Sir Sidney in action. It was again impressive to come aboard a beautifully run eighty gun British battleship. Totally fluent in French having been involved in our revolutionary wars on the royalist side, I heard him regale Kleber with incredible stories. He had blown up the arsenal in Toulon when Napoleon was fighting there as a captain of artillery to regain the city for the Revolution and later as a Royal Navy captain he was captured and spent time in a French prison.

He was extremely pleasant and friendly, described himself as a "Francophile" and was good at buttering up the Turks who he seemed to understand and who thought he was marvellous, the Caliph having for a time appointed him commander in chief of the Turkish Army! He and Kleber got on well and together they soon worked out an agreement by which the British Navy would ship the French Army together with all its arms back to France while the Turkish Army would take over Egypt. The treaty signed on the 28th of January 1800 was called The Convention of Al Arish and honour on both sides appeared to be satisfied.

Sadly, it was all too good to be true. Both the British and French governments rejected it saying that Kleber and Smith had over-reached themselves and that they did not have the authority to make peace like that. Britain demanded unconditional surrender from the French. They also demanded all our arms and did so in the most insulting manner as if to deliberately undermine what Smith had done. Kleber was furious.

*****

The Turks under their Grand Vizier then decided to invade Egypt with an army of 40,000 men, stopping at El Arish to massacre the French garrison of 250. We had only 10,000 men to put up against them, but by the ruins of Heliopolis just north of Cairo, Kleber took them on. He was at his most inspiring and our troops responded, their discipline and bravery were such that despite being outnumbered four to one the Turks broke under fire and were completely defeated.

Cairo was then as peaceful as it had ever been when two months later he was walking on the terrace of the palace used as his headquarters. He was in conversation with a visiting officer and I was collecting some papers he had just asked for. A young man approached and Kleber thought he was begging when he produced a knife from under his robes and stabbed Kleber to death. It was June 24th.

His name was Suliman El Halaby, a Kurd, and he came from Aleppo in Syria. At his trial it came out that he was studying Islam at Al Azar and had told his teacher that he wished to commit jihad for the glory of God by killing an infidel. He was publicly executed after a trial before a huge crowd in a way too dreadful to describe, maintaining complete silence until finally crying out at the top of his voice, "Allah Akbar, God is great and Muhammad is his Prophet."

I thought co-operating in this barbarous execution shamed us and I am certain Kleber would have hated it. Yes, he deserved to die, but not like that.

*****

No-one was more devastated by Kleber's death than me. For two years I had hardly been out of his sight, and I had seen him in public and in private. He had trusted me completely and had used me as a sounding board to try out ideas and phrases before using them on Napoleon and the other generals. He was also a true believer in the Revolution and the new French Republic and thought that what we were doing was building a better world, despite the obvious contradictions and shortcoming. For him Liberty, Equality and Fraternity really meant something as did his membership of the Free Masons.

I had been privy to most of his secrets and I had been constantly inspired by his dedication to the tasks he was given, even when he did not agree with them. His care and concern for the welfare of his men was second nature to him. Working for him had been tough for he had quite a temper and did not tolerate fools, inefficiency or dishonesty. He had though treated me very well and I had learnt much from him. To serve him had been a rare honour.

Bioletti in Saint Domingue
- 1801 to 1803 -

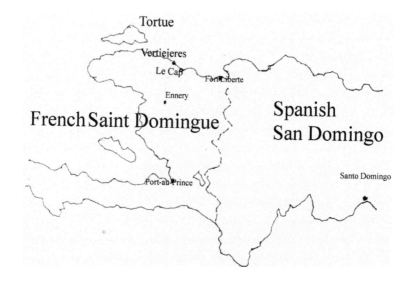

Chapter 21
Out of Egypt

Kleber's death was met with widespread condemnation and sadness across all ranks for he was loved and trusted far more than Napoleon and an enormous military funeral was organised for him. At the end of it I saw Pauline Faure. She was on her own and dressed in black, her blonde hair hidden by a concealing bonnet. We had of course met when she had visited Kleber, though we had hardly spoken. She saw me and came over and said. "You know Bioletti, he often mentioned you, said you had saved his life and did a wonderful job for him."

"Thoughtful of you to say so." I replied. "In all the time I worked for him, I never saw him happier than when he was with you. You really made him laugh and relax."

"Yes," she said, "He was very special. I really admired him. He was a great lover and a real friend. Perhaps more so than someone else I could mention. Yes, in both departments. He was someone I knew I could trust. I shall really miss him. What the future would have been for us I have no idea. The tragedy is he had much more to give and to do, for himself and I think for France."

We walked on silently. "And another thing Bioletti, he told me we both share something in common."

"And what's that?" I asked surprised.

"We both have fathers who are clockmakers. He said when your soldiering is over you might become one. Was he right?" she asked.

"He said he thought it might be a great job for me and yes I might, but after these years in the Army I really have no idea. It's more complicated than that. And what did you do before you met your gallant chasseur?" I asked.

"You mean my husband! Millinery. I made and sold fancy hats for ladies." she said.

"Enjoy it?" I asked.

"I enjoyed being part of a family business. Buying, making, selling, turning in a profit. That's a good life, at no-one's beck and call. Someday I want to run my own business like my parents have. Not be run by anyone."

"You mean by a husband?" I asked.

"You mean like the dashing chasseur? I am not against husbands, but he was so controlling, so manipulative, so jealous! Always wanted to keep me in my place and that place was to be good in bed, look pretty and do what I was told. And that's what I did. I was such a good girl until the "little corporal" came along. All that slavish adoration from such a powerful and brilliant man. Yes, quite turned my head." she said reflectively.

"And he liked you dressing up like a soldier?" I asked.

"He loved it." She replied, "Found it a real turn on, and he seemed to need a turn on. He also liked to upset others and watch them trying to hide their feelings in front of him. Sometimes I thought it wasn't really me he was mad about, but someone I reminded him of." She said pensively.

Her puzzling comment stuck in my mind until much later when I was to meet another Pauline, Napoleon's sister. We continued talking like this all the way back to the house which Napoleon had set up for her. We found our clock-making fathers had endowed both of us with a fascination for dates and numbers, for handling figures and for speculating about how to control and measure time. We just hit it off and found lots to talk about.

When we reached her door she said, "Bioletti, now we are both pretty much on our own I would like it if you felt like calling to take me out for a walk along the Nile, or out to those pyramids or to one of those little bistros our camp followers have set up, but on one condition. I've had enough of romance here in Egypt. Could we just see each other as friends? I think you're the sort of rare person who could do that.

"Of course," I replied, hoping for something more.

"I want to calm down." She went on, "Sort out my thoughts and get back to France as soon as I can. Obviously there is nothing left for me here. And you?" she asked.

"I have no idea what will happen to me next. I guess the Army could send me off on some campaign any time." I said, "Of course I would love to see you and yes I think I can manage a Platonic friendship – unless of course you change your mind!"

"Platonic! Wow what an educated chap you must be." she laughed.

After that we met twice before I was sent off by the Army. Each time she appeared in a neat brown cotton dress with long sleeves and a full bonnet so as not to be easily recognised. She was sharp, observant and intelligent and we found we had much to talk about and share. She really was not looking for romance and stuck to that, which I thought was rather a pity.

*****

For me things changed very quickly. Based on seniority General Menou succeeded to Kleber's position. A very physically unattractive man, pot-bellied, notorious for his slovenly dress, a convert to Islam married to a plump Egyptian woman, he did not like or admire Kleber and the first thing he did was to get rid of all the officers at headquarters who had been working with him. He also accused Kleber's adjutant general Boyer of embezzling funds and he was sent back to France to face a court martial. That did not upset me, true or false. Of course there was then no place for me and I was ordered to report to the sergeant major in charge of skirmishers and allocated a place in their barracks.

It was a rude return to the basics of soldiering after living in Kleber's grand Cairo mansion and it made me very aware of how well I had eaten and what an interesting and comparatively safe life I had when serving as an *ordonnance*.

After only a few days I was sent off with a company of skirmishers to support an attempt to flush out and defeat Murad Bey from his hideout in Upper Egypt. This went on until the news came through that he had suddenly died. When we got back to Cairo Pauline was gone.

In March 1801 the British General Abercromby landed near Alexandria with 17,000 men and three weeks later I took part in a badly planned and badly led battle against British troops that included Scottish highlanders in kilts. What a sight they were, and what a sound with their screaming bagpipes, but tough soldiers.

The British, as if to rub salt in our wounds, also brought over a few regiments of handsomely attired and well trained Indian troops to fight us. I was very lucky to be only slightly wounded in one leg for casualties on both sides were high. We were thoroughly defeated and stumbled back to Cairo.

*****

General Belliard being in charge then decided in late June to sue for surrender. In his negotiations with the British he reached an agreement which when it was announced everyone thought sounded very similar to that made between Kleber and Smith, except now thousands more had died for nothing on both sides.

On 6th July we marched out of Cairo "with full military honours" that is with our muskets and flags flying and Kleber in his coffin on a gun carriage. In truth we looked a sorry sight. We then embarked on boats up the Nile after we had handed over our arms and artillery to the smiling British and from there we embarked onto British Navy ships and transports and an uncomfortable but uneventful journey back to France. We were lucky to receive such treatment for Britain and France were still at war in Europe.

In this account I have failed to mention the savants who came with us and who I was able to talk to on the journey back. Often ignored and treated by many military as irrelevant – we were after all fighting a war, I came to realise on that trip that their achievements were perhaps the only lasting positive outcome of this whole Egyptian campaign. They had worked extremely hard under tough conditions researching ancient and present Egypt, and had discovered a great deal about both. They were allowed by the British to keep all their meticulously researched documents, but had to surrender all the artefacts they had collected, the most important being the Rosetta Stone, the key to deciphering ancient languages. These were now all destined for the British Museum.

Of the 40,000 soldiers who had set out, the British repatriated 24,500 of us, also thousands of sick and wounded. That means around 15,000 had died in battle or from disease.

So I had survived two of Napoleon's campaigns, was still in one piece and was only twenty-three years old.

Chapter 22
Off to the Other Indies

The British Navy landed us at Morlaix, a small Breton fishing port in the Finistere area of Northern France. Perhaps it was chosen because during their blockade of the Channel no French warship could go there. The blockade however was now lifted for an uneasy peace had been agreed between Great Britain and the French Republic with the ending of the Egyptian campaign. It was known as the Peace of Amiens.

And so I arrived back in France. Thin, hungry, sunburnt, and nursing a cut that had nearly healed. Our treatment at the hands of the British had been as good as could have been expected. We ate the same pretty poor diet as they did, and tried to sleep cramped up in the same hammocks as they did. The jack tars were kept busy and worked hard, but when they finally got off duty were happy to drink grog with us. This was a strange mixture of rum, lemon-juice and water none of us had ever tasted but they were very happy with it. The lemon juice they told us was to stop scurvy and it seemed to work. I enjoyed trying to learn some English and make myself understood to them which most of my French comrades did not.

I felt rather isolated having to muck in with a team of skirmishers who did not know me except as the Italian *ordonnance* who had served General Kleber. That counted for something for he was generally well thought of. I had also accounted quite well for myself in that last battle in Egypt when things descended into hand to hand combat. Still, coming back to France just made me more aware of how alone I was. Coming ashore emphasised for me that I was not French and I had no family to return to. I knew that my membership of the French Army, which now I learnt had just taken over complete control of Piedmont and Turin, annexing it into France, would make my return there neither popular with my uncle and his family, nor safe for me in Turin.

I was nothing but an almost penniless soldier, part of a military unit, living under military discipline and the only money I had was the sparse and irregular pay of a private. This meant I had no option but to wait and see where the Army would send me next.

*****

We were billeted in some rather grubby barracks in the town and the sergeant major, his name was Girard, set about making a very careful check of all our records, where we had been and what we had done which was slightly intimidating. The political atmosphere had certainly changed. Napoleon after his return to France and his sudden overthrow of the Directory was now very much in charge as First Consul and dictator and as we constantly read, he was setting about working on all sorts of reforms in the Law, Education and government.

The Republic however had now lost all pretence of democracy as centralised military rule with a powerful bureaucracy took its place. Attitudes like those of Kleber in favour of liberty, equality and fraternity had become definitely "unfashionable" and for some dangerous. Those who expressed them were labelled I thought most unfairly "Jacobins." It was also very clear that we had returned to a France that for years now had been at war with Britain and most of Europe.

Sergeant-major Girard's instructions were to give us no home leave and after two weeks of lounging about, eating lots of fish, and as soldiers do exploring Breton cooking, wine and women, we were informed we were to be marched to Brest 36 miles (58km) away. This came as a great surprise for our army paper was full of news about the "glory" Napoleon and a new Army of Italy were earning with a string of spectacular victories crossing the Alps, in Italy and then again in Austria at Marengo. We expected we might be sent to join them. Brest however did not fit in with that, being as we all knew the largest French naval base next to Toulon. For the second time we could not imagine why we were being sent there.

After a two day march we arrived to discover a sight which reminded us of Toulon three years earlier. The harbour was packed with ships of all sizes being provisioned for a long voyage. Again there were huge camps of tents set up on the edge of the town to accommodate thousands of troops and hundreds of horses. It seemed the army included those of us who had survived Egypt plus a lot of new conscripts. This time however, on arrival we found our destination was no secret, perhaps because the British Navy blockade was no longer operating. The army paper informed us that we were off to the West Indies, in particular to Saint Domingue.

From the map it also printed we could see that this large West Indian island of Hispaniola was divided in two, the western half ruled as a French colony and called Saint Domingue and the eastern half ruled as a Spanish colony and called Santo Domingo. We were off to the French half. Still what the paper was not at all clear about was why we were going.

Was it anything to do with coffee and sugar? We all knew most of our coffee and sugar came from there. We also knew without much thought that these had been grown by black slaves from Africa. I then remembered something else. When back in 1789 as a schoolboy in Turin I heard news of the French Revolution, I remembered being inspired when I read the Declaration of the Rights of Man and the Citizen which had been adopted by the National Assembly in Paris. I also remembered reading that the Assembly had included delegates from Saint Domingue and it had voted to implement the Declaration and abolish slavery.

More than that I and the other soldiers knew nothing about Saint Domingue except we had seen caricatures of a black general. It seemed he had emerged as leader there and taking the Revolution at its word had declared he would free the island from slavery. His name was Toussaint Louverture.

*****

A few days later Sergeant-major Girard sent a note saying he wished to see me at his office in the main barracks.

"Bioletti," he said, "I have been watching you and looking at your record. An impressive tour in Italy followed by your work as *ordonnance* for General Kleber. How did you get on with him?"

"I thought he was a great man. It was a real privilege to serve under him." I said.

"I agree." he said, "A true soldier of the Republic."

We had quite a long conversation about my work in Egypt which tentatively moved into discussing Kleber's political views and opinions. I also got the distinct feel that the sergeant-major was a member of the masonic brotherhood and had got to know Klever at lodge meetings in Cairo.

"I think if he had lived he might have found things pretty difficult right now." he said, "Have you heard that when Napoleon left Egypt Kleber wrote a very critical report about him and about the whole Egyptian campaign which he sent quite correctly to the Directory?"

"Yes I did." I replied cautiously.

"And do you know it was intercepted by the British who after reading it splashed it all over their newspapers? Then to cause maximum upset in France they sent it on to Paris where it was published in our newspapers just before the Directory was abolished and Napoleon took power as First Consul." he continued.

"I know the paper you are referring to, but I never knew what happened to it." I replied.

"So, you agreed with what he said?" he asked.

"Well, yes. He made some strong points." I replied cautiously.

"Not something to broadcast now though."

"Certainly not." I nodded.

"Well Bioletti, you must be wondering where all this is leading? It so happens that a senior officer who has spent most of his rather distinguished military career in Saint Domingue is here "on leave to visit his parents" he says and he is looking for a man to become his *ordonnance* before he returns to the colony. This will be a sensitive and I think dangerous posting, though from what I have heard the whole of this expedition is going to be dangerous for everyone on it, regardless of rank, myself included. You however have particularly valuable skills and experience, not to mention what we might describe as "good revolutionary values." These may be just what this officer is looking for in an *ordonnance* he can trust. Are you interested?" he asked.

"Neither you nor I sergeant-major have any choice as regards going on this campaign, and I still have no idea what the point of it is, still I have found the role of *ordonnance* suits me well - provided I am assigned to serve an officer who I can respect." I replied.

"Good point. Some of them must be hell to serve." he said. "I think you will get on with this one though. Come here tomorrow at the same time and of course our conversation did not take place."

*****

The next morning suitably clad with my uniform up to parade ground standard I came in to his office to find an officer seated there talking to him dressed in the uniform of an adjutant general. I saluted.

"At ease Bioletti," he said. Of medium height with a pleasant easy manner which immediately made me think, "Here we have a real diplomat," he set about asking me a wide range of questions about the Egyptian campaign and how I had worked with General Kleber. He then said, "No doubt you are wondering why, in looking for an *ordonnance*, I have not sought out a soldier who is already familiar with the island."

"The thought had crossed my mind sir." I replied.

"Listening to you talk about Egypt and working for General Kleber shows you really have come through a baptism of fire facing both extreme physical danger and considerable tests of your discretion, intelligence and trustworthiness. I hope I can take it you were up to dressing and looking after him properly as well.

"Oh yes sir." I replied. "I also learnt to enjoy cooking fresh foods for him and worked hard to keep us both healthy."

"Well Bioletti I can assure you this post will demand all your exceptional abilities, but the big difference is you will be entering a world not only of physical danger, but of far greater political complexity than Egypt. I will need to be able to trust you completely. Even more than General Klever did, I will need to be able to use you as my surreptitious eyes and ears. To do that it will be important you understand the tricky politics going on all around you."

"Being trustworthy I am sure is vital sir," I replied, "But when it comes to the tricky politics why would a local not be able to understand and do that far better than me?"

"Just because such a person would be local, with his own local relatives, friends and lovers. Put a local in a tight corner and he might well put them first - before me and before France – as sadly was the case with my last *ordonnance*." he said.

I thought it better not to ask what happened to him. "I see sir. That makes sense, but as a raw outsider how am I to get all this political knowledge you say will be so important?" I asked.

"From me Bioletti. From me. I think I understand the situation and know the people on the island pretty well, in fact far better than the man who has been placed in charge of all this by the First Consul. We have a long ships journey ahead of us and we will have plenty of time to talk.

And another thing. Once we get there it will be good if you do not come across as having any interest in politics. That way you will hear much more in the way of gossip which you can then feed back to me. Do you think you will be able to do that?" he asked.

"I am quite happy with that sir. It happened with General Kleber. It would make the life of your humble *ordonnance* much more interesting."

"I hope so Bioletti." he said with a laugh. "You are now the third man I have interviewed. I think we understand each other and I am offering you the job."

"Thank you sir. I hope my service will be satisfactory." I replied.

Chapter 23
Ordonnance to
General Jacques Boye

"Right Bioletti, come with me. First, let me introduce myself. I am Adjutant General Jacques Boye. By the way as an Italian are you keen on singing and do you know any opera?"

"Just what I learnt at home sir." I said, "My mother sang well."

"You will find music is a bit of an obsession with me. I have just bought rather a good violin and a whole case of sheet music as I am just as keen on singing. We will have to get that going on this voyage with so many men whose morale needs attention."

"Yes sir. Of course." I replied. It sounded like we were in for an interesting voyage. It was also the start of a working relationship that would continue for far longer than either of us could possibly have imagined.

On the 25th of October 1801 we set sail from Brest in a 76 gun ship of the line of the French Navy, the *Revolutionnaire*. This was not the flagship for as I soon learnt Boye was not part of the invading campaign, but an officer returning after visiting his ill father, the mayor of Caussade. This also meant, despite his rank, that he had not been appointed adjutant- general to the commander for he was part of the French Army as set up on Saint Domingue.

The *Revolutionnaire* was neither as clean nor as well run as a British Navy vessel and it was certainly the longest journey anyone on board had been on after years kept holed up out of range of Nelson's guns. Still the captain did his best and there was regular firing practice to speed up the performance of the inexperienced gun crews. This also involved shipping away in the holds everything from the captain's furniture to our baggage and hammocks to turn the ship into a fighting machine. Whenever this took place he had all of us military crammed on the top decks to keep out of the way or ordered into the rigging to get us used to acting as sharp-shooters from there. Sometimes confusion reigned and it was just as well we did not need to see action.

*****

Boye as the most senior army officer on board had a decent cabin, but overall the ship was pretty crowded with soldiers filling up every corner and puking whenever we had a rough sea. I seemed to have become almost inured to sea-sickness, almost but not quite. I remained a hater of ships hammocks.

Boye told me the whole fleet consisted of over fifty ships and that we were carrying twenty thousand troops, this being the largest ever overseas expedition of the French army. He believed there were however another thirty ships setting out from different ports with several thousand extra troops. Did that mean I wondered that this campaign was even bigger than Napoleon's Egyptian adventure?

I asked Boye why Napoleon had not come to see us off in person and why so little was said about the expedition in the Army paper. He told me this was because Napoleon was fighting in Austria and did not want to draw attention to the number of troops he was sending to fight overseas. However, as he always did, it appeared Napoleon had planned the whole thing in detail.

*****

Leading the campaign I learnt was General Charles Leclerc who was with his staff on our flagship *L'Ocean*. I remembered him as a cavalry officer at Lodi in the Italian campaign and I remembered hearing about his marriage to Napoleon's very young sister Pauline at Mombello outside Milan. Boye, had only met him briefly just before we sailed. Boye told me his second in command was a General Rochambeau who had been involved in Saint Domingue for many years. I immediately picked up that he and Boye did not see eye to eye.

"Have you ever met or served a real *aristo* of the old school Bioletti, one who has evaded she who has cut down so many with all his views intact?" he said. "Watch and learn Bioletti, and see to it that you are always suitably subservient. He does not tolerate what he sees as insubordination or lack of respect."

Of Leclerc Boye said, "They say he is quite inexperienced, is only 29 and worships the First Consul, copying his dress and mannerisms. It seems to me quite mad to insist as I hear Napoleon has, that the girl-wife Pauline should accompany him. Does he expect Leclerc to become some sort of settler?"

Each day when the weather was fair, we exercised together on the quarter-deck, slightly to the irritation of the other officers, but they were not senior enough to have an *ordonnance* of their own, so again I was something of an outsider. We then spent time until the mid-day meal discussing Hispaniola and the colonies of Saint Domingue and Santo Domingo.

*****

I soon learnt from him that at thirty-five he had lived and worked on the island since 1793 when he had left France as a young captain in the National Guard. It was among them that he had developed his liberal, democratic Girondist views, views that if known became a life-threatening risk during the Terror.

Transferring from the Guard to the regular French Army as set up on the island he had quickly been promoted to Adjutant General and had been appointed as a Deputy of the Colonial Assembly working under the authority of the two Commissioners who were sent out to run the colony by the French National Assembly, Polverel and the Girondist Sonthonax. Clearly I was working for a man of some ability.

He explained to me what then happened. "Both these men, Polverel and Sonthonax, had been given the difficult task of getting rid of slavery as required by the Rights of Man. At the same time they were expected to get the colony back to work in order to regain the spectacular productivity it had lost during the disturbances and slave revolts sparked off by the Revolution."

"Was that very important?" I asked.

"It certainly was. Before the Revolution Saint Domingue had been the most lucrative of all French colonies by far and a key contributor to the French economy. After the Revolution and their revolt both economies were in a very bad way. It was an impossible task the Commissioners had been given," Boye told me, "You see Bioletti, what made the economy of Saint Domingue so profitable and productive was slavery and no-one really knew then or now how to get it really profitable and productive without it."

I found that hard to believe. "Surely sir, free men would be more productive working for a decent wage than slaves under the lash?" I queried.

"Wait till you see how it all actually works. When you have had real experience of the place I think you will recognise how difficult it will be to combine high profits with ending the gross exploitation involved in slavery." he said, "The strange thing is Napoleon seems to think sending this huge army out to Saint Domingue can somehow bring this about. I wonder how he imagines he or his General Leclerc will ever be able to do it, for that I think is what this campaign is expected to achieve."

*****

After our morning sessions my usual duty was to stand behind Boye and generally act as a waiter for the assembled officers for both lunch and dinner. Listening to their conversations could be boring, but often very interesting and informing. It also meant eating the same food as they had which was very much better than the ships biscuit, soup and salted meat the rest of those on board had to put up with. Inevitably on a long voyage like this that was expected to take six or seven weeks, the quality of the food got steadily worse as the last pig and chicken came to its inevitable end.

Breaking the monotony and boredom was the fact that Boye was not alone in his love of music and singing. Several of the junior officers unpacked musical instruments, though none were as accomplished at playing or in conducting and leading a choir. He extended this to include the soldiers which went down very well. He was good also in mixing popular songs and drinking songs with opera choruses and classical instrumental pieces. He told me, "You have a good voice Bioletti, so get involved with music and you will make many friends."

*****

My next lesson was rather different and came up on a calm day after the sergeants in charge had all our soldiers up on deck for games and physical exercise. "Bioletti" he said, "Have a guess. What do you think will be possibly the greatest single danger to the lives of all these fit young men when we reach the island?"

"Revolting slaves, the pox, infected loose women, plague?" I suggested.

"Yes, we have all of those, except plague so far, but the worst of any of them is something you may not have heard about. Yellow fever. It is a plague on its own."

"What does it do?" I asked.

"For some it does very little. They take to bed with a high fever and aching muscles and after a few days they are better. For others, particularly those who come from Europe and have never been near it before, it can be catastrophic. The high fever and minor aches can quickly turn into back ache, nausea and violent vomiting. Following three or four days of this the patient goes yellow in the whites of his eyes, then yellow all over and the outcome is a painful death."

"What causes it?" I asked as the sweating young conscripts ran past us.

"The doctors all think it is caused by a *miasma*." He replied. "Know what that is Bioletti?"

"Something to do with bad air sir?" I suggested.

"Something like that." he replied, "Actually, the theory is that a miasma is a poisonous vapour or mist which contains tiny particles floating in it which we breathe in. Miasmas are set off it is said when there is smelly, stagnant water, filthy conditions in the home and rotting meat or fish. It is also considered to be much worse in the hot misty season in the West Indies when there are lots of insects and mosquitos about."

"And can one person infect another?" I asked.

"The doctors think not."

"So what treatment is there?" I asked.

"None. The doctors recommend we keep things clean and avoid places where the miasma is, but once you get it there is no treatment. Some get better, some die. If you get better it appears you never get it again, even if everyone around you has it."

"It sounds to me very like the bubonic plague I saw in Egypt, though with different symptoms. There we argued about it being

137

infectious and Napoleon's chief medical officer, Desgenettes, insisted on putting those with it in quarantine even though Napoleon thought it was a matter of will-power who caught it. Nevertheless he backed Desgenettes and quarantine wards seemed to stop its spread." I said.

"That doesn't work with yellow fever." he said, "There is no evidence one person can catch it from another."

"So there is nothing anyone can do about it. We just have to see who is affected by the miasma and who is not?" I replied. "And what about you sir?"

"I caught it years ago, was pretty sick for a few days and then recovered and have been fine ever since." he said.

"So there is nothing I can do but wait and see? I take it that is why so far we have been told nothing about it." I said bitterly.

"Not quite Bioletti." he replied. "I am not convinced by this miasma theory, though obviously I am in no position to question it publicly. I think it is an infection and if it is not passed on from person to person like Desgenettes thinks is the case with plague, then it could be some insect, like a flea, mosquito or tiny bug. Also it seems something happens to us if we survive which stops us ever getting it again. Some of the slaves in Saint Domingue have a practice which often, though not always, seems to work for them. They of course think it has to do with magic which you and I know is nonsense and no white on the island thinks he or she could learn anything from a slave. I have however seen it done and seen it work."

"So what do they do sir?" I asked.

"A man or woman who has recovered from the fever makes a small cut in the arm and a similar cut in the uninfected person and with much chanting rubs in his or her blood. The arm is then bandaged. The receiver then gets a mild version of the fever a couple of weeks later and never is infected again."

"You would not know sir, but that is exactly what Desgenettes did in Egypt. He took blood from a plague victim and rubbed it into a cut he had made in his arm. Despite being in daily contact with plague victims he never developed it. He did not feel able to try it on others though. This happened when we were retreating from Acre."

"So Bioletti," he said, "Are you ready to give it a try – without the chanting of course?" I agreed and he did it the next day. Yes I did get the symptoms for a few days when we had almost arrived at Saint Domingue, but never after that. I am sure it saved my life.

Chapter 24
We Entertain a Slaver

The journey across the Atlantic was long and hard with every type of weather from times when we were becalmed under a burning sky to violent storms. When we were about two thirds through our journey on a calm day we saw two merchant ships approaching. They were about the size of frigates and were flying the tricolour and the first pulled in close to us.

"Right, Bioletti," said Boye, "This is where your education really begins. They are slavers."

"French slavers?" I replied.

"Oh yes. In fact I think I recognise one of them."

With that we received a signal for permission to visit and a long-boat was sent across and a party of three came on board. Smartly dressed and smiling self-confidently the captain presented his card and was escorted to the quarter deck where he was invited to stay for lunch by our captain. He was then announced as Captain Gaugy, Master of the *Seraphique* of Nantes.

He told us he and his "little fleet" were on route for Santo Domingo, the chief town on the Spanish side of the island.

"We have just come from Angola," he said. "This is now my fourth voyage from there and very rewarding they have been too. I hope this voyage will work out successfully, for I intend this to be my last round trip. As usual we will load up with sugar at Le Cap, but when we get home to Nantes I will be selling up to retire with my wife and family. We have acquired such an attractive little property a few miles outside the city on the Loire."

"And how did you find Angola?" Boye asked him politely.

"We have been very lucky in having been able to build up a

good relationship with the same African chief, Chief Obukwe, who in return for guns, cloth, assorted beads and baubles and of course some barrels of our cheapest brandy and some gold coin, provides us with about 800 slaves for each ship. Dealing with the same man is so much better than having to deal with several marauding slave traffickers. They are just bandits, and are usually fighting each other for the slaves they have captured from various villages. Chief Obukwe always puts us up, lays on a feast and treats us very well. "

"And tell me Captain," asked Boye, "How many of those 800 per ship do you hope to land in Santo Domingo?"

"It is so hard to say," replied Gaugy. "It depends you know on the weather and of course on the quality of the "property". If some of them come aboard with some ghastly illness, it can spread to a lot of them and our losses can be considerable. Then again if we get becalmed we can run out of food and be short on water, then it is best to just get rid of some of them rather than endanger the health of the rest of us.

"You mean dropping them over the side?" said Boye.

"I am afraid so. Such a waste." said the captain, "Still while it can be highly profitable, slave trading is always a risky business."

"I'm sure" said Boye.

"But, to answer your question if we take 800 on board on average we expect to be able to have about 550 still saleable when we arrive."

Boye nodded and continued, "Am I right in thinking I have met you before Captain?"

"Why, of course sir. Now I recognise you!" replied Gaugy, "You were attached to the naval ministry and were liaising with the Spanish in Santo Domingo, their main port."

"Yes Captain, and you were making sure that you would be able to sell your cargo on the Spanish side since General Toussaint Louverture has forbidden the landing of any more slaves into Saint Domingue."

"You are so right sir. What a foolish decision. Given the short life span of these blacks when they get there, how does he think they can possibly find enough men to work the plantations?"

"I think he hopes that if his Africans are free, they will work better and be more productive than if they are kept as slaves." said Boye rather repeating what I had said earlier.

"But I am sure you know sir that cannot work. They are such lazy devils and so hate labouring on the plantations, even on Louverture's own plantations they say. No doubt you know he has had to face several revolts against his policy of saying the freed slaves must stay and work on their old plantations." said the captain.

"Which brings me to why I have asked to come on board. When I dropped off my last cargo of sugar in France and was loading up with goods for Obukwe, I heard rumours that the First Consul was planning to send an expedition to Saint Domingue and Martinique to sort things out with this upstart black General Louverture, but what are you intending to do?" he asked, "Clearly you are that expedition. Some think because his *creole* wife Josephine de Beauharnais comes from Martinique and her family own a large plantation he is sending you to re-introduce or maintain slavery on all the French islands. What I want to know is can that be true? I do hope so."

Our ship's captain said he had no idea about that, but Boye replied, "Captain Gaugy, I can assure you that the First Consul has said that he has no intention of re-introducing slavery on Saint Domingue. That is clear and definite, however there are those who wish to see Saint Domingue become independent, independent of France like the United States has become independent of Britain."

"Is that what the black general wants? Independence?" asked Gaugy.

"Absolutely not," said Boye, "General Louverture has said many times, in fact he has said it to me personally, that he wishes to see Saint Domingue and if possible the whole island being a true, self-governing part of the French Republic built on the principles of the Revolution and the Rights of Man. This means I can say this to you. The purpose of this great fleet and army coming to Saint Domingue is to strengthen the bonds between the colony and France and protect it from outside interference either from the United States or from a meddling Britain."

Boye could sound so authoritative when he wanted to. The conversation then turned to discussing the peace which had been agreed between France and Britain which they all agreed was unlikely to last long, but which was very welcome in the West Indies as it marked a pause in the English blockade which had such a negative impact on French and Spanish shipping. It also meant an end to the interference of English troops on Hispaniola.

"Good riddance to them," said Gaugy. "And did you hear they say the English lost nearly half their soldiers to Yellow Fever?"

And so the lunch time conversation continued, one French gentleman to another as if they were discussing the price of sugar, which in a way they were. The use of the word "property" to describe slaves I noticed was the accepted way of totally denying the reality of what was being discussed.

After lunch the weather changed and a wind started to blow. Gaugy excused himself and returned to his ship, and it was agreed he could tail our fleet until we were near the island when he would go on to Santo Domingo. As the wind started up we noticed naked bodies being thrown over the sides of the slavers. Almost immediately these attracted the attention of sharks which seemed to be following both ships. I asked Boye to explain.

"Unless you were to visit one of those ships, which I can assure you is not encouraged, except of course when they are all spruced up to host a sale, you could not imagine how they cram their human cargo in." he said quietly, "Shackled, completely naked and with not enough room to stand, freezing in the storms and roasting in the heat, poorly fed they lie in their own stinking waste. Not surprisingly many die and only the most hardy survive. I think they have been using this break as a chance to do some house-keeping, pump sea water over them to wash out their deck and get rid of the dead bodies that have accumulated."

*****

A few days later it was calm again and Boye asked me if I now had any questions. My first was about Louverture, but he checked me. "Before we discuss him Bioletti, I need to tell you more about the population.

First we have estimated that when the Revolution started in France there were about half a million slaves on our side of the island. They all come from various parts of Africa, either stolen by Arab slave catchers or as often prisoners of war from tribal conflicts. Their sale gave their rulers access to European weapons and goods. Almost all were set to work on the sugar, coffee, indigo and cotton plantations, mostly sugar. Over the last fifty years some have escaped and have taken to the forests and mountains of the island. They are called *maroons*. They raid, steal and burn the plantations whenever they can, are much feared and practice an African style religion with much drumming, dancing, chanting and ancestor worship called, Vodou.

On the plantations the slaves did not live more than a few years being driven to work under the lash. Female slaves died quicker and many committed suicide believing the spirits of their ancestors would take them back to Africa. This is why the slavers continue to do such good business and why most slaves are African born; the plantations keep running short of labour."

"Does this make the African slaves a pretty united group?" I asked.

"Not really." Boye replied. "They arrive illiterate and with many languages and come from different places and tribes. They have also been worked so hard and relentlessly and have been subjected to so much beating, brutality and really fearsome tortures that most are reduced to sullen and terrified subservience, if they survive. They still often act as if they are stupid and "do not understand" to avoid attention and hard work. Some have watched their masters and play at being "the good slave" to become household slaves and nursemaid slaves. Some of these have earned their freedom and have adopted white ways. They are slightly better treated and see themselves as superior to the field slaves or plantation workers cutting cane or cropping coffee."

"So we have black Africans and their white rulers," I summarised.

"Well, no, it is more complicated than that. However, let us first look at the whites. Ruling over this half million has been a small population of only some thirty thousand odd whites. They consist of those who have bought, inherited, or manage plantations. Those who are island born like Napoleon's Josephine are called *creoles*. You will soon recognise their accent. Those who own plantations see themselves as almost the top of the social tree."

"Almost? So who is really at the top of the tree?" I asked."

"Inevitably I suppose, there is also a group of lesser, impoverished or disgraced aristocrats whose families own plantations and have chosen to live here who have settled from France. They like to assume social superiority and you can imagine how the wives of the *creole* plantation owners love to fawn over and sleep with such people."

"So where do you fit in sir?" I asked.

"Yes, there are then army officers like me, civil servants, teachers, clergy, surgeons, barbers and tradespeople and the usual set of inadequates at the bottom who nevertheless see themselves as infinitely superior to anyone who is not white.

"Whites and blacks. Is that it then?" I asked.

"Not quite. Now I am going to explain the uniquely French take on black/white relations. Human beings are human beings and a pretty girl is a pretty girl whatever her colour."

"Oh yes, sir. I do agree." I said.

"Many black slave women, given their options, have been prepared to accept or even encourage the attentions of their white masters and pregnancy has followed. Here the French response has been different to the response of the English and the Americans to this situation where the children are simply rejected, sent away and classed as black slaves. Here these children of black slave women and their masters have been considered to be free and are called "people of colour" or *mulattoes*. They are often educated locally by the Catholic Church or even sent to school in France. They are then encouraged to join the local branch of the French Army as I have done, and the best and brightest become army officers.

"There can't be many of them surely given the race hatred towards the slaves you have described." I said.

"That Bioletti is where you are wrong." Replied Boye, "There are as many *mulattoes* in Saint Domingue as whites, and though the cheated white women hate it, the white fathers have also given their offspring property, estates of their own and yes to work them, slaves. And the result is that as things stand about a third of the plantations are run and owned by *mulattoes* and worked by their own slaves/plantation workers."

I was completely amazed at this news and found it hard to take in. "So are you saying the *mulattoes* can own slaves and are accepted and treated as equals of the whites?" I asked incredulously.

"Oh no," Boye replied, "Remember the white women. They would not put up with that! They have got their menfolk to enact local laws discriminating against the *mulattoes* so they cannot dress like them or socialise with whites when white women are present, even if the "people of colour" can get rich and own "property" –

which has included slaves."

"That I find less amazing. In Cairo our soldiers went with Egyptian women, but no white woman would mix with that sort of Egyptian woman." I said.

"One final point for today," said Boye, "You and I were both inspired by reading the Rights of Man and the Citizen and its condemnation of slavery when the French Revolution took place in '89. Who do you think reacted in the same way in Saint Domingue?"

"The *mulattoes*?" I suggested.

"Yes." said Boye, "And the tiny number of educated, freed slaves, like Toussaint Louverture, and as I will later explain, some of the planters.

"So now sir please, tell me about him."

Chapter 25
The Liberation
of Louverture

" A fascinating and impressive man." Said Boye, "His origin was unusual for he was the son of an African chief sold into slavery. He was raised on the Breda plantation owned by a French aristocrat and managed by a man named Libertat. There he was obviously comparatively well treated for he quickly showed himself to be quite unusually intelligent. He was educated by his white god-father learning French, reading classical philosophy and Machiavelli. Oh yes! He also studied medicine as far as he could and slave folk remedies."

"Like the one you used on me?" I asked.

"Yes, I certainly heard about it from him. He also was raised and remains a Catholic, is opposed to Vodou, and read Abbe Reynal's book attacking slavery. As the coachman and as an overseer for Libertat on the Breda estate he worked as a slave until he was freed in 1776 at the age of 33. He was then able to marry (slaves are not) and had two children who were later educated in France.

He did not lead but then became involved in a *mulatto* and slave rebellion inspired by the Revolution as it was taking place in France. First he worked as a doctor to the rebels, but soon as a strategist and negotiator where he stood out for his intelligence and good sense and is particularly remembered for preventing the massacre of white prisoners." he continued.

"Was the rebellion successful then?" I asked.

""Basically yes." he went on, "Much of the countryside was

taken over by rebel *mulattoes* and slaves, and many plantations were burnt and their owners and managers killed. At this point Louverture attempted to negotiate with the Colonial Assembly, a body consisting mainly of plantation owners, but they foolishly refused to see him. This was just after I arrived from France and transferred from the National Guard to the local branch of the French Army as a second lieutenant. I was soon promoted to military commander of Port au Prince and then promoted to Lieutenant Colonel by Commissioner Leger Felicite Sonthonax who represented the French Government of the Directorate. On that same day in 1793 he proclaimed the emancipation of all slaves on French Saint-Domingue!

"That sounds amazing. What was Sonthonax trying to do?" I asked.

"This is where you see things get complicated." said Boye. "Sonthonax, like me, is a Girondist, a liberal, believing in liberty, equality, basic human rights and the abolition of slavery as core Revolution values. He simply saw the planters on the Colonial Assembly as anti-revolutionary royalists and thought that by declaring the slaves to be free the rebels and Louverture would back him."

"Was he right?" I asked.

"No, for as a local Louverture recognised two things Sonthonax had missed." he replied. "The first was that many of the planters saw themselves as being inspired by the Revolution and were not like the royalists in France. They did not want the French king back. They however wanted freedom for themselves and the *mulattoes* and the liberty to be able to vote.

"That sounds quite liberal and in tune with the Revolution." I said.

"Well, not quite." Boye continued, "They wanted the liberty to vote and declare the colony independent of France as the American southern slave owning states had declared independence from Britain. That way they could keep their slaves and trade profitably."

"Yes. Complicated, and what was the second thing Sonthonax had missed?" I asked.

"Sonthonax was a lawyer, a politician and an outsider. Louverture however knew from his own experience as Sonthonax did not how the plantations really worked. He recognised that for all the appalling cruelty exercised by many of the plantation owners, white and *mulatto*, and their dreadful attitude towards their slaves, they had the specialist know-how, financial and practical skills needed to run their estates profitably, and if they were all driven out or killed, as Sonthonax was in danger of encouraging, the result would be complete economic collapse of the colony. To stop this happening Louverture insisted that freed slaves remain on their plantations as paid but compulsory plantation labour. This unsurprisingly has not been popular with them. Louverture however is convinced that the long term freedom and development of the former slaves and all the people of Saint Domingue depends on the economic viability of the colony or the people will starve."

"So what happened next?" I asked.

"Yes, it has gone on being complicated, but the same issues keep returning. Louverture rose to command a rebel army and proved to be a brilliant tactician and an inspiring general bringing on several other formidable fighters, in particular another former black slave Dessalines who has been promoted to general. I have worked a lot with Louverture together with a friend of mine Colonel Vincent who Louverture has used as an advisor. We both think he is one of the most extraordinary men we have ever met. His ability to analyse a problem and appreciate how his opponents and allies are thinking is amazing as is his attention to detail and skill in administration. I have never met Bonaparte, but I would put him in the same league."

"That sir, is a very big claim to make." I said surprised.

"Yes it is." He replied, "And to bring you up to date after first fighting with the rebels and the Spanish, Louverture and Dessalines joined us in the local French Army to back France. The reason they did was because the English, who were at war with the French Republic, thought our local conflict over slavery gave them a chance to take over the island and add it to their collection of West Indian slave colonies like Jamaica, an aim that was the opposite of what Louverture and Dessalines wanted. The British then invaded with thousands of redcoats and several hundred slave-hunting dogs that they had bought in Cuba, and allied themselves with the *creole* plantation owners and successfully took over several coastal towns. I was put in command by Sonthonax over a mainly *mulatto* force. Though totally outnumbered they fought very well. We also had a deadly ally that killed those fresh young Englishmen in their thousands. Yes their thousands. It was dreadful to see. Like to guess what that was?"

"The Yellow Fever your men had acquired some resistance to?" I guessed.

"Absolutely. And the dogs trained to chase unarmed runaway slaves cowered whimpering as soon as they heard a musket. They were useless. Fighting to preserve their freedom my troops and those of Louverture and Dessalines who joined us were exemplary and so we were successful in driving the British with all their sick and wounded to the point of surrender. With Louverture we then negotiated with Sir Thomas Maitland their commander a complete British withdrawal from the island in 1798."

"That sounds impressive, so what happened then sir?" I asked.

"On coming over to our side both Louverture and Dessalines had of course joined our colonial French Army and both were promoted to the rank of General. It did not then take Louverture long to become the overall Governor of the island exercising complete power. He sent Sonthonax back to France when he saw the days of the Directory were numbered, and defeated a *mulatto* general who led a revolt against him in the south of the island. He has now expelled the Spanish so uniting the whole island for the first time and he has got trade in sugar going with the United States. He has just introduced a Constitution for the island which claims that all citizens of the island are free and French. Slavery is forever abolished and every man is admissible to all employments, the only distinctions to be recognised being the virtues and talents of individuals."

"And does this constitution enshrine democracy, free and fair elections?" I asked.

"Ah, no" he replied. "Remember from the time of the start of the Revolution the island has been facing war, insurrection and lawlessness on quite a scale. More than half the whites have left and marauding bands of starving ex-slaves are everywhere and possibly as many as a third of the pre-Revolution slaves are now dead. Law and order needs to be restored first. No doubt he sees democracy as the aim for the long term. No. Not surprisingly his constitution echoes that brought in by our First Consul! All power is centred on himself and he has appointed himself Governor General for life."

"And what do you and your friend Colonel Vincent think about that." I asked.

"Poor Vincent. He has had a very tough time. We came over to France together, I to see my father, he to show Louverture's constitution to Napoleon as Louverture had asked him to."

"Did he intend supporting it then?" I asked.

"Certainly not. He thinks Louverture has gone too far and before he left he told him so. His constitution reads like a declaration of independence. It rejects the right of France to pass laws to apply to the island, perhaps because he fears there are those who might wish to re-introduce slavery - though I find that hard to believe. He also makes no provision for French officials to exercise any authority on the island. It implies he is equal to the First Consul

"So how did the First Consul react?" I asked.

"I had a letter from Vincent just before we sailed. Napoleon was furious for on the basis of reading many letters Louverture had sent him he had already decided he was a threat to his Empire. To bring him down he had decided to despatch this huge invasion fleet. Vincent then told him what we both thought would happen if he tried to invade Saint Domingue."

"And what is that?" I asked.

"This whole vast invasion force could be defeated, just as the English were, by a combination of Yellow Fever and other illnesses that will kill our fresh white conscripts by the thousand. Add to that the difficulty of fighting a skilled and determined enemy used to jungle fighting as our French troops certainly are not and defeat becomes highly likely. Imagine saying that to Napoleon! Bravely he then tried to convince Napoleon that Louverture is an exceptional man and dealing with him and accepting his position in Hispaniola remains the best option for France."

"So what did Napoleon do?" I asked,

"He placed Vincent under house arrest on Elba and has banned him from returning to the island." said Boye.

I was stunned as this all sunk in. Clearly Boye as a leading officer of the French Army of the island had been deeply involved in complicated and shifting alliances and conflicts. This meant that he could now be at some risk from those who would see his admiration and respect for Toussaint Louverture as deeply questionable.

*****

A few days later as we were getting close to Saint Domingue Boye received a message from Leclerc saying that he would like Boye and his *ordonnance* to join him on the flagship and we were duly transferred to *L'Ocean*.

As we came aboard this huge one hundred gun ship of the line, as big and as grand as the *Orient*, we were met by a figure I did not expect. It was General Pierre Francois Boyer, General Kleber's former chief of staff who had been packed off to Paris by General Menou charged with misuse of funds after General Kleber's assassination.

After greeting Boye somewhat coldly and introducing himself as Adjutant General or chief staff officer to General Leclerc, he turned to me.

"Bioletti!" he said. "What a surprise. So you have wormed your way in somehow to being an *ordonnance* again."

"Yes sir," I replied.

"Well, General Boye, you will need to watch this one carefully. Easily gets ideas above his station."

"Don't worry about that General," replied Boye, smiling glassily, "I will see to it he knows just what his place is." And with that they went off to meet Leclerc while I wrestled with our baggage. Interesting, I thought. Napoleon by-passes the local experienced officer of suitable rank in order to bring in as adjutant general an officer known for ambition, efficiency, brutality and ruthlessness.

That evening at dinner, which I attended as waiter standing behind Boye, we were joined at the meal by Leclerc's wife Pauline. Dressed in the height of Parisian fashion, which meant a sleeveless diaphanous gown with plunging neckline and no back and her rich brown hair piled high, she was simply ravishingly beautiful. No matter that her conversation was rather flippant and inconsequential, she had every man in the cabin hanging on her every word, including me. I nearly dropped a plate because she glanced in my direction. I noticed something else about her. She reminded me strongly of that other Pauline so briefly beloved of the First Consul in Cairo, Pauline Foure. No she was not her double, but her face, her figure and the way she moved bore a striking resemblance.

Making as great a bid for attention as Pauline, and dressed in a most extravagant uniform for his rank, was the unmistakable General Donatien Rochambeau, Leclerc's second in command. You could however miss that for he behaved as if it were he rather than Leclerc who was in charge.

After dinner Pauline withdrew, dessert wine was served and Leclerc took over. Blond, arrogant in manner and self-consciously handsome he called us to order and expounded the plans that had been given him by Napoleon.

The first was to do everything possible to re-assure the local population that we were coming in peace to restore order after the "rebellion," but at the same time defend the freedom from slavery the locals held so dear.

The second was while this was being done our troops should be landed and should take up all the key strongholds as our bases for future military operations.

In addition in order to get all the troops loyal to Louverture to accept his authority as the representative of France, Leclerc explained that they were to guarantee all officers in this colonial French force equivalent rank in the mainland French Army and all the men the option of enlistment into it.

Leclerc then turned to Boye and said, "General, as someone well known and I hear trusted by many blacks and mulattoes, when we reach Le Cap I would like you to take a long-boat with a letter from me for the general in charge there who you tell me is a *mulatto* named Christophe. In the nicest possible manner I should like you to tell him he has to surrender control of the town to me and my officers. In return his rank in the French Army is guaranteed."

This announcement was met by nods and knowing smiles particularly from Rochambeau. Now we knew why we had been summoned to join *Le' Ocean*.

Chapter 26
The Leclerc Invasion of Saint Domingue

So it was that a few days later we climbed into a long-boat rowed by four French sailors. The sea, almost mirror calm, was a brilliant azure blue, the sky cloudless and before us was the harbour of Le Cap "the Paris of the West". On either side fine stone buildings glistened white in the morning sun flanked by palm trees. Behind them wooded hills combined to make an unforgettable sight.

We disembarked to be met by four black soldiers, tall and well built in immaculate French Army uniforms. They saluted and when they recognised Boye broke into friendly smiles before taking us in a carriage to the governor's palace. On our way we passed handsome public buildings, fountains, a theatre and shops that looked smart and fashionable. At the front door of the palace we were cordially greeted by the imposing figure of General Christophe who again obviously knew Boye.

I was taken by the soldiers to the main kitchen where I was offered oranges, apples and wine and asked about our journey while the two generals conferred. It was the first time I had heard the creole patois they spoke. It was not a long meeting before we were escorted back to our long-boat. Boye was in no mood for talking. The next day we returned with a fresh letter to be more rapidly escorted back to our long-boat. No apples and oranges this time.

"The man is not a fool," Boye said to me quietly. "He says he is legally under the command of the Governor General, i.e.

Louverture, and so cannot hand over his position to Leclerc. I fear things are about to turn nasty."

Leclerc's response was to up anchor that night and sail around the coast with several ships landing a considerable army of some 6,000 of us with the plan of going inland and then entering Le Cap from the land side. I think his intention was to march into Le Cap with an overwhelmingly large force and take over the town's fortifications without a fight, with *L'Oceon* and his other battleships providing the threat of artillery support from the sea.

At the same time he landed Rochambeau with a smaller force of a thousand men to remain behind as back-up near Forte Liberte.

We found ourselves moving through a dense and unfamiliar woodland jungle filled with weird sounds and some very unpleasant insects and on several occasions we were met by strange black figures who appeared and disappeared among the trees. They did not attack us, but made us very uneasy and aware that our every move was being watched.

After a night of this a messenger caught us up from Rochambeau reporting that his men had been attacked and he had responded with full attack on Forte Liberte. "We have captured the garrison here and have taken no prisoners" his letter reported.

"That means he has massacred all opposition. His chance to avenge the planters killed when the slaves first revolted." Boye told me. "His behaviour has of course left Leclerc with no choice but to forget any peaceful occupation of Le Cap for this action will get straight to Christophe."

Later that same night we saw an ominous red glow in the sky and a light wind carried a miasma of wood smoke over us.

"I know what that means." Said Boye. "Before I left for France Louverture told me that if the French were to send an army to put down the slave revolt and the government he had set up, he would burn down the towns and retreat with his troops into the mountains. This is what Christophe has just done"

We pressed on and on getting to Le Cap the next morning and found the city still burning and Christophe's force waiting for us. Well trained and experienced but totally outnumbered they fought hard and before he finally surrendered we had some five hundred casualties.

For the first time we saw something else. Many of our men were going down with a high fever and recurrent vomiting. It was the Yellow Fever Boye had told me about.

Out in the bay *L'Oceon* rode at anchor and Boye and I accompanied Leclerc back on board for he was anxious to see how Pauline and his baby son Dermide aged three were doing. The sea was no longer calm and as we watched for a further two days Le Cap continued to burn and dense black clouds of smoke and ash drifted right out to sea depositing cinders on our decks.

Leclerc and his generals were now bent on taking over and pacifying the island. He was also keen to rebuild Le Cap and as soon as the fires were over covered the town with proclamations in French and creole declaring "Black and White, all are children of the Republic" and that the First Consul had declared he strongly supported the freedom the slaves had so bravely fought for.

*****

While using Boyer as chief of staff on the military side, Leclerc now turned to Boye for advice about the local politics and in particular the relations between the black generals and Louverture which were not straight forward, there being tensions between mulattoes like Christophe and blacks like Dessaline. To this I heard Boye add, "These generals are also divided on how best to treat the former slaves while at the same time making the plantations productive. Freedom of movement, wages and numbers of days to be worked each week are all being argued over. They also have differing attitudes towards the local whites and toward France."

When on our own he explained to me that initially the "rebels" were looking for a continued association with the French Republic and liked the idea of being incorporated into the French Army while retaining their ranks. They were also attracted by the ideas and culture of the Revolution, though quite quickly suspicions were growing about how much Leclerc and his fine words could be trusted.

Boye from his many contacts on the island quickly picked up that the presence of Rochambeau with Leclerc was also fuelling suspicion.

"Did I tell you Bioletti? He is still a plantation owner and former Governor General both of Saint Dominique and of Martinique. Oh yes. He was dismissed by Commissioner Sonthonax for being against freeing the slaves."

Port au Prince, the other major town on the island, had been controlled by General Dessalines who had withdrawn without burning it down. This meant it was now open for occupation by Leclerc. This left the governor's palace unoccupied and thoughtfully not vandalised. Pauline hated being stuck on *L'Ocean* and wished to be on land so Leclerc installed her there, together with her entourage of musicians and a nursemaid for Dermide. Almost immediately she became the centre of attention from all the leading white and some mulatto ladies of the town.

Boye and I were put up in a pleasant villa nearby run by a *creole* landlady and a surprisingly large black staff. One quickly saw that anyone who was white or *creole* had a deep aversion to any form of physical labour and given the huge supply of blacks willing to be servants I quickly found I could get all my uniform and polishing duties – which can be quite time-consuming - efficiently done for me and returned spotless, ironed and polished.

*****

Soon we joined Leclerc on campaign against the man who had vacated Port au Prince, General Dessaline. He was unwilling to surrender and had holed up in a fort, Crete-a-Pierrot a few miles inland. Boye was there in an advisory role to Leclerc and I was around as his bodyguard. Against his advice Leclerc and Boyer clearly thought taking the fort would be easy, but as I heard Leclerc say later, "It was the hottest affair I have seen in my life." In one day 600 of our army were killed or wounded, including 50 officers. Boye and I were not sorry to miss out on the actual fighting. It was a bloody business. Before finally surrendering Dessalines' troops showed extreme bravery and well-trained discipline. Not what Leclerc and his men expected, though no surprise to Boye. On entering their camp however our troops discovered most had melted away into the jungle leaving piles of slaughtered whites and blacks. Disturbing.

We were surprised when the night before our attack we could hear his troops all singing *The Marseilles* and other revolutionary songs accompanied by a band. When I asked Boye what this meant he said that he thought Dessalines had persuaded his men that the First Consul had betrayed the Revolution and they were its true followers.

True to Napoleon's directions on surrender all Dessalines' officers were officially received into the French Army. A dramatic parade was held and their ranks publicly confirmed and the men all enlisted. When news of this got about the remaining rebel groups in the North and West who were far from defeated all surrendered. The exception however was Toussaint Louverture who said that at sixty he was too old to accept military rank and that he would retire to his own estate with his wife and children at a place called Ennery.

With that Leclerc played another of Napoleon's cards sending Louverture's two teenage French educated sons with their priest mentor to their father to ask him to accede to Leclerc's request that he surrender. Louverture however continued to refuse.

It looked now like a period of calm with the island under Leclerc's control. He was however well aware that appearances could be deceptive for the black generals and their men could quickly reform if they became dissatisfied. With this in mind he set off to Le Cap to oversee its rebuild and to tour around and inspect all the other bases.

At the same time he was not a well man and was faced with an increasing number of soldiers going down with Yellow Fever. Before they set off he told Boye that he was rather unhappy leaving Pauline in Port au Prince without really good security for as he said, "I fear any black or mulatto may fawn on us one moment and be ready to cut our throats the next." He was quite right. In the next few weeks he soon found that despite the parades and promises rebel formations continued to form and men to change sides.

At first his policy was to try anyone who was caught deserting before having them shot, but as the numbers going down with Yellow Fever increased, we heard he was adopting another policy. If one person deserted to the "rebel" side, be it a soldier or a plantation worker, Leclerc ordered that everyone else in that unit or working on that farm should be summarily shot. His thinking was that if one went others might follow and if the penalty was known that would act as a disincentive to changing sides. In fact the opposite effect quickly took hold and as the numbers executed grew so did the numbers going over to the "rebel" side. Dark days were upon us.

Chapter 27
Cleopatra of The Indies

Boye then decided to offer Leclerc my services while they were both away, suggesting I remain in Port au Prince and oversee the guard responsible for the security of the governor's palace.

"He is not just a good *ordonnance*," he told Leclerc, "In the sense of looking after one well. He has served right through both Napoleon's Italian and Egyptian campaigns in active battlefield service. He knows how to handle himself in a crisis or an emergency and I trust him."

Well, that was nice to know. Before he left Boye took me aside and told me he had put me forward for this job because it would be a great opportunity to be his eyes and ears, to hear the gossip and find out what the locals who came to visit Pauline were thinking and doing. "She is already the focus of the wildest of rumours as I am sure you will have heard from the other ranks. Her amorous behaviour may or may not be of interest, but what I really am interested in is anything you can tell me or find out about this whole mission for I feel Leclerc is keeping something very important about it very close to his chest. Be careful, but you may even come across some drafts of his correspondence with Napoleon which could shed light on this."

"So you are asking me to act as a spy sir? If caught I would be executed for treason." I responded.

"Telling me what you hear and see should involve you in no risk Bioletti," Boye replied, "Beyond that it will depend on what you come across and what risks you take. Of course if you were caught searching files or documents I would not be able to help you, so any initiative you take like that has to be yours."

"Sir, since you are suggesting I take quite a risk, could you share with me your suspicions as to what may being kept secret about the aims of this mission?" I said.

"Alright Bioletti. I have put years of my life into working here and have come to believe slavery the most appalling of human institutions which is almost as evil in its effects upon the slavers as the slave. You just don't know how much I have seen of it at first hand. It corrupts everyone and it is a complete denial of our common humanity. The future of this island has to be one free of slavery and the honour of France and of our Revolution and of our Republic demands we stand by that. What I fear is that one way or another what our First Consul and Leclerc have in mind is some form of betrayal of the former slaves and those who support them."

"And if that turns out to be true, what do you think you could do about it?" I replied remembering the Italians and the Egyptians.

"As yet I have no idea," said Boye regretfully, "Let's hope I am wrong and that the aim of this great invasion force is to turn us all in the end into one great happy family - all free and French."

After this conversation I was moved by a team of black servants out of my lodgings and into a rather nice guest room in the palace. This placed me in a conveniently central location so as to be able to keep an eye on Pauline and the whole security set-up.

*****

The Governor's Palace was a fine colonial-style building with large reception rooms, offices, a ball-room and over twenty rooms where guests could be accommodated, together with kitchens, laundry, servants (formerly slave) quarters and a suite of rooms for the Governor that Pauline would now continue to live in.

The residence was surrounded by fine gardens with palm trees, orange trees and local varieties of plants and flowers in abundance and the whole estate was surrounded by a high perimeter wall. There was a guardhouse for the sentries and kennels for the guard dogs used to patrol the perimeter.

Since that first dinner on *L'Ocean* I had observed Pauline but had never spoken to her. In the close confines of a ship where a look or a word could trigger gossip, and my status so subservient, that was hardly surprising.

The night before the generals were off to La Cap Leclerc

invited P.F.J. Boyer and Boye to join him for "an intimate family dinner" with Pauline. I was told to ready myself to be "properly introduced." at the end of their meal when I was duly called in.

"Ah Bioletti," said Boye, "Please come in. Madame Leclerc I would like to introduce you to my *ordonnance* Private Bioletti. He takes care of me very thoroughly, and your husband and I have decided that while we are away he should join your staff and particularly keep an eye on you as your bodyguard so that you might feel safe and secure here."

"Bioletti!" said Pauline, "Don't tell me the man's an Italian. I just love Italians. Fancy, there you were on the ship and I never knew."

"No madam," I replied soberly.

"So tell me Bioletti, how are you going to look after me?" she asked.

"He has quarters here in the palace and he will be around keeping an eye on things in general and in particular making sure you only see the persons you wish to see, my dear." said Leclerc. "And at night he will take his turn with the others already here to be on guard duty outside your chambers and around the house."

"You will also find he sings quite well and can work with your musicians." said Boye.

"And I knew him as the *ordonnance* of that tough old bird General Kleber in Egypt." said Boyer. "Very good he was at keeping him looking smart and cleaning his boots." he sneered. "And of course at keeping himself out of harm's way as *ordonnances* do. Pity he wasn't around when Kleber got stabbed by that Muslim fanatic in Cairo." he added.

"That of course was before I met him and keeping out of harm's way was not quite what I have heard about his Egyptian service when he was recommended to me." Said Boye, "Before that he fought as a skirmisher in Italy."

"Really," said Pauline, "I so love Italy. All that art, culture and music."

"Lodi, Mantua, Rivoli?" asked Leclerc.

"Yes sir." I replied, "All of them."

"Very good," said Leclerc, sounding impressed. "Perhaps our paths crossed? I am sure you will take good care of Madame. That will be all." And with that he dismissed me.

The next day after the departure of Leclerc and his entourage the palace was rather still and quiet when I was summoned to the sitting room after lunch. There Pauline was playing with her little boy attended by her French maid. She quietly told the woman to take Dermide off for a walk in the garden.

"Well Bioletti," she said speaking to my surprise in quite heavily accented Italian, "Tell me about yourself. Where are you from and how did you get into the French Army? And don't look so surprised. We Corsicans are all pretty bilingual, speaking French in public and our own form of Italian at home."

It was the first time I had been addressed in Italian for a long time. I told her about growing up in Turin and being inspired by the Revolution as a result of our French teacher, how I had joined up in the Revolutionary Army after I had seen my school friend shot and how I had been inspired by Napoleon in Nice at eighteen and later in action in Italy.

I was surprised how much I opened up to her. I thought she was a really good listener and showed none of the silliness she exhibited at the dinner table.

Two days later I was summoned again to see her on my own. This time she was sitting in the gardens.

"It sounds as if you have had a much better education than I have." she said, "And you are still only a Private. Poor you. Do you like what you do and do you get on with your General Boye?"

"Well, actually, yes I do." I replied.

"Does that mean I can expect you to share with him all the gossip you hear about me and that you will tell him everything I say to you?"

"Not at all!" I replied rather shocked she had smelt out my possible role so soon. "The whole point about being an *ordonnance* is that you can be trusted not to share confidences or gossip."

"I hope I can believe you." she said, "You don't know how many times I have been let down like that, or all the lies that people I have known have spread about me."

"I won't pretend I have not heard gossip about you." I said. "I suppose it is the down side of being the sister of someone so famous. People will want to say, "Do you know what I heard about Pauline" or some men will want to boast, "You will never believe how I got on with Pauline." even if all they say is lies."

"Not just men, women too." She said bitterly. "Now the reason I wanted speak to you is that this evening I have some guests coming for dinner and afterwards we shall have some music and I will be joining our two musicians to sing. We rehearse later this afternoon and I would like you to join us so I can hear how you sing. Perhaps then you might be able to take part in our little concert?" I could hardly believe my good fortune.

The rehearsal and the evening went very well for she was very relaxed and pleasant and had herself a rather beautiful, if essentially untrained, voice. Subsequently we sang duets together and practising these gave us good reason to visit corners of the gardens and be alone together. On these occasions we sang and then chatted on and she really seemed at ease with me when she suddenly said seriously, "Right, Bioletti, I have decided. I hope I am not being a fool but I really like you being so direct with me. No one else would have admitted to hearing rumours about me in the way you did. Most simply deny having heard anything. You will already have seen what flattering rubbish I have to put up with from most of my guests."

"Yes, Madame, I certainly have." I replied.

"Well then, let's hope you are as honest as you are direct. From now on you can call me Pauline – when we are alone like this. Then I can also talk to you in my native Corsican Italian - which I'm sure you've noticed, no-one else here understands. Otherwise of course in company expect me to – you know - keep you in your place."

"Quite understood Pauline, and please, my name is Alberto." I replied.

And so it was from then on. I was Bioletti the guard, footman and extra singer in public and Alberto in private and she made time almost every day for us to be able to chat.

I remember her saying, "You know I have no real illusions. I am just an uneducated Corsican girl with a famous older brother and an awful mother. Did you know we had no money for school fees when I was the right age and my mother took in washing! But as I am aware you have noticed I have other charms. Oh yes Alberto! I am well aware of how you look at me! And of course I really enjoy looking as beautiful and attractive as possible. I just love fashion and dressing up and I love upsetting other women when their men just can't keep their eyes off me, particularly when they think they are cleverer or more important than me." And she roared with laughter.

On another occasion she said, "We must be around the same age. How old are you?

Twenty four." I replied.

"Just two years older than me and you have already fought through two campaigns and are well on your way to doing a third. No woman could do all that." she said wistfully.

"Not exactly my choice you know Pauline. Once you get into the Army you just have to make the best of what comes your way. It has though been a pretty eventful life so far and I really am lucky still to be in one piece." I said.

"No, it's not that I want to be a fighting soldier Alberto," she replied, "It is that with all their talk of liberty and equality most "revolutionary" men don't think liberty and equality applies to women, but are rather like the planters here who think liberty and equality applies to them, but not to persons of colour.

"Do you mean you think women should have the vote?" I asked.

"Well, some day that might come, perhaps when all men have the vote, but that sort of politics doesn't interest me. No, I was thinking of something much more personal." she said this with a big smile and then changed the subject.

*****

Of course I was completely smitten, as I had never been in all my life. The time she chose to give me became the centre of each day, in fact it felt like the centre of my life. Everything about her, her voice, her laugh, her face, her neat figure, her dainty feet, expressive hands – everything about her just overwhelmed me.

When I was with her I was simply obsessed by her and found it very hard not to show it. At the same time I took my professional duties even more seriously, making certain that no-one could approach her that had not been questioned and cleared by me or one of the other guards.

Certainly the looks and behaviour of the passing mulattoes or blacks we saw in the streets made me feel edgy when they crowded around. This happened several times when with a guard of four soldiers we escorted her to visit a dress shop or milliner in the main boulevard, something she loved to do. I felt particularly anxious when news came through of the attempt made on Napoleon's life in Paris when he and Josephine were driving to the Opera.

In public at some of her concerts and dinner parties it got through even to my enamoured self that she could be quite rude and silly. It was as if she had an act and a particular persona to live up to, so when we were alone I gave it to her straight about the need for care in what she said and not causing unnecessary offence or of doing impulsive things which would lay her open to risk and criticism.

"Alberto, you make such a fuss, but you can't imagine what it is like being me with all the innuendo and sly looks I have to put up with." she said, "I think "What the hell. Let's give them something to make a fuss about." Still, don't stop your criticisms. They do make me think."

The *creole* women who came to visit her were quite something. Turning up with at least three or four black servants each they were annoyed to be told the servants should be sent to the kitchen while they visited Madame Leclerc for they thought their status was enhanced if they had their servants standing around. They appeared dressed in frills and garish colours and their conversation consisted mainly of complaints about their servants, gossip about the latest fashions, and tales about who was sleeping with whom.

One attractive young woman named Michelle Gaudreau, wife of a prominent plantation owner, seemed to strike up a particular friendship with Pauline. Fascinated by Pauline's wardrobe she begged to look at and try on her things. Pauline was I thought remarkably accommodating and they would disappear into her bedroom with much giggling to appear later, flushed and wearing each other's clothes.

Dermide and his nurse-maid were often around but I was sorry to see that looking after him or showing interest in what he was doing was not something Pauline found easy. He spent a solitary life with the nurse-maid and no contact with other children. The gossip I heard was that Pauline had found giving birth very painful and protracted and she had never been able to feel close to the child, also it was said the doctors had told her she could never have any more.

*****

During one of our conversations Pauline said, "And that stuck up Boyer said you were in Cairo? I would just love to go to Cairo. All that Egyptian Art, their paintings and their pyramids and I hear they have huge mysterious temples. I so wanted my brother to take me with him when he went to Egypt. He said he would. Then we could have sailed down the Nile like Anthony and Cleopatra, he the Roman General with me as his Queen."

"But you are his sister." I said.

"Yes, but didn't you know. The pharaohs often married their sisters. You should know Alberto," she continued defiantly, " I love my brother more than any man."

"Even though he stopped you marrying the man you were engaged to and got you to marry Leclerc." I blurted out.

"So that has got about among the lower ranks has it?" she said bitterly. "Of course. Napoleon broke up the engagement for my own good. I was just a child then, he was my first love and I was pretty besotted by that Stanislas Freron, He certainly knew how to pleasure me and I have to remember I learnt a lot about that from him. I was fifteen and he was over forty and very experienced. What I didn't know was he had a long term Italian mistress who was pregnant and he already had two children by her."

"That I did not know. It must have been very painful for you to learn." I said.

"Napoleon was quite right seeing the engagement was broken off and choosing Charles for me instead. In many ways he is a lovely man – even if he doesn't give me quite what I want." she finished off.

All this threw me into the most confused state of mind. My imagination took me down paths I did not want to go and others that obsessed me. The one thing I did know was that I was utterly in love with her. I also had never felt so powerless. I was after all a private, a nothing, and she was, whatever she was saying, the clearly much loved sister of the most powerful man in all Europe if not the world, and the wife of my commander in chief.

The nights of course were the worst of times, especially when the drumming started – usually in the early hours to continue relentlessly, pounding on and on. Everyone said it was the *maroons*, the runaway slaves from the mountains, but who knew, it could be the more recent insurgents. It was certainly menacing.

Taking my turn I came on duty outside the door to her chamber at midnight, to stand in uniform with a primed pistol and my trusty short sword. I would stay there until relieved at 6 a.m. The heat was oppressive and so was the sound of cicadas.

One evening after a particularly boring dinner party for an older French officer and his prying and insincere wife, Pauline had said little and could hardly maintain politeness. I was on duty outside her room when at around two I heard the lock turn and the bolt of her door being drawn back and there she stood in a plain white chemise.

"Alberto, I can't bear this terrible drumming and I can't sleep. Can I come out and sit by you out here?" she said. No we did not rush inside her room and do as I had imagined countless times as I lay alone on my bed. Instead I fetched a small chair which she sat in and brought from inside her room a glass of the local lemonade she liked and her wraparound gown.

"Cover yourself in this and slip back into your room if you hear anyone coming. The other guard will not be around to check for nearly an hour." was all I said. She thanked me, sat silently in the chair staring into the distance and after some time stood up, gave me a gentle kiss on the cheek and slipped back into her room while my heart pounded.

The next day when I met her in the garden she said, "Alberto I have been quite depressed. All sorts of things about this spooky place get me down but I want to say I do not know any other man who would have treated me with such kindness and restraint as you did last night. Now I really do feel I can trust you."

"Pauline," I said, "I would do anything to earn your trust and make you happy."

"I think you would," she said, "But honestly Alberto, I am not like you. I can see the state you are in, but though I think you are a really attractive man, since that first silly mistake falling for Freron when I was so young, my emotions have never been so deeply stirred, except by the one person who I can never have."

"You mean your brother?"

"Yes. I am afraid so. Don't ask me to tell you more about that, but when he married that miserable licentious *creole* Josephine and I saw them together I was just so jealous! As a result I behaved really badly. If I hear he has got involved with anyone else, like I hear he did with some girl in Cairo, it just makes me madly jealous all over again."

Remembering Pauline Foures I kept quiet about that. "So what about your husband?" I asked. "Doesn't he make you happy?"

"Charles just wants someone to look good and pleasure him in bed - which by the way is something he is not very good at doing for me. He isn't even interested in his son. Instead I think he is almost as obsessed by my brother as I am! Seriously. Have you watched him? I'm sure you have heard it said about him too. "The blond Napoleon!" Also all he is really concerned with is his own reputation, his wealth and his "glory."

She paused and then continued, "He is though quite kind and generous to me, so now I would not like to hurt him anymore, for I have already – several times." she said quietly.

"How?" I asked.

"Oh, well there were these three silly generals I was seeing in Paris. I had such fun setting them up against each other until one of them got suspicions, told the others and it all came out into the open, making poor Charles look such a fool! So you see I am not the sort of innocent, sweet person you should fall for deeply." I looked crushed.

"Come on Alberto, let's forget all that." she then said, "Charles may be home tomorrow or not for weeks. Who knows? Let's just make the most of this time we can have together and enjoy the present. When you think about it really, it is all we could ever have hoped for. So let's just enjoy ourselves. Tonight I want to sing with you after dinner. You know I really love music, it is the best thing next to the pleasures of love!"

So that night I sang my head off with her musicians, drank lots of good wine and at one in the morning slipped into her bedroom for the first of a series of the most amazing experiences of the pleasures the body is capable of. We also laughed a lot, relaxed and talked both afterwards and the next day about what we had done. This was something I had never discussed with anyone before, yet with her it just seemed natural and nothing exceptional, like discussing a good wine or a good meal.

At the same time it is impossible to describe the mix of exhilaration, pride, joy, regret and sadness that I felt – all at the same time.

*****

A few days later she received a note from Michelle, asking if she could call after lunch. When she arrived she looked desperate and had obvious bruises on her face and her arms. Pauline waved for me to keep my distance while they walked in the garden, Michelle being obviously very upset. Later when she had gone home Pauline said to me, "The man she has married is a monster. He takes her every night he is at home, and he does it in such a violent way. You should see the marks she has. And that's not all. He often has two, yes two black women who he has known since he was a child when they were slaves on his plantation. Each now has a baby of his and he tells Michelle both of them satisfy him much more than her."

"Do you think there is anything you can do to help her?" I asked.

"Michelle says her husband is off to Martinique for several days." She replied, "Something to do with training a consignment of dogs from Cuba my husband ordered when we got here. General Rochambeau is also interested in them she tells me.

"What sort of dogs?" I asked.

"Oh I don't know." she replied looking suddenly embarrassed. "Bloody Cuban slave-hunting dogs if you must know. They think the Army might use them in dealing with these rebels. Anyway, nothing to do with Michelle except that he hit her and now she is alone so I have invited her to come and stay here while he is away. We have no shortage of space."

So Michelle came to stay for nearly a week. The two became inseparable to the extent that I began to feel jealous of the time they spent in her room together and talking to each other in the garden. Pauline picked up on that and invited me to join them, describing me as "Bioletti, my tame Italian *ordonnance*, who has become really quite a friend." She did this without intimating to her the nature of our relationship. Who knows what Michelle must have thought.

To an extent this placated me though I continued to feel there was something going on between them. At the same time I also felt some sympathy for this young woman who found herself in such an unpleasant and difficult situation with her husband. Seeing that Pauline seemed to trust me she also quickly started to talk about herself to me.

"So your husband has gone to Martinique? I asked.

"Yes. He is a great friend of that detestable stuck-up General Rochambeau." she replied. "You must know he was previously Governor of Martinique, and then of Saint Domingue just before the Revolution and he still has an estate here."

I remembered Boye had mentioned that. She then went on to describe how Leclerc had imported at great expense a large number of hunting dogs with their Cuban handlers to Martinique.

"Rochambeau has a real passion for dogs and for training them, just like my husband, and they think they could be a great help in catching rebels and terrifying all the blacks who set eyes on them. My husband is getting a pack of one hundred dogs with their handlers now in Martinique ready to be brought over here." she went on.

"And what will they do with them over here?" I asked.

"The same sort of thing I suppose. Get them ready for hunting and controlling these rebelling former slaves. In fact my husband said it was all part of the plan Leclerc and Rochambeau have to re-introduce slavery."

"And what does your husband think about that?" I asked.

"He says he can't wait." she replied, "He thinks freeing the slaves to be the worst thing ever to hit this island. It certainly has made his job trying to run a profitable plantation much tougher, and that certainly has not made him an easier man to live with." She then went on, "My husband is also keen to see how the work has been going to re-introduce slavery on Martinique since Leclerc's campaign arrived here." I looked a bit stunned. "Why Bioletti, did you not know about all this?" she asked.

"Well, no. But then I'm not interested in political things." I muttered.

"You'd be surprised at what Bioletti finds interesting," Pauline added with a laugh, "And tonight you will see one of them – his love of music - when he sings."

That was the first rumour I heard that the real aim of this campaign was the re-introduction of slavery and I was stunned. After its abolition at least six years earlier how could such a policy be imagined and what could be a greater betrayal of all the Revolution stood for?

I did not know anything about Martinique except that Napoleon's Josephine came from a plantation owning family there. Certainly what I had already learnt about Saint Domingue and Toussaint Louverture made me think that reintroducing slavery sounded not only wrong, but impossible without setting off a most terrible war.

It did not however take that long to hear the rumour repeated again and again by other guests of Pauline and among the guards. I wondered how aware Boye and Boyer would both be that it was now doing the rounds and I continued to hope that it might not be true.

*****

Talking to Michelle and listening to Pauline's guests was also an education as to the feelings of local *creole* whites towards their black former slaves and the mixed race *mulattoes*. The revolts had resulted in some very violent murders of plantation owners, their managers and their families with the result that they all had horrible stories to tell of the killing of relatives and people they knew. Not surprisingly they did not say much about how those involved had treated their slaves, except that a twelve hour, six day week under the lash of an overseer in the fields with a minimum of food was regarded by them as normal and not unreasonable treatment.

Many were also pretty sentimental about their household slave servants who they had grown up with and who looked after their children, seeing them as "good blacks" who they thought they treated very well, but they were also quickly ready to justify extended beatings and terrible tortures for those who crossed the line into rebelliousness or disobedience. There was also a widespread terror among them of the possibility of being poisoned, something very difficult to pin on one person. In the end they all agreed, the blacks were just dangerous savages who could only be kept in their place if they had a hearty fear of their owners. I wondered if that was really so different to the way the nobility treated the peasantry in Italy.

Soon after our discussions Michelle returned home to the tender attentions of her husband. He turned up at the palace to collect her, as arrogant and self-confident a man as I expected. Pauline then took to her bed with a nasty fever. I was naturally terrified that she had contracted Yellow Fever, but within a week the high temperature which left her exhausted and covered in perspiration was gone.

In fact the illness had certainly weakened her, but being the person she was her response was to turn her convalescence into an opportunity to indulge her Cleopatra fantasy and demand that she be carried around in a litter by four servants, strapping black men of course, for much of the day. Was this affectation or need? I will never know. It did not however inhibit her ardour or capacity for love-making for having made much of how tired she was all day, when night came and her team of black bearers were dismissed - from whatever duties she had asked them to perform - she easily secreted herself into my room.

After one such meeting we ended discussing Michelle and her husband and I asked what she thought about slavery.

"I think it is rather disgusting." she said. "We should all be free and paid a wage for our work, though if you think about it poor Michelle is little more than a slave as far as her husband is concerned."

"But she chose to marry him." I replied.

"Oh no she didn't, no more than I chose my husband! Liberty, Equality, Fraternity," she said slowly. "Listen Alberto, what I am going to say now I didn't think up all by myself. Oh no, I am not clever enough for that, but when I was in Paris I attended the salons of some of the top revolutionary ladies, Madame de Stael and her group the *incroyables*. Ever hear of them?

"Sorry, no," I replied.

"Well, I can assure you in Revolutionary society in Paris they are pretty highly thought of. They were also pretty terrible to me. They laughed at my ignorance for not having read all that the philosophers of the Enlightenment carried on about. Oh yes, they enjoyed making me feel stupid, but they pointed out that Revolutionary men, even when they thought about emancipating slaves, were not so keen on emancipating women.

They also pointed out that while men thought it quite alright to carry on taking pleasure with the women they desired, inside or outside of marriage, they were not at all happy about seeing a woman behave in the same way, except if she were one of their whores, in which case they could say that she was doing it for money and not for her own pleasure.

So you see I, like several of those *incroyables*, are just teaching you men what liberty, equality and fraternity really means - if you include us."

"And your brother, does he agree with you?" I asked.

"No, he does not. He thinks it is the duty of a wife to be "faithful" to her husband and please him in every way and look after his children and accept his authority. Typical soldier. He was terribly hurt and jealous when he heard about Josephine and Hippolyte Charles! He also hates the thought of a white woman being with a black man even if he does not worry if it is the other way around."

"Is that because he thinks white people are essentially superior to any person who is not white?" I asked.

"Well, don't you?" she came back.

"I try not to and I don't think so. I have met some very clever and able people who are not white and I have heard of others." I said.

"So have I," she replied, "But most of them are just stupid."

"Quite unlike most white people?" said I. "And what about you getting jealous of Josephine, not because she was unfaithful but because she married your brother?"

"And I told you I will not talk about that." She said angrily.

"And am I not supposed to feel jealous when I see or hear you are involved with someone else, because I have to tell you the very thought makes me feel quite sick with jealousy." I responded.

"I know," she replied, "And there is just nothing I and you can do about that."

The next night she came I raised slavery with her again. "Tell me Pauline, your guests said it again at lunch today, that people are all thinking that the purpose of this great army being here is to re-introduce slavery. Do you think that is what your husband wants to do.?"

"He never discusses military or political matters with me. Thinks I am far too stupid, so I give up trying." she replied. "I can though tell you one thing, he knows the reason Napoleon appointed him commander in chief of this army is because he can be trusted to do what Napoleon wants. He does not take big decisions on his own, in fact he does not seem to take even quite small decisions on his own. Still I don't know what Napoleon has told him to do. This time I think I shall ask him and try and get an answer out of him."

She fell silent after that and we lay together thinking until we fell into an uneasy sleep. It was to be our last night together for the next day first Boye and then Leclerc came back unannounced. Boye looked tired and exhausted and his uniform was in a terrible state. He had been rushing around the island on horseback.

"Sorry to bring your little idyll with the lovely Pauline to an end Bioletti," he said, "But we will all be moving back to Le Cap in one big party as soon as we have both had our kit all cleaned up, so plenty for you to do."

"Of course sir. You look exhausted."

"And what news have you for me?" he asked.

"All sorts of people are saying that the real purpose of this whole campaign is the re-introduction of slavery, and frankly what I have been able to find out about white opinion while staying here is that all the local whites think that is why you are here and want that to happen." I replied.

"You confirm just what I have learnt." he replied. "And to add to the bad news I was present while Leclerc supervised the execution of five hundred black troops suspected of getting ready to rise against us yesterday. That was also the day after he supervised the arrest and preparation of the return to France of all white women who have been or are in relationships with black or *mulatto* men on the direct order of the First Consul because they "prostitute the honour of France" or words to that effect. Add to that hundreds of our men have died of Yellow Fever while we have been in Le Cap. These are dark days."

Pauline arranged one last meeting walking in the garden. "I'm sure you have heard that French nurse-maid reported sick this morning. I fear she has the fever." she said, "And my dear Alberto, we always knew it would end like this, without warning and with no going back. I hope you will be able to remember our times together with kindness. You are the best Italian I have ever had." she said smiling. I can't remember what I mumbled, but I knew she was quite right. For us it was over.

Chapter 28
Into the Darkness

The news steadily got worse. Pauline followed Leclerc to the beautiful island of Tortue off the coast of Le Cap. He liked it so much he asked Napoleon to give it to him as part recompense for his service. The climate there was certainly more pleasant than in Le Cap where we were now based and which became hotter and wetter as we suffered violent rain, thunder storms and clammy, damp heat. Everywhere soldiers were going down with the Yellow Fever and Leclerc had a large hospital built for them on Tortue, hoping this would keep them away from the miasma enveloping Le Cap.

Toussaint Louverture was now at his Ennery estate supervising the harvest, and I accompanied Boye on a visit to him. His was an imposing presence, very black, tall and with greying hair, he spoke elegant French with a deep resonant voice and what struck me was how sad he seemed. Leclerc was still seeking to get him to make a formal surrender as all the other "rebel" officers had now done, but he continued to refuse. He and Boye had a long conversation walking in his garden together while I was entertained by his formidable looking guards, again wearing immaculate French Army uniforms. As with Christophe's guards they were very friendly towards me having seen Boye visit Louverture on many previous occasions.

As we rode away Boye told me that Louverture was now convinced that Leclerc's real aim was the re-introduction of slavery and nothing Boye could say could counteract that, in fact Boye felt, after listening to Louverture, that his suspicions were well founded.

"I think I have been a blind and trusting fool." he said to me.

"Despite the news you brought me I have just not been able to believe that Napoleon could so betray all the Revolution and the Republic stands for as to seek to re-introduce slavery. Louverture tells me he has written over a hundred letters to Napoleon assuring him of his wish to see the island and all its people free and French, but he has received not a single reply. What I did not tell him is that I have seen much of Napoleon's correspondence with Leclerc which refers to Louverture in the most disparaging way and his generals as "those gilded Africans" who are first to be deported before the "final step" is taken. There can, I must now face it, be little doubt as to what he means that final step to be."

He went on to tell me how while on the one hand Louverture was convinced the facts showed the French Army was there to re-impose slavery, at the same time his sadness was not just caused at this betrayal of the Revolution, but he saw it as a betrayal of all that French civilisation and his Catholic faith stood for. This really pained him. He told Boye it was only because he had been given the chance to adopt and understand French culture, civilisation and Christianity that he had been able to recognise the evil of slavery properly, and the difference freedom could make. He saw his revolt and that of the slaves of the island as inspired by both French revolutionary thought and as deeply by French culture. He could not see how tribal Africans could build a new society on the island without adopting much of the knowledge and culture of France as well as the values of the Revolution. He certainly did not trust the British, Spanish or Americans to give what Revolutionary France could give them.

In an attempt to make himself popular Leclerc was involved in two strange events. News reached us that on Tortue he arranged a ball for Pauline and all his staff. As well as her *creole* friends he invited leading *mulatto* guests and the music provided had been wild. The guests it was said had then indulged in the most explicit and provocative dancing to the "great embarrassment" of the French officers present. In other words the ball effectively increased tension between *creoles* and *mulattoes*. Not what he had intended.

The second event was just rather bizarre. In an attempt to imitate Napoleon with his savants in Egypt Leclerc set about trying to appear a patron of science by collecting unique and exotic local wild-life. He sought out plants, animals and birds to send back to France, alive if possible, or if dead to be stuffed. He also wrote to the Spanish governor of Cartagena in Columbia who sent an amazing collection of wild South American animals including mountain lions, panthers, bears, monkeys and parrots. These were paraded through the streets before being housed in the stables of the governor's palace in Le Cap prior to being shipped on to France.

*****

It was at this time I met a second Boyer. To avoid confusion there is my general, Jacques Boye whose career had been mainly in Saint Domingue, and who had risen to Adjutant General, and there is General Pierre Francois Joseph Boyer who was Leclerc's and formerly Kleber's adjutant general, I now need to introduce the *mulatto* Jean Pierre Boyer.

The first I knew of him was when a rather scared looking black man delivered a letter by hand addressed to Boye. It was from Jean Pierre telling Boye that he was in prison in Le Cap and he feared for his life. By this time the situation had become so precarious and the security of any white man and of any white Army officer so at risk of sudden attack, that it was clearly necessary that I accompany Boye everywhere he went as his bodyguard.

The prison in Le Cap was a stinking, depressing hell-hole. Built with slaves in mind it was nothing more than a series of fetid dungeons. To enter the packed cells was impossible. Boye gave the name of Jean Pierre to a guard and he was brought out to meet us. To my surprise the two embraced and both Jean Pierre and Boye wept. A tall good-looking young man of colour with a sensitive face, his perfect French and confident bearing, despite his filthy clothes, made it obvious that he was French educated and had a military background.

"Jean Pierre," said Boye, "It is so good to see you again. What has happened for you to be here? I thought you were in France. When did you get back to Saint Domingue?

"Jacques," Jean Pierre replied, "I can't tell you how glad I am to see you. Conditions here are appalling. Didn't you know? I was part of a group of *mulattoes* living in France who were actually officially approached to join this expedition of Leclerc's."

They talked earnestly together and it was only later after asking Boye about it that his story made sense to me. The first thing

181

that needed to be done however was to get Jean Pierre released. I thought Boye might write an order for his release for I thought he was sufficiently senior to do this without reference to anyone else. He however said, "I'm sorry Jean Pierre, I have got to be careful here for I have just learnt that Leclerc , following an order from Napoleon, is expelling any whites, military or civilian who are suspected of backing the rebels. They are being sent, of all places, to Corsica. To write an order for your release might get me locked up in that prison waiting for the next ship going there."

"I quite understand." Jean Pierre replied. "There is however another way to get me out. These guards are not well paid. In fact they grumble they have not been paid for the last three months."

And that was all it took. A not very large bribe changed hands and Jean Pierre was able to accompany us back to the house with no paper-work and no names having been given or recorded, and given the general chaos that was developing there was a good chance that the loss of a prisoner would not be noticed, followed up, or linked to Boye. Back in our rooms I provided him with a good bath and some of Boye's clean, fresh clothes.

Again as part of the small French educated elite on the island they had known each other for years, in fact somewhere down the line they were distant cousins. I learnt Jean Pierre on finishing school in France had joined the Revolutionary Army, had shown great ability and had risen to command a brigade before returning home and working with the Commissioners after the first uprising. Like Louverture he was against any attempt to go for independence from France, and had then returned to France with Commissioner Sonthonax.

When he read Louverture's constitution in France he had, like Boye, thought it went too far. His critical opinions had been noticed and he had been invited to join the Leclerc expedition which he was told aimed to stabilise the island and preserve the freedom of the former slaves.

Over a meal that evening, which I cooked and served, Boye said, "So Jean Pierre how did you get yourself locked up?"

"It was when I saw and heard our generals like Dessalines having to "surrender" to the French Army and to become part of it to keep their ranks, and when I saw and heard so many of our soldiers being disarmed after they had been apparently enlisted in the French Army that I became suspicious. I put two and two together and guessed I could see what the real purpose of this huge invasion is."

"And what do you think that is?" said Boye.

"The re-imposition of slavery. If it had been a stabilising operation they could have done that with an army a quarter of this size and they would have provoked no opposition." replied Jeanne Pierre. "Now, as you can see, the country is being torn apart with uprisings and then there is the news from Guadeloupe where the Army is supporting slavery."

"I see," said Boye. "So what happened next?"

"I made the mistake of expressing my opinion in front of the senior officer appointed to be the minder of our group." said Jean Pierre, "He quietly left the room, came back with two guards and it was off to prison for me. Now they are "thinning out" our numbers, which I think means each day a few are being taken out to be shot."

"I'm sorry but you can't stay here, it's not safe for either of us. I am not part of the invasion team despite my rank and I have to tread very carefully." said Boye, "You need to get away from here as soon as you can. Do you know where to go now?"

"I certainly do. General Dessalines." said Jean Pierre. "Don't worry about my safety now that I am out, in fact I think I am now safer than you, so thank you Jacques for getting me out and you Bioletti for all your help with something to wear, and for a great meal."

That was the last and only time I saw him and no one could possibly imagine the circumstances which would again bring Jean Pierre and Boye together many years later.

Chapter 29

Louverture Betrayed

A few days after this took place Louverture decided to face Leclerc and he turned up in Le Cap at the head of his dragoons on horseback. On seeing him ride by all the people in the street burst into spontaneous applause. Leclerc was having his meal on board a ship in the harbour and was alerted that Louverture had arrived. He rushed back to his residence and invited Louverture to dinner and I was involved in getting the food organised while Louverture's men stood outside leaning on their drawn sabres.

Inside the meeting did not go well for Louverture confronted Leclerc with having come to a peaceful island only to precipitate a vicious war. Leclerc attempted smarmy behaviour embracing Louverture and saying, "General, we can only praise you and admire you for the way you have borne the burdens of governing Saint Domingue." Again Leclerc offered him the rank of lieutenant-general which he refused.

Things did not improve when the meal was served. As each course was brought in Louverture carried on talking and refrained from eating and drinking, except for a glass of water, and at the end cutting himself a small piece of gruyere cheese. It was obvious he feared being poisoned. Nothing, I thought could more clearly show the breakdown of trust which had occurred between them.

When Leclerc talked about the overwhelming size of the army he commanded, Louverture responded saying simply, "Providence will save us." Providence was the name of the hospital in Le Cap, the hospital which was overflowing with Yellow Fever patients. Getting his meaning Leclerc and his aides were furious and upset. Boye told me afterwards that there were

3,600 men then in hospital and they were dying at the rate of 30 to 50 per day.

Louverture then returned to Ennery having assured Leclerc that he was simply now a retired farmer attending to the harvest. Leclerc for his part made fulsome promises to the effect that Louverture was safe and free to run his estate with his position respected. An increasing number of blacks however kept on turning up at Ennery.

When Leclerc heard that he became worried and suspicious particularly as he continued to be faced with the desertion of locals from the Army and insurrections by workers on the plantations. These often turned violent and bloody while at the same time more and more of his men were succumbing to Yellow Fever. He was also afraid Louverture had enough support to mount a rebellion against him.

Leclerc thus decided in June to break his word to Louverture and ordered his arrest and deportation to be carried out by deception. It was a terrible mistake.

On the pretext of discussing a business deal Louverture was lured away from his home by a man he thought he could trust. His two guards then suddenly found themselves disarmed by a large party of soldiers and finally when alone he was bound like a common criminal, his wife and family arrested, and his home at Ennery trashed in a fruitless search for cash. He was then secretly put on board a waiting frigate bound for France. As he embarked he said to the ship's captain, "In overthrowing me you have cut down in Saint Domingue only the trunk of the tree of liberty. It will spring up again from the roots for they are numerous and deep." These words were remembered and repeated everywhere. As news got about of Louverture's betrayal, trust in Leclerc and his intentions sank to a new low and defections to the "rebel" side increased.

*****

For Leclerc however the Yellow Fever epidemic continued to kill and disable his troops, though there was as yet no mass uprising on the rebel side and the black and *mulatto* generals were still apparently loyal. Leclerc, Boyer, Boye and many of us however were sure a general rebellion against Leclerc and the French Army was close. News reached the island daily in personal letters that slavery was back in Guadeloupe and new discriminatory laws came through from France. Leclerc repeatedly begged France for another 10,000 troops at least, but only 1,500 were sent.

His health continued to deteriorate and he asked to be relieved of his post as the numbers of troops loyal to him diminished. He also became reckless giving orders for mass executions on the farms of workers suspected to be on the edge of rebellion. This act of desperation resulted in thousands of deaths.

Knowing he was dying, he asked Boyer to take his report back to Napoleon and on November 2nd 1802 he died. My Boye estimated that of the 34,000 French soldiers who had landed, 24,000 were dead and 8,000 were in hospital, A few over 2,000 remained.

At Leclerc's "full military honours" funeral - which of course we were all expected to attend - Pauline appeared, tearstained and with her hair cut off. Suitably clad in a black gown that showed her figure off well, she came over for a brief word with Boye and me. I had not set eyes on her since we left Port au Prince. We both expressed our sympathies at her sad loss.

She looked exhausted and said she had not been well and that Leclerc had suffered an agonisingly painful death. She said she had placed her hair in his coffin and had his heart removed and placed in an urn she was keeping.

We thought this all very extreme and theatrical, but said nothing. No, she was not looking forward to the voyage home, but was desperate to see France and her brother again. Leclerc's body was to accompany her in a lead lined coffin.

Boye then moved away and Pauline said quietly to me, "Did you hear Alberto what happened to that black General Louverture?"

"No Pauline." I said, "Not since his arrest."

"That was a terrible thing my Charles did. He told me he thought it would solve his problems and it is one of the few political things he ever told me about. He told me he had orders from France to separate that poor man from his wife and sons even on the boat and when they reached France they were just abandoned. He was sent across France and locked up in a dungeon in a castle in the Jura Mountains. There he soon died of the cold and the poor treatment he received. So sad." she said.

I did not ask her what her brother had to say about that guessing he must have been the source of the "orders from France."

That was the last time I saw her. Since our time in Port au Prince the rumours and gossip about her had gathered like her own personal miasma. There were tales of the many men she had reputedly pleasured, including to my surprise Boyer who had publicly massaged her feet, of what she had got up to with her women friends and black bearers, of the semi-public baths she had taken, apparently a la Cleopatra, in a bath filled with milk after being born in by a black bearer. They added up, given the sickening violence and massacre currently taking place that everyone was aware of, to a dreadful and deeply depressing picture. The only good thing about it being that our little dalliance appeared to have gone un-noticed amidst such colourful goings on. I comforted myself that all or most of it might not be true, but the vicious gossip of her enemies.

*****

The crisis then escalated. Boye was summoned to a meeting straight away with Rochambeau who informed him that he would now be taking over as commander in chief and as Boyer would soon be off to brief Napoleon, Boye would now need to work with him to prepare to take over the role of adjutant-general.

Chapter 30
Boye's Bitter Promotion

The role of Adjutant General meant being chief administrative officer, seeing to it that the commander's strategic decisions were put into practice. It would also mean a significant shift in duties for me for I would be expected to deliver orally or in writing Boye's orders to the units around the island as well as doing more duties organising our horses and being prepared to act as his bodyguard and cover his security.

You could hardly find two men more deeply opposed to each other than Rochambeau and Boye. Rochambeau was an unreformed aristo, former governor general of the island before the Revolution, friend and ally of the white plantation owners, and a fellow land and slave owner. He had never accepted or seen the point of emancipating the slaves and he certainly saw black and mixed race persons as inherently inferior to white Europeans, and in particular, the French. He was also a highly intelligent and well-read man, particularly in the classics. As a soldier he was ruthless, brave and well organised, always taking it for granted that he was born to rule. He could also, when he put his mind to it, be amusing and charming.

Boye on the other hand was a committed revolutionary with a comfortable middle-class background, efficient, capable, diplomatic, and wishing to see the advantages he had experienced in life open to everyone. Above all I saw he was a man who had come to recognise the multi-faceted evil of slavery and he was someone who had made a wide range of friends of different colours and backgrounds. Boye, like Kleber and Diderot was someone I had come to admire. Neither of us could imagine the horror that was to come or how that admiration was to be tested.

*****

Rochambeau next told Boye that he wished to have a staff meeting for all his white officers. No *mulattoes* and of course no blacks were to attend or be told about it. He was also inviting along the white planters' militia that had just been formed since the French had arrived. He also invited some of the plantation owners who had fled before we had arrived, but who on hearing about the expedition had been returning to Saint Domingue in some numbers.

"They have the great advantage of long experience in dealing with blacks, and they have the future of their property to think about. In this setting we have much to learn from them." he said. I looked down the list he handed to Boye and sure enough there was the dog-loving husband of Michelle.

Held in the Ball Room of the rebuilt Governor's palace in Le Cap, the room was full when Rochambeau strode in. As Boye's *ordonnance* I was able to sneak in at the back. Rochambeau surveyed his audience serious and unsmiling.

"Gentlemen of France," he intoned in his courtly accent, "With our troops over-extended and decimated by Yellow Fever and combat with the locals, and with our total numbers being but a small fraction of those of our enemies, as I see it we have few choices.

The first I say is to write to the First Consul and say that using the normal conventions of war as we would in Europe, that is taking prisoner those who surrender, treating them with humanity, making treaties that we stick to as between civilised equals, if we do these things there is no way we can win here if winning means, and now let us be explicit about this, - the re-imposition of slavery."

Around the room where the planters were spread there were murmurs of agreement and from many others also for this was the first public recognition of why we were there.

"If this is the case what are our options? The first is again we could write to the First Consul and say, "Using normal conventions we cannot win here. There are too few French troops and too many local black and mulatto men, many well trained and experienced officers. We should withdraw in good order, bands playing, say we have achieved a great victory, the pacification of the island, and sail for home leaving the blacks and *mulattoes* in charge."

"And what about us white people?" called out a large plantation owner. "How long would we and our families survive?"

"Good point." Said Rochambeau, "Almost unthinkable isn't it?" There were general mutterings and murmurs about the rape, pillage, torture and destruction that could be expected if the black "rebels" regained power. Rochambeau then continued, "The other option is to employ the tactics which have already worked very well on our fine plantations until the pernicious poison of so-called Revolutionary rhetoric was heard here. I speak of course of the use of severe punishment, acts to induce terror and executions which also involve the deliberate imposition of extreme pain. To what end? In order to force our "property" into abject obedience, an obedience based on fear. Be in no doubt. This can be done very effectively as it has been done from the days of the Greeks and Romans with their slaves and by other peoples long before that and by many like the Turks, Arabs and the African tribes where our blacks come from who use slaves to this day."

Again there was much murmuring of agreement from both planters and officers.

"What about those who have tasted freedom and have come to value it?" said Boye.

"Good point, General," said Rochambeau. "The apparent courage of captured slaves who have faced torture and death with relentless defiance should give us cause for thought. They often chant "Freedom or Death". Have I got that right? So what should we do? My intention is to write to our First Consul and say that as a result of the insurrections most of the men and women of colour who have been infected by Revolutionary thought, should be dispensed with."

"You mean killed sir?" someone said.

"Exactly." Said Rochambeau, "Let me read to you from a copy of the letter General Leclerc wrote to the First Consul in October just before he became so seriously ill. I quote, "Here is my opinion about this country. All the blacks in the mountains, (that is those who have rebelled) men and women, need to be destroyed and children older than 12. Half of those in the plains must also be killed and not a single black who has worn rebel uniform left alive. Otherwise every year you risk civil war."

There was silence while the enormity of what Leclerc had advised sank in. "That's a lot of people sir." piped up someone.

"A lot of depraved and infected savages, yes." said Rochambeau.

"But if we did that who would be left to work our plantations?" said another.

"Again, good question." said Rochambeau. "We will simply need to import large numbers of fresh, compliant slaves from Africa unsullied by revolutionary nonsense."

Hearty laughter echoed around the hall. He ended the meeting by saying that we were going to need to get this programme of eliminating "infected" slaves operating as quickly and as energetically as possible. He then set up groups of officers and planters to discuss different strategies and methods for getting rid of them. All agreed by the end of the evening a good start had been made.

Things then happened fast. That same night Rochambeau gave orders to detain all black officers and they ended up in the same stinking prison Jean Pierre Boyer had been so recently held in. General Christophe narrowly escaped capture, but General Dessalines had already got wind of the plan and had retreated to re-organise his men into an army.

Dessalines certainly was a formidable operator. As Boye told me this black general was the first person to come to the conclusion that Louverture's wish to see Saint Domingue both free and French was an impossible delusion. The way ahead he saw had to be the expulsion of all French and the creation of an independent country.

Relying on Boyer's organisational skills before he left, Rochambeau's next move was quite unexpected. He saw the *mulattoes* as a threat to the whites for if the black insurgents got rid of all the white plantation owners, the *mulatto* plantation owners had the skills needed to replace them, take over and run their farms, so he set out to eliminate them too. His first move was to organise a special "ladies only" ball for the wives of all the leading *mulatto* plantation owners. It was laid on as a very grand affair – one which would outdo Pauline's ball on Tortue. This would be held in the Governor's Ball Room.

At midnight the proceedings came to an abrupt halt and he announced that while they were there being entertained, all their husbands had been executed and their properties confiscated.

This had the counter-productive effect of driving the blacks and the *mulattoes* together for in the past they were often on opposite sides. Now they saw the *creole* and French whites as their common enemy.

*****

The next day was the occasion for a bizarre spectacle in Le Cap. Arriving in the harbour was a boat carrying a hundred slave-hunting dogs, each with a Cuban handler. These were huge animals with greyhound bodies and mastiff heads unlike any dog I had ever seen. Rochambeau announced their arrival as the "terror weapon" that would bring the rebels to their senses and all the plantation owners and other members of the white community lined the streets throwing flowers and cheering as they passed. A seating arena was hastily erected in the grounds of a former Catholic school and that evening a military band was set up to play. The planter wives turned up in their best finery and a stake was erected in the centre.

Having urgent business to attend to for Boye I was spared seeing what happened next but I heard the band playing, the crowd cheering, a man screaming and the sound of the dogs baying as an execution of some hapless rebel took place. It was to be the first of several. A shocked and saddened Boye told me the details later as he had been present with Rochambeau and he described how Boyer had actually taken part.

"It just shows the depths of depravity slave owning and the fear of slaves triggers. It can turn decent people into monsters." he said. A few days later Boyer sailed for France to brief Napoleon. I was not sorry never to see him again.

Next all the arrested *mulatto* and black officers held in the prison were executed, the more senior in publicly humiliating and painful ways. Then, following up on his policy of terror and racial extermination, Rochambeau ordered and encouraged French troops, aided and abetted by white planters, to engage in an orgy of cruelty and mass executions that beggars belief and which I cannot bring myself to describe.

If, as was certainly Rochambeau's objective, the aim of such behaviour was to cow those who survived into accepting the re-imposition of slavery, it was a total failure. Certainly many thousands died, many showing exemplary courage and defiance as they went to their deaths, saying it was better to die than live as a slave.

*****

Regarding the dogs Boyer and Leclerc never asked Boye what had happened when he was fighting the British and they had tried to use similar dogs against him and his mainly *mulatto* troops. They thought the dogs and their handlers would help French troops find rebel assailants in jungle warfare. In fact again faced with armed enemies who fired muskets at them, as had happened with Boye, the dogs simply cowered terrified at the feet of their handlers and were quite useless. They ended up being eaten when the French found themselves under siege.

While never taking an active part in the atrocities Rochambeau ordered, I needed to visit centres where such things were taking place. I will never be able to forget what I have seen, nor will I ever forget setting off one evening to take a walk along the beach at Le Cap with Boye for us to find the sand strewn with the rotting bodies washed up of those who had been taken out to sea to be drowned and gassed, men, women and yes small children.

And what of the role of Boye and I in all this? From the start we were appalled, but as Boye said, it seemed that although Leclerc had kept it to himself almost to his death, the basic policy, the reason we were in Saint Domingue, was to re-establish slavery. That, we had to recognise, was the policy of our supreme commander, Napoleon.

It was also pretty obvious that the only way slavery could be re-imposed was by a mixture of the execution of those who resisted and the use of terror and torture to obtain compliance from those who survived. Did this mean such policies were recognised as being necessary by Napoleon?

I had seen his growing callousness and cynicism in Italy and even more in Egypt, but this took things to a new level of contempt for any form of morality. Yes, Rochambeau was extreme in his behaviour, but his views and past behaviour was well know and predictable. Napoleon had appointed him knowing that the chance he would end up running the show or at the least encouraging Leclerc not to go soft in any way, was high. The man was doing no more than zealously carrying out the task he believed he had been given in the way he thought best. Responsibility for placing him in that position has to be Napoleon's.

What could either of us do? Boye as adjutant general was now aware how easy it would be for morale and discipline to fall apart in the Army. If that happened we could all end up being massacred by Dessalines and his troops and backers. Rochambeau could also be dangerous. Arrogant and opinionated he did not brook opposition and was well aware of Boye's record and views. This meant we could easily get shot for indiscipline or insubordination if we questioned or subverted his orders, or end up doing forced labour in Corsica.

Boye never actively participated in any of the horrible acts, but he certainly passed on orders to carry them out, as did I in my more humble way delivering them. Inevitably we both felt guilty and compromised. We were not alone, but those who expressed any criticism of Rochambeau's policies were few and far between and not under his direct authority. We both felt, and will I am sure continue to feel for the rest of our lives, shame and guilt for our involvement in what must be seen as our own and France's darkest hour.

*****

In the meantime Dessalines attracted the united support of both blacks and *mulattoes*, those who were educated and those who came from the plantations. His men fought skilfully and implacably as guerrillas, rather as I had as a skirmisher, except they knew their countryside extremely well and were masters of appearing and then disappearing.

Dessalines also deliberately matched atrocity with atrocity. When Rochambeau had five hundred buried alive, Dessalines hung five hundred whites from trees so they could be seen by the French side.

For blacks and *mulattoes* the clear objective now became the expulsion or execution of all French whites and the setting up of an independent republic. So it was that this terrible war of torture and annihilation went on across the island. In the end Boye and I with Rochambeau and his remaining army were steadily driven back and surrounded by Dessalines' troops in a small fort, Vertieres, outside Le Cap. There we were caught, running short of food (when the dogs were eaten) and facing certain extermination if we were taken.

Chapter 31
Defeat

Out at sea loomed the powerful presence of two great ships of the line, *H.M.S. Hercule*, and *H.M.S. Bellerephon*. Yes that same *Bellerephon* that had been so badly damaged at the Battle of the Nile, but was now of course completely refitted. They were there because the Peace of Amiens was now over for Britain had again declared war on France and the Royal Navy had placed the French islands under blockade.

In desperation Rochambeau sent Boye and me out in a small boat to see if Captain John Loring of the *Bellerephon* would accept a French surrender to the British rather than let us be massacred by Dessalines' men. Loring then contacted Dessalines who agreed and a ten day cease fire was organised. That was long enough for the French troops and a few white civilians to embark on three French ships from Le Cap, the *Surveillante*, the *Clorinde* and the *Vertu*. Loring, following normal practice, insisted in the surrender document that Boye signed that these would then become British prizes and those on board escorted as prisoners to Jamaica. Naval and military personnel would then be sent to England as prisoners of war while wounded French would be sent straight back to France. Dessalines had been buying supplies from the British and was more concerned to see the French leave rather than exact revenge and extend the battle and lose more of his men fighting so he agreed to the cease-fire.

We, Rochambeau, his young *mulatto ordonnance* Pierre Courpon, Boye and me, then boarded the French frigate the *Surviellante*. This, Boye told me, was the same ship he had sailed on when he had come to Saint Domingue in 1791.

Once aboard the weather deteriorated and a storm blew up

197

and Rochambeau started to complain that the British surrender terms of demanding the French ships were too harsh, and ordered the captain to use the storm as an opportunity to make a run for it, frigates being generally faster than ships of the line. A signal was sent to the *Clorinde* and they also attempted to escape.

This proved to be a near fatal mistake for both ships for as soon as the *Bellerephon* saw what the elderly *Surviellante* was trying to do it gave chase, turned out to be faster than expected, drew alongside and opened fire with a devastating broadside, the most terrifying experience of my life. The sight of canon-balls crashing through our bulkheads, spreading lethal ripped and splintering wood, followed by the sea pouring in as we started to sink, while the wind howled and the ship pitched, was unforgettable. It has given me nightmares ever since.

Surprisingly quickly the *Bellerephon* had long-boats by our side to rescue us and take us on board. There our treatment was humane and correct despite the failure of Rochambeau to abide by the surrender agreement Boye had signed on his behalf.

The fate of the *Chlorinde* was similar for when it attempted to run from the harbour it went aground in range of Dessalines' batteries that prepared to pound it with red hot shot to set it on fire prior to the massacre of any survivors. A dashing young British acting lieutenant, Nesbit Willoughby (acting because on probation after a court-martial for insubordination!) promptly boarded the *Chlorinde* almost alone and persuaded the French captain and the general on board to surrender to him and run up the Union Flag. This done Dessalines' men did not fire. The ship was then re-floated, the lives of the 900 men on board saved and a 40 gun battleship became a Royal Navy prize. After a nine day journey we arrived in Jamaica on the 9th of December 1803. It was there that we heard about Willoughby's brave exploit.

*****

Those days gave Boye and I time to reflect. Thirteen months had passed since the death of Leclerc to our capture and this marked the total defeat of Napoleon's plan for Saint Domingue and of Rochambeau's command of the campaign. It also marked the victory of the first successful slave revolt in history so far as we knew under the leadership of the former slave General Dessalines. It was also a fact many of us found hard to acknowledge that it was the correct behaviour and prompt intervention of the British that had saved all our lives.

Those of us taken prisoner to Jamaica were then all that was left of an invading force of over 34,000. If our losses were a catastrophe, how much more were the losses suffered by the people of the island who had endured the imposition of our ghastly cull? We had no way of knowing, but when Boye and I talked it over, we considered at least 100,000 had died, possibly two or three times that number. It was generally known that prior to the uprising the slave population had been around half a million and that number was now drastically reduced. What we did know was the killing, wounding, destruction and burning brought about by the war had reduced the "Pearl of the Antilles" and it's surviving people to the most abject poverty.

It was almost Christmas when we arrived in Jamaica, a feast the English all took as a great opportunity to celebrate their local victory so it was on the 27th of December 1803 that we set sail for England.

In Jamaica we were lucky to escape the fate of many on the *Bellerephon* for again the dreaded Yellow Fever took hold of their crew and over sixty of them died.

*****

The vessel we sailed in was another Royal Navy prize, the captured French frigate named, as it now seemed ironically, the *Revolutionnaire*. Manned by English officers and crew and loaded to capacity with prisoners, conditions were pretty cramped. The voyage took five weeks. Rochambeau and Boye were the most senior French officers on board and Pierre Courpon and I were the only *ordonnances*.

It had surprised me to find Rochambeau had chosen a *mulatto* to be his *ordonnance* given his much publicised hatred of *mulattoes*. Perhaps it was a way for him to re-enforce his sense of superiority which seemed so important to him. Rochambeau and Boye maintained a polite distance with no discussion between them about what had happened. I had hardly spoken to Pierre before, but now we needed to get on. Not surprisingly he seemed guarded and not easy to get to know, but together we practiced our English and engaged in grog drinking and banter with any Jack Tars ready to be friendly.

There were many sick and wounded men on board and with Boye's encouragement I volunteered to spend part of each day assisting the ships surgeons in providing what help and care we could. The two surgeons were both French and one way I could really help they suggested was with cutting hair and shaving wounded men. As news of my new skill spread many who were not ill requested my services. With neither beards nor wigs being any longer fashionable there was no shortage of work.

The surgeons reminded me that a common skill barbers were expected to have was the ability to pull infected teeth and they initiated me into the grisly and pain producing skills needed so this could be done as safely and quickly as possible. Boye commented that it could turn out very useful to have such skills when a prisoner in England.

For the first time I discovered that both Boye and Rochambeau were fluent English speakers, Rochambeau because he had spent years in America prior to his service in the West Indies and Boye because he had both fought them and dealt diplomatically with them when they had tried to take the island and because he had a great interest in languages and literature.

"Do all you can Bioletti to learn English for who knows how long we are liable to be held in England." he said and he certainly helped, getting me to read English texts and papers and checking my pronunciation. As regards what we were to expect in England he said, "The custom is officers who sign a parole agreement not to escape are held in parole towns where they are free to move around. Other ranks can have a tough time being consigned to hulks. These are decommissioned warships tied up in the naval ports. With luck they may be prepared to let us keep you as our "servants" as they say.

And so it was that we arrived on the 3rd of February 1804 in Portsmouth.

Bioletti in England
- 1804 to 1811 -

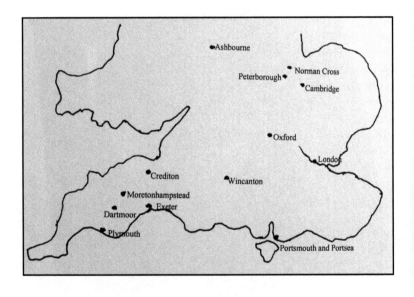

Chapter 32
Prisoners of
the Old Enemy

3rd February 1804 Portsmouth, England

Our first chance to see the land of the old enemy. It was a bitterly cold, wet, grey day when we arrived, something we were to discover the English are used to. The size and bustle of this great naval port was awe-inspiring for we were surrounded by massive fortifications and artillery batteries on the hill tops and on the Isle of Wight, and in front of us were the shipyards. These were immense, with huge factory buildings looming behind them. It made Toulon look small in comparison.

As we came in we were faced by a forest of masts and so many great warships. We passed a series of dry-docks where we could see ships being built and others refitted. There were squads of marines in red marching about, the jack tars everywhere, and the noise and clatter of horses, carts and workmen coming and going. In front of us already neatly moored was the *Bellerephon*.

We had heard it proudly declared by the tars on our ship that Portsmouth was the biggest centre for making things in the country with ships, sails, rigging, cannon, small arms, munitions and much else being produced. There was no doubt about it, we had arrived at the home of the largest, most advanced and powerful navy in the world.

We were landed and escorted by marines to be processed in a huge warehouse with our names, ranks and details of background carefully taken down. I was entered as Albert Violett, Alberto Bioletti being too much for the naval clerk to manage, particularly when he had the complicated names and titles of the two generals to deal with.

Pierre and I were entered as "servants" to our respective generals, "*ordonnance*" not being a term they understood. We were then sent to a barrack block, the generals to officer's quarters and a few days later we were informed that we were to be sent to Ashbourne in Derbyshire on parole. Being men of such senior rank Boye told me, they were not required to sign parole papers, as those who were of lesser rank were expected to do. "I think they expect senior officers to be men of honour who will simply behave as expected," he said. "I do hope our General Rochambeau will go along with that."

We were told it was a 200 mile journey to Ashbourne which we would find is a small market town set in the middle of Derbyshire and like all the parole towns far from the sea. We would be sent by carriage escorted by two guards. The more junior officers would be expected to march and many we heard were being sent to Chesterfield. The other ranks with us were lined up and marched off to the hulks which we could see tied up in the harbour. This very depressing option left Pierre and I feeling very lucky to be with our generals.

*****

We read in the English newspapers that Napoleon had declared himself Emperor of the French and was massing a new and vastly bigger *Army d'Angleterre* at Boulogne with the intention of invading Britain. No doubt it was this news that added to the sense of urgency so obvious in Portsmouth.

Travelling by coach in winter, though a bumpy business, was much to be preferred to having to march. Add to that being able to stay each evening in a post-house inn or tavern where we were amply fed on roasts, stews and pies with no shortage of beer was enjoyable after our long voyage and miserable diet of ship's biscuit. Of course the food was strange to French tastes and gave occasion for Rochambeau to complain. This was ignored by our guards who spoke no French, were very reserved and had been given clear instructions to keep us separated from the locals for anti-French feelings, what Rochambeau dubbed "Francophobia", was high because of the threat of invasion. Mostly we stayed in small villages, but we did pass rapidly through the outskirts of Oxford.

On reaching Ashbourne we found we had been assigned a very pleasant furnished cottage with ample accommodation for the four of us. Almost immediately however Rochambeau started to cause problems, behaving with condescending rudeness when visited by the Commissioners of the Transport Board, the body that was responsible for the care of prisoners of war.

It was not surprising that news of his behaviour did not go down well with the Board, or with local gentry. Also it was no surprise that our presence in the local taverns on occasion resulted in rudeness and threats of violence.

After eight months of rescuing us from the said locals, bearing the brunt of insulting remarks from the generals and having to deal with a run of infringements of their parole conditions from the trivial to the serious, the Transport Board officers lost patience with our "pesky" generals. As a result the four of us were threatened with imprisonment in an ordinary prison in Wales.

The fuss the generals made about that however was such that instead they were given the option of signing a fuller and more restrictive parole agreement than was normal, or be sent to Norman Cross; the new, specially designed facility or camp for prisoners of war. That was actually quite a generous offer.

Rochambeau of course, refused to sign saying it was beneath his dignity to do so. As a result, hardly surprisingly, we were sent under armed guard by coach across England to Norman Cross just south of Peterborough. What this might mean we had no idea.

Chapter 33
Norman Cross

O n arrival we looked out of the coach windows to see an enormous great fort covering many acres. It was built of fresh timber and brick construction with a forbidding tower in its centre armed it seemed with cannon. All around this fort was a deep moat which we were to learn was to make tunnelling out impossible. There was only one entrance which was through an imposing high archway. We however were taken straight to the administrative offices situated outside the camp alongside a barrack building. There we could see regular soldiers being put through their paces drilling on the parade ground.

We however were taken straight to the office of the Agent, Captain Pressland (R.N. Retired) who was in command of Norman Cross. The four of us were ushered into his office and kept standing in front of his desk. This was unusual treatment for a general. He sat behind his desk and proceeded to quietly deliver a devastating dressing down to the generals which he followed by reading out his orders for what we were to expect.

In his tirade he declared that their bad behaviour in Ashbourne went far beyond anything the Transport Board had ever had to put up with from any other senior officers. This being the case, at considerable expense, he had had to prepare for our arrival by building special facilities for the four of us in the camp hospital building. In this we would have small rooms, a common room and a small walled exercise yard.

We were to be incarcerated within this area with guards from the duty regiment at the doors in order to make sure that we were not able to foment disruptive or rebellious behaviour among anyone held in the camp. Initially additional food, newspapers, periodicals or writing materials would also be forbidden and there was also to be an absolute ban on any communication with other prisoner of war officers.

With that we were dismissed and taken to a bare room where we were held until nightfall. There predictably Rochambeau exploded in rage. Then, when all the prisoners were confined to their barracks for the night, we were hurriedly taken into the camp to the hospital for what turned out to be months of pretty miserable confinement.

Once a week we were visited by Captain Pressland and the French physician in charge of the hospital. Initially he simply enquired briefly after our health and left, but after some weeks he came in and said, "Gentlemen and orderlies, I would like to explain your situation here and how you can improve it."

"It is quite outrageous." expostulated Rochambeau. "You have absolutely no right to treat senior officers like this and when word gets back to France you British will pay for it."

"For holding you in a French run hospital after you have broken all the rules accepted by honourable men on parole on both sides? I think not." replied Pressland. "No, let me explain. Norman Cross is an institution quite different from anything that any country has attempted before in dealing with prisoners of war.

As I am sure you are aware until this conflict with your Napoleon the custom after both land and sea battles was to return the wounded to their own country and other prisoners in agreed exchanges, as we did to you French after Egypt and your Spanish allies after Trafalgar. However this system has broken down since your Emperor refused to release British soldiers who surrender. In fact he has even held English tourists – including members of the nobility and many ladies and gentlemen of quality, from returning from their holidays in France! He has them all holed up in Verdun where we hear they are regularly cheated by the corrupt governor who has been put in charge."

"That is a libellous accusation." declared Rochambeau, though Boye said nothing.

"The point is," declared Pressland, "We British are now faced with many thousands of French soldiers and sailors who have surrendered, and there are far more of you than there are British prisoners being held in France. So, since your Emperor is bent on invading us, we have no intention of returning you or them to strengthen his army or his rather weak navy until he is defeated."

"Or you are by him," responded Rochambeau.

"What about other ranks?" Boye then asked. "Yes, officers, like English officers in France, are quite well treated if we sign a parole agreement. For the majority however what we saw in Portsmouth and know since we arrived is that they are sent to rot in your dreadful hulks."

"As a naval man I am well aware of that." said Pressland. "And I can assure you men like me do not like that at all. The problem is we had no idea we would be faced with having to deal with so many thousands of prisoners. Yes. The hulks are now dangerously overcrowded and unhealthy. Still, conditions in them are I think better than being simply consigned to local prisons as is the fate of other rank prisoners in France. The point is our government has set out to remedy the situation and their first attempt to do that is by constructing this camp at Norman Cross.

"By building one huge great prison instead of using a lot of little ones." sneered Rochambeau.

"Not at all." said Pressland. "Norman Cross has been humanely conceived. That is to say it is not meant to punish you, officers or men, or treat you like criminals for being prisoners of war - if you behave yourselves. We would much rather see you all being industrious, improving yourselves and looking after each other. That way we can all get on in a decent manner until this war is over."

He then went on to say that if each week the report he received from our guards was positive, and our behaviour was quiet and peaceable, we could expect our conditions to improve. It was however up to the two generals to see to it that this happened. He then left us.

In the discussion that followed between the two generals Boye remarked that he was quite impressed. Rochambeau said that we still had a lot to learn about what was actually going on in this "so called camp."

When Pressland next inspected us Boye asked if it might be possible for some of the restrictions to be lifted on us "orderlies" so we could bring in some extra food to supplement the very limited diet we had. Nothing was agreed but a couple of weeks later it was stipulated that Pierre and I were to be allowed to move around the camp and bring back food and necessities for our generals. Nonetheless we had, like all the prisoners, to be back in our quarters to be locked in for the night.

Two soldiers from the guard regiment were always on duty day and night at the entrance to our little prison to check what Pierre and I took in and took out and to see we had not brought in or taken out any written messages or papers to the generals. In fact of course it was not difficult to keep the generals informed of what we had read and heard as regards news of the war or what was being reported in the English papers.

This change in our circumstances meant that for the first time in weeks Pierre and I were able to explore the place and find out what was going on. We could also see for ourselves if Pressland's claim that Norman Cross was a "humane institution" stood up.

The biggest objection to this claim however it emerged was not, as Boye and I we had to admit, an intentional one, but had to do with size. Over the next few months we learnt that numbers at Norman Cross fluctuated, going down when prisoner exchanges were sometimes organised, but going up, sometimes dramatically, after some naval or continental battle. Then they could and did reach six thousand which was over a thousand more than Norman Cross was designed to accommodate.

The difference this made was that while the barrack block accommodation for officers and NCO's was more spacious than that for ordinary soldiers and seamen, the other ranks had to sleep in rows of hammocks crammed tightly together. This meant that when their blocks filled up there was severe overcrowding and this seemed to set off some nasty outbreaks of typhus and other diseases. The French doctors and surgeons, who ran the hospital block, did their best to see that these blocks were kept clean and the sick treated, but often that did not amount to much and the result was rather a lot of deaths.

Being kept where we were in the generals' little prison did it seems mean the four of us were lucky to escape whatever it was that set off such maladies. Otherwise the claim that Norman Cross was an "humane establishment" did indeed seem to stand up.

The camp was divided into four large quadrangles, three for other ranks and one for officers. Each quad had a large "airing yard." Here inmates were expected, except in the most inclement weather, to spend our daylight hours before being locked up in the barrack blocks for the night. In the briefings issued to all inmates Captain Pressland told us the reason for this was, "Because fresh air and exercise are good for your health. Can't have you all lying about in the barracks being lazy and getting up to mischief." None of us would want to disagree with that.

About a quarter of the Norman Cross inmates were officers, mostly of junior rank, together with some more senior who had broken parole and so could not be trusted in the parole towns. The rest were ordinary soldiers and seamen.

Most days the gates between the four airing yards were kept open and we were all encouraged to move about the interior of the camp and set up "workshops." With our army and navy being made up largely of conscripts there were among us men with all sorts of skills and crafts. We had carpenters, chefs, tailors, boot-makers, bookbinders, clockmakers, barbers, and others ready to practice their skills or learn new ones.

We had no idea how long we would be there, but we knew the war had to end sometime and then we would have to go home and earn a living. We also if possible needed to earn some money, something Captain Pressland encouraged us to try and do.

Rochambeau and Boye had us order complete new uniforms from the tailors and new pairs of fine boots both for them and for us. On one occasion Rochambeau came out all dressed up in full uniform into the exercise yard, announcing to the guard that he was certain that Napoleon would be here, "In a matter of days." This was typical of his over-the-top patriotic optimism. Still the uniforms were very well made and were badly needed as by the end of our time in Saint Domingue all our clothing and boots were in a sorry state.

So how busy were all these men? One in twelve inmates were assigned in rotation to baking and cooking duty and there were also classes to teach the illiterate - and we had a lot of them - to read, and for others to learn English or French.

It was also possible to buy at the main gate copies of the latest English newspapers. Their hilariously scurrilous cartoons and attacks not only against the French and Napoleon, as we would expect, but against the members and policies of their own government went far beyond anything tolerated in France, certainly not by our "sensitive to criticism" Emperor. They amused and amazed us, but just seemed to be taken for granted by the English.

There were of course constant discussions about how the war was going. Rochambeau was not alone in thinking that any day soon we could all be "liberated" by an invading French Army, in fact I think many of the English were of the same opinion, though they would not see it as liberation, believing themselves to be much freer and better off than us.

In addition to the sessions when Pierre and I were free to roam about, we spent many hours closeted with the generals. When they were still restricted we played chess, dominoes and cards, wrestled and did exercises with them, singing and generally whiling away what was for them and for us a boring time.

When six months had passed, Captain Pressland visited us to inform the generals that as he had heard no ill reports of the behaviour of any of us, they were now free to come out and mix with other officers and live in the same way as the rest of us. We were however to stay where we were as regards accommodation and if there was any disruptive behaviour from any of us, the tight conditions would be re-imposed.

Rochambeau looked furious, but had the good sense to say nothing and Boye thanked him civilly for his consideration in having allowed Pierre and I to serve and support them as we had.

*****

This description may make you think we, or certainly Pierre and I, had a rather easy time at Norman Cross in this "humane establishment." There was however something which every evening from the start to the end of our time there filled me with dread as we were locked up. It was the coming night. Our accommodation was cramped. A day room and four small cells for sleeping in was what we had, but that was not the cause.

*****

The experiences we had undergone in Saint Domingue were something we now found we could not escape. They came back to haunt us, to be relived in dreams, nightmares and flashes of memory so vivid we could lose track of where we were. Every night then, and yes for many years after, I awoke either with nightmares of my own or from the screams and cries of one or more of the others. Pierre often cried out like one under torture and then would lie shaking, awake and trying to control his sobs. Boye woke shouting out orders and with cries to God that he might be forgiven. I had several recurring dreams that replayed themselves with such intensity that I could not tell if I had woken up or was still asleep. That frightened me. The worst of these was of being on a sinking ship under fire with a volley of huge cannon balls crashing all around me. This, my *Bellerephon* dream, just would not go away. There were other dreams of the atrocities I had seen that are too terrible to describe.

It was Rochambeau however whose behaviour was most disturbing for he never seemed to hear or wake up because of our cries, but had a rigid, almost nightly ritual of his own which he replayed over and over. It started in the small hours when the camp clock struck. He would then get up from his bed and with his eyes wide open, but oblivious of our presence, he would cram on his hat and swagger around the day room giving terrible orders to an invisible audience while grinning and laughing. It was horrible to see. He would then suddenly stop, climb back into bed and fall into a deep sleep until he awoke in the morning declaring that he had never had a better night.

Asked more than once by Boye if he remembered getting out of bed and putting his hat on he just looked puzzled and denied he had done any such thing. Of course we all knew what lay behind this behaviour of his and it stirred up in me conflicting emotions - disgust, fear, self-hatred and memories I wished to forget.

When day came we said nothing about our experiences to each other and the generals said we should tell no-one this was happening lest we all be suspected of harbouring madness. They also both let it be known that we should take care never to discuss with others the campaign Rochambeau had led in Saint Domingue. The reason they gave was that they had heard Napoleon had said it was his greatest failure, so to talk about it would be bad for morale.

I also discovered moving around in Norman Cross that if I came across others who had served in Saint Domingue discussion with them never got beyond talking about the heat, the flies, Yellow Fever and the atrocities carried out by the revolting slaves, never about what had been done by us. Most made it clear they would rather talk about anything else but their time on the island.

*****

Life in Norman Cross was however very far from being all gloom. I was also able to practice and develop my skills as a barber - cutting hair, shaving men and on occasion pulling teeth. I found it paid well enough for men imprisoned can get even more pre-occupied over their appearance than they do when free and I enjoyed the chat and gossip that is so much a part of the job. Pulling teeth was also a much appreciated skill for all too obviously those with severe toothache who did not have it done, simply died painfully.

My real passion and interest however was and is clock making and I met some fine craftsmen. I was though frustrated, for it was almost impossible to get sheets of brass and the right tools to build clocks. All the same we spent hours drawing and discussing designs and the mathematics involved in working out cog and dial sizes.

One man, already a master clockmaker, did make an amazing clockwork automaton. It was a clock which drives eleven moving costumed figures – and the whole thing, cogs and spokes and the little figures were not made from metal, but carved out of bone.

And were we being watched? Oh yes. Security around the perimeter of the camp was tight. Always on duty was the regiment of regular soldiers we had seen drilling on our first day. Kept quite separate from the camp staff they were there just to be on guard duty around the perimeter and were replaced with a fresh regiment every two months. They were clearly told to have no personal dealings with us. They also manned the central guard-house tower in the middle of the camp which we had noticed on arrival. We had been right in noticing cannon. There were six. These were constantly manned as a deterrent against riot and could cover any of the quads with rounds of grape shot if ever it were needed. Thankfully it never was. In fact Norman Cross was as peaceful a community as I have ever lived in.

Escapes from Norman Cross were rare and when somehow a man did trick his way out he was usually quickly picked up and returned for a spell in the guard house below the gun-tower. It had a "black hole" basement. There they were held for some days on half rations. Relations with the small regular English staff inside the prison however were generally good and friendly. Captain Pressland, if a little pompous, seemed to me a fair and straightforward man, though Rochambeau would never admit it.

One "airing yard" contained a huge pile of beef, pork and sheep bones – these were either left over from camp cooking or dumped by local butchers. Dried and cleaned these bones were carved with amazing skill as I have mentioned with reference to the automaton. Men made beautiful model ships, toys, games, sets of dominoes, and most lucrative and much prized by locals as well as among us, erotic models of ladies in interesting poses and "toys" to go with them. These Captain Pressland tried to ban. "They are disgusting, shocking and depraved." he said. As a result they had to be offered "under the counter." We found it interesting to see that they upset some of the English more than their political cartoons.

On two days a week inside the camp and every day at the main gate we had a market. As well as the inmate stalls English traders from the area came in with their wares. This meant if we had cash we could buy extra fresh food, vegetables and other necessities. These markets also attracted English visitors who came in bringing their wives and children for a day out. Yes they were inclined to find all foreigners exotic. They also came to the main gate to see what was on offer in the way of new "naughty carvings" or manufactured goods.

Boye as an accomplished violinist and musician had of course lost his very fine instrument when we were captured in Saint Domingue. We had no luck finding a replacement in Ashbourne so I was given the task of seeing if I could get an instrument for him through an English trader when he was confined. When they heard he was able to pay a good price I was provided with three for him to try out, and one proved acceptable. This made a huge difference to his life and to ours listening to him. Being also keen on singing he encouraged both Pierre and me to sing, both together and apart. Once the time in confinement was over he also led and got us to join the main Norman Cross Choir.

At other times we took part in games in the airing yards and carried out exercises to keep ourselves fit. Fives against the barrack walls, fencing with canes, running and athletic competitions were all popular. Others played a wide variety of board games, drafts, chess, cards. I enjoyed playing bagatelle and got interested in how the tables were made and I met a carpenter who was really helpful in showing me how to do this.

*****

Internal discipline among prisoners was left by the English to be carried out by elected committees of prisoners in each quad. These settled petty disputes and generally worked well. The one thing that was not tolerated by prisoners was theft from one prisoner by another. If caught this could result in a public thrashing. This rarely happened, but it had a bizarre consequence.

A strange and unexpected sight found in the other ranks quads were men wandering about virtually naked and so thin they appeared to be starving. On inquiring about them when we first saw them I learnt that they were compulsive gamblers who having gambled away what little cash they had ended up losing bets on their clothes and meal tickets. When a team of inspectors turned up from London led by a Dr Johnson they discovered many prisoners running around emaciated and naked and declared they were shocked.

On their return to London an order came from the government that such men be provided with soup and a free outfit. This consisted of a cap, jacket and trousers all in yellow, and a waistcoat and neckerchief, two shirts, and two pairs of stockings in red together with a pair of shoes. Adopted voluntarily by nearly half the inmates this "uniform" became quite the fashion before we left.

The Transport Board declared that it spent as much on rations for French prisoners as it spent on the rations of British soldiers and sailors. They also set up a committee of senior French officers to inspect the food as it came into the camp for quality and freshness. Despite this much of the regular ration of bread and beef delivered was pretty disgusting and we all suspected someone down the line was on the take.

Because our generals (and some of the other officers) were men of means, receiving regular payments from France, we were able to see to it that they, and of course we, were well fed and had access to the best the markets could offer. Still, time hung heavily even if we were not confined, as at first the generals were confined to their prison in the hospital block. We were still a long way from feeling free. Add to that no alcohol except weak beer and no women. The practices some men resorted to in order to deal with that lack I think are best left unexplored.

By talking with the Englishmen in the market and with some of the staff, I became increasingly fluent in English. More importantly Boye had good English and he leant me several books; on occasion he asked me to read aloud to him and Rochambeau. When confined it was a good way of passing the time, and he would pick up and correct any errors in my pronunciation. He chose Tom Paine's book "The Rights of Man" which was very popular in France when the Revolution started.

Boye said Paine had been elected to the National Assembly in Paris for what he had written. Rochambeau too had good English. He told us he had read Paine during his time in America with General George Washington and General Lafayette, something he constantly alluded to. There, he said, Paine was even more widely read than in France and that General Lafayette had worked with Paine. Rochambeau however made it clear that he agreed with little they had written. He pronounced many words in the Yankee fashion or with a strong French accent, something to note, not copy. We also read some racy and amusing novels. I particularly remember *Tom Jones* by Fielding which describes in vivid detail the amorous exploits of a young foundling.

Still our final year in Norman Cross – though we never knew how long it was going to be – was certainly much better than the six months of the two general's confinement. Once released we saw little of Rochambeau during the day for he consorted mainly with a few other senior officers of noble birth who seemed to take their dignity as seriously as he did his. We were glad of this for his behaviour with us, including with Boye, was so condescending and his comments so often supercilious.

We all pitied Pierre who had to serve him for unlike me he was given almost no time off. Boye and I always got on well and it was a pleasure to serve him. He was well read and thoughtful, had attended the Sorbonne and we had long discussions about many subjects. He enjoyed enlightening me and I learnt much from him.

*****

217

Our time in Norman Cross came to an end when we were summoned to meet Captain Pressland in his office. There he explained that since our behaviour had been acceptable it had been decided by the Transport Board that we could go to the Somerset parole town of Wincanton, provided the generals were prepared to sign in his presence the parole certificates he had prepared. They agreed to do so though Rochambeau managed to sign with bad grace. We were then given a date when we would leave.

Pressland had a coach reserved for the four of us with two English militia men as escorts. The senior guard was charged to carry to the Wincanton Agent our parole papers and doubtless an account of our past and a letter of warning about the potential for disruptive bad behaviour of our generals, particularly Rochambeau. They were bluff and pleasant enough fellows but since they could not understand us we four could all converse freely. They both fell asleep easily and drank heavily in the evenings.

To pass through villages and the green English countryside after being restricted to the confines of Norman Cross for a year and a half was a pleasure indeed, and having a coach to ourselves seemed like luxury.

It was also an experience to spend a night in an Oxford public house frequented by some obviously wealthy and well-born students. "Undergraduates" they called themselves and they were mightily intrigued to meet and chat to two of Napoleon's generals and try out their French on us and tell us about their grand tours on what they referred to as "the Continent."

One said he was from the Hoare family and was intrigued to hear we were going to Wincanton for this was quite near the family estate Stourhead which he said had been built by a Wincanton builder named Nathaniel Ireson. Also with them was a student who told me not all the undergraduates were as rich and privileged as Master Hoare.

"His family you know run one of the richest banks in London and their Stourhead estate in Somerset has one of the grandest houses and most beautiful gardens in England. Their bank is one of the main financiers of Britain's war against Napoleon." he told me. He had been to the Grammar School in Bristol and had won a scholarship to study at Trinity College. He was as he described it, "reading Law," and hoped to become a solicitor.

Our escorts however had never been to Wincanton before and so could tell us nothing about the town save that they had heard it was a hub for the stage-coach trade between the southern port of Plymouth, Exeter and London together with routes to Wells, Bath and Bristol so we had little idea what to expect.

Chapter 34
Wincanton Swagger

30th June 1806

Our journey to Wincanton had taken four days and three nights stopping over at Oxford, Newmarket and Basingstoke. The weather was fair for March, the roads passably free from mud and the inns fed us well. Still, when we reached Mere we were glad to hear that was the last change of horses.

We arrived at Wincanton in the evening and were taken straight to our designated house at the top of the High Street. It was a neat, thatched, two-storey cottage with an overgrown vegetable patch of some size at the back. Inside it boasted a large living-room with a fire and a stove and three bedrooms – one for each general and one for Pierre and me to share.

A meal of beef stew, bread, vegetables and pints of cider had been prepared for us which was brought over from a nearby tavern, the Dolphin, and served to us by a good-looking young woman with flashing eyes and a "Keep your distance" look. I have to admit from the first moment I was much taken by her. Tall and elegant, she carried herself as well as any grand lady with her dark hair swept up in the latest style under her cap and her maid's uniform crisp and spotless. I quickly found she could stare us down with a haughty look and toss of the head as she laid out the food, but in answer to our inquiries she did deign to let us know her name, Mary, Mary Feltham.

"Were you born here Mary?" I asked.

"No sir. What a question. I am from Crediton in Devonshire."

"And what brought you here then?"

"My father has a dressmaking and tailoring business there," she said, "And he has supported my brother John and his wife Jane to come here and open a similar business across in the High Street. I live with them and work as seamstress and dressmaker. Two nights a week I serve at table in the Dolphin. It be a nice change after the hours of close work sewing. The point I would make sirs, in telling you all this, is that if you need smart, well-cut, new clothes, or repairs done or replacements made to your fancy French uniforms, Feltham's is the place to bring your custom."

"It is unusual for a young lady to work on men's tailoring," I said.

"Yes. Of course it would not be proper for me to do the measuring on a man. That is done by John, still I do much of the cutting and stitching. Men's tailoring is not however my speciality."

"So what then is your speciality? " I asked intrigued.

"I do dress-making. I copy the latest styles from the fashion magazines that come from Bath and London, measure up the young ladies who come to me, and provide them with dresses and ball gowns they can be proud of. Don't think for a minute that we here in this Somerset town are behind the times as regards fashion, for we are not."

This tirade certainly shut us up for a bit. Mary departed and we unpacked while the generals sat at table to eat first. It had not been Rochambeau's custom to share a table with us *ordonnances* at Norman Cross – something we were glad of. Meals with him would have been stiff and stilted affairs.

About an hour later there was a knock on the door and a sergeant in yeoman uniform announced that the Agent, Captain George Messiter was there to see us. This quite surprised us. He was accompanied by his clerk, a rather sombre-looking young man clad in black and carrying an official looking leather case. Messiter strode in with an air of authority. He was a self-confident, good-looking man and we soon learnt a solicitor by training, owner of a local bank and of several properties, including the house we were in as well as being commander of three companies of the local yeoman militia. He was and looked every bit the English country gentleman.

We hastily cleared what was left of the meal away and he was invited by the generals to join them at the table. Speaking in his less than perfect French, something he was nevertheless clearly proud of, Messiter exchanged pleasantries and made enquiries about our journey and what they thought of the accommodation. He then adopted a serious expression and suggested that Pierre and I might have some unpacking to do.

What happened next was both overheard by us and quietly passed on to me later by Boye who felt that Pierre and I should know just what transpired. The clerk opened the case and Messiter took out a stack of letters from Captain Pressland including the parole documents which had been brought with us by our guard. He laid these out in silence in front of the two generals and invited them to look at them. Boyer quietly did so but Rochambeau crossed legs and arms, sat back and said, "Well sir, what is it you have to say? Pray speak English for I think my English may be better than your French."

"Very well", said Messiter, ignoring the incivility of his response. "The behaviour of both of you, but particularly of you General Rochambeau, has been both difficult and reprehensible."

What followed was a thorough dressing down and warning of the generals on the lines of what we had heard from Captain Pressland and which made it clear that Messiter had been very thoroughly briefed about us. He concluded by saying, "You were both given the opportunity to sign parole papers – which you recognise are legal documents and which have weight in a court of law as evidence of good character, and here they are now. Do I need to say more?" Both Boyer and Rochambeau shook their heads.

"Good," said Messiter. "You will find I seek to run my Agency here in a fair and considerate way. In the end this war must finish, and as you know we British find much to admire about you French, particularly when it comes to food, art, fashion and of course wine."

Slightly hollow laughter followed which we could hear from our room and we were invited to join them all for a glass of Burgundy from a bottle that Messiter had thoughtfully brought with him which we consumed politely standing while they chatted at the table. He also invited them both to come next week to dinner at his home on Sunday. "Roast beef," he said "A special English custom. I shall send a carriage to pick you up at noon." We were amazed at such civility. We were also told we could

223

sleep in late, settle in and would then be expected to attend roll call in the Market Place at 5 p.m. the next day. It would be a day to remember.

*****

Swagger, swagger. Oh yes General Rochambeau always had to swagger. And my general, Boye, had to go along with him, booted, spurred, white breeches, (culottes) scarlet sash, epaulettes, braided jacket and of course the hat, the ceremonial military hat, its broad brim folded up on either side and surmounted with a brave tricolour cockade. How Rochambeau loved the hat!

"Liberty! Equality! Fraternity. Long live the Revolution!" he cried as he thrust on the hat with a sardonic laugh since of course he believed in none of them. He had just taken it from Pierre who stood impassive, ready, a slight knowing smile on his face. Rochambeau then adjusted it, examining himself in the hall mirror and taking care to get its angle just right.

My general quietly accepted his hat from me and slipped it on. We two, Pierre and me, were also dressed in our best uniforms, our boots shining, tight white breeches, spurs, tailored dark blue jackets, tall hats, but not so tall as theirs, white gloves and yes, cockades. To get the four of us to look like this had taken Pierre and I since daybreak polishing, ironing, brushing and washing. Next Boye inspected us both, nodding approval while Rochambeau fiddled with his sash and continued to eye himself in the mirror as he pulled on his gauntlets and picked up his swagger stick since of course he had no sword.

"Right," he said, "Time to show this miserable little town and its arrogant Agent what French officers and their "orderlies" can look like and how we behave."

Pierre rolled his eyes and opened the front door. Rochambeau led the way out onto the High Street. We formed up four abreast, the two generals in the middle and proceeded, not marching in step, but with the exaggerated swagger Rochambeau so liked to adopt, to strut down the street towards the Market Place.

As I thought would be the case, news of our arrival the night before had got about the town and our first attendance at roll-call was eagerly anticipated for life in a parole town is enlivened by mysterious new arrivals. Looking out we saw more than two hundred French officers standing along each side of the road waiting for us. Among them were also some townspeople and several young women of ample proportions and over made-up faces clinging to the arms of their officer escorts.

Out of the corner of my eye I noted a group of poorly dressed local lads with broken boots scuffing along to come up behind us. One detached himself from the others and ran up beside Pierre, pushing against him. He looked up, laughed in his face and shouted out to his mates. "Hey, look at this one lads! What have we here? I do believe we've got a real French darkie!" (that was not the word he used.) This provoked a gale of laughs and hoots of derision from the others.

With that Rochambeau strode up to him and struck him hard across the face with his stick. Blood spurted from his nose. The boy screamed and ran off swearing about "those bloody Frenchies," his "mates" gathering around him. Some of the officers murmured approval, others look appalled at the violence of Rochambeau's reaction. We moved on down the High Street where more spectators had gathered.

What was not expected by them was the sartorial splendour of our full dress uniforms for they were all wearing civilian clothes. Some clapped politely as we passed, some with perhaps too much enthusiasm looked as if they were suppressing a smirk. All however, as we approached, disentangled from the ladies, stood to attention and doffed their hats, in recognition of Rochambeau's and Boye's rank and seniority. This Rochambeau acknowledged with a little bow and his best sneering smile. All then fell in behind us until some hundreds, far more than I expected, were lined up as if on parade in the Market Place.

Messiter, as Navy Transport Board Agent and militia commander was there, again in civilian clothes. He stepped forward and addressed us in French with his heavy English accent.

"Gentlemen, today I would like to welcome to our little town of Wincanton two of your distinguished officers, General Rochambeau and General Boye who have come with their orderlies Courpon and Bioletti. Last night they arrived from Norman Cross. I hope their stay here will not be unpleasant for them and without incident for us until this war is over. Let us all make the best of things and continue to live here in a peaceable manner."

Rather to my surprise there were cries of approval, smiles and nods. Clearly here was a man well thought of. With that he turned and left us giving a wry smile as he noted the defiant splendour of our uniforms. A yeoman sergeant then stepped forward to carry out the roll-call. He proceeded to do murder to our names as he struggled to pronounce them in his strong Somerset accent.

I counted our ranks as he was doing this and saw there was a total of some five hundred of us. I had no idea there could be so many placed in this small English town. This done we were dismissed, broke ranks and set off towards the coaching inns which punctuate the High Street. Yes. This place was a far cry from Norman Cross.

The four of us were led across the square to The Greyhound, a fine coaching inn with a handsome assembly room upstairs. The senior officers present gathered around our generals and I heard them invite them to take a glass of port and join in a game of cards in the "salon" upstairs. As they introduced themselves I picked up there was a rear admiral, two naval captains and several colonels, but no generals. They were no doubt keen to take the opportunity to introduce themselves and size up these new arrivals.

Before ascending the stairs Rochambeau looked around at the junior officers crowding the bar. He jumped on a chair and banged with his cane for quiet.

"Gentleman, fellow officers of France," he declared. "We come here today after a year and a half of harsh treatment. Harsh treatment at the hands of the English at two of their depots, Ashbourne and Norman Cross. In both we suffered a shameful lack of respect, particularly when it seems, as I am sure we all know, that soon the tables will be turned and those who guard us now will be defeated and under guard themselves. That will be when this island is invaded by our great Emperor."

There were cries of, "Here, here," and the inevitable "*Vivre l'Empereur*," but also some knowing smiles. He continued, "I am also sorry to see that tonight we alone have dressed with pride as officers of France and I hope that now many more of us will take to wearing our uniforms on suitable occasions, like the Emperor's birthday. Will we not do that just to remind our captors who they are dealing with?" This elicited some more applause. With a satisfied look he jumped down and went upstairs.

Boye then came over to us carrying two pint glasses of English beer.

"They call this their best bitter", he said. "And Courpon," he continued, "So sorry you had to put up with that loutish rudeness. Such a bore."

"Yes sir, but on this occasion I appreciated my general's action."

Boye nodded and chatted about what a pleasant town it seemed and assured us we were now both off duty until the morning. He then slipped upstairs to join the senior ranks.

We then found ourselves plied with drink and questions by a circle of enthusiastic "new friends," young officers only too eager to talk to us, learn our news and hear about our generals and Norman Cross which they knew nothing about except it was some sort of prison camp. They too sympathised with Pierre expressing their disgust at the rudeness of the locals, but pointed out that he was probably the first man of colour any of them had ever seen. One said to us, "I liked the way your General Rochambeau dealt with that young guttersnipe. Showed he's prepared to stand up for you."

We just smiled at each other knowing his behaviour was nothing of the sort. He had struck out because disrupting our progress had affronted his precious dignity and taken attention off him and his uniform.

We questioned them about life in Wincanton and soon felt that we were indeed lucky to have ended up in this plain little market town. They confirmed that here there was quite a lot going on and we could experience a level of freedom and comfort at the hands of our "enemies" that was remarkable, so long as we kept the simple parole rules. These were no more onerous than not going beyond the marked town boundaries, attending roll-call twice a day, keeping the curfew at night and otherwise behaving in a decent and peaceable manner. If we did that we could expect to be treated with surprising friendliness by the English who also welcomed the business our presence brought.

As "other rank" orderlies, in fact as the only parolees in the town who were not officers, we again felt particularly lucky to have avoided incarceration in the rotting hulks of Portsmouth.

At half past ten on hearing the ring of the "ting-tang", bell of the town hall clock, which warned of our curfew, we bade all a good night and walked somewhat unsteadily back to our new home. Soon after the generals arrived bringing with them a bottle

227

of that Scottish whisky, so forbidden at Norman Cross and in a rare display of bonhomie Rochambeau offered us all a tot before we retired for the night with the toast, "To the good people of Wincanton and a happy time until we see victory for our Emperor right here!"

Chapter 35
Love in Wincanton

Every morning in Wincanton we awoke to the sound of horses galloping past and the clatter of coaches. The town certainly was a stage-coach and post-chaise hub. Seventeen of them arrived and departed daily, except on Sundays, their routes being to and fro from Plymouth, Exeter, London, Bath and Bristol. The post-chaises carried military despatches, newspapers and the private post of those who could afford it. They arrived at great speed to be met by the next team of post riders booted and spurred who saw to it they change a team of horses in two minutes.

The sound of their arrival attracted crowds of parolee's and passing locals, some to cheer, some to look downcast depending on the news passed around of the latest battles in the war. The news from Europe was that Napoleon, now Emperor, was driving all before him in a series of spectacular victories which seemed to make him more and more invincible. This made a possible invasion of England seem increasingly credible.

We were now free to wander about the town as far as its boundaries. What remained a bore and reminded us of our position were the morning and afternoon roll calls in the Market Place and the half past ten curfew by which time we were all expected to be back in our lodgings. Time was measured by a fine town hall clock with its resonating "ting tang" bell.

With access to alcohol and female company the main restraint on what parolees could do was what we could pay for. We were paid an allowance by Britain which was pretty basic out of which most had to pay their rent. In addition prisoners with means such as Rochambeau seemed to have little difficulty in receiving funds from their families in France despite the ban on ordinary correspondence. There was a scandal about a boarding house in the town inhabited by a group of very young French midshipmen that we heard had been reduced to eating a diet of "onions, leeks, cucumbers and dandelions." We organised a whip around to help them and a deputation saw Messiter and he got the basic allowance increased.

As at Norman Cross that however was hardly a problem for us. Based on what the generals gave us to spend we could purchase fresh fish, excellent meat including game and vegetables and of course often we went out to eat, drink and generally socialise.

The town boasted no less than nine inns, no doubt as a result of the coach trade. They catered for all tastes from the decidedly rough "Trooper" to the more genteel "Greyhound" and every grade in-between. Many had meeting rooms for hire for special meals and gatherings and some offered bedrooms for "special entertaining" hired out by the hour. This was a facility Rochambeau took to using which we all much preferred to his bringing his pick-ups back to our cottage.

There was also a large and strong Lodge of Freemasons. While linked to the English Freemasons we had a French Lodge. After some months I was gratified to be asked to attend and think about joining. Not only was I impressed by what I learnt about their moral teaching and work for charity, but it showed I was socially accepted by officers. Boye was a longstanding mason and he pointed out that the masons as an international brotherhood with members in all the armies and professions of Europe were honour bound to help each other in extremity even when on opposing sides in war. In some circumstances this could be very useful.

*****

And what of our duties? With no real military duties what was left for us was keeping our generals happy and making sure their clothes and uniforms were laid out ready for them to wear and that all our quarters were kept neat and clean. Our real role though we knew was simply to signal by our very presence both to the English and other officers the status and importance of our generals. While Boye usually wore civilian dress, Rochambeau put on uniform whenever he could.

They were both soon getting invitations to dine out with

members of the local gentry such as the families that lived at Dial House and the The Dogs. I noted Rochambeau was seldom invited a second time to any one family and Boye began getting a name for being very attentive to the young ladies of the families he visited. I hoped he might have some luck, but observed that such young women "of quality" were pretty closely chaperoned. Naturally their parents were protective and on guard against the development of "unsuitable relationships" with the dashing, intriguing foreigners.

When it came to village girls however, our presence seemed to have attracted quite a few who came to seek work or liaisons in the town. In addition there were a few officers who were able to afford to have their wives and children join them from France. It was an odd feature of the war that unarmed "cartel boats" ran continuously across the Channel taking business mail, cash and some prisoner exchanges. Clearly it suited both sides.

Boye had no desire to have me fussing around him so most of my time was my own. You will not be surprised to hear that Rochambeau's approach was different. He kept Pierre hanging around doing almost nothing much of the time.

Rochambeau also liked to take Pierre along when he was invited out to a grand house, expecting him to play the manservant. His colour always provoked comment. Pierre told me that Rochambeau liked to steer the conversation away from any discussion of his command in Saint Domingue. Instead he loved to regale his hosts about his travels in Massachusetts, New England and Virginia in the United States and to repeat the story of how he assisted his father, the General Jean Baptiste, Comte de Rochambeau who was sent by Louis XVI with four thousand "crack French troops" to assist George Washington and the Americans in their War of Independence against Britain.

He loved to describe how he was present when the English under General Cornwallis had to surrender, the first time an English army had surrendered to Frenchmen for over a hundred years.

"And do you know," Pierre told me, imitating Rochambeau, "That when the battle-field was cleared and the men had surrendered my father invited the English officers to sit down to a fine dinner at which they all discussed how the fighting had gone in a most gentlemanly fashion. This was behaviour the

Yankees just could not understand, except of course for George Washington. He was the only real gentleman among them, the rest being little more than tradesmen."

Yes. You can imagine how well that went down with his hosts – who always, Pierre says, smiled and remained polite, but were clearly irritated by the arrogant way he expressed himself, even if some of them might have agreed with his sentiments.

Pierre was also expected to stand behind Rochambeau's chair or with the other staff. He had to eat with the English servants who had never been with a black man before, stared a lot and asked embarrassing questions or whispered to each other without addressing him.

*****

And what of Mary Feltham? I told myself not to get carried away by her, particularly when a casual remark I made the next day to the barman in the Dolphin brought from him the sharp remark, "Don't think you will get far there mate. She is a respectable girl and she knows what you Frenchmen have in mind. There's no shortage of others around here if you are looking for that."

A week or so passed and I found seeing other obviously available women in the pubs just underlined how much I wanted someone who was quite different. Catching a glimpse of Mary walking past head held high in the street just confirmed this. I could not get her out of my mind. In the end I decided to make an attempt to meet her and see what came of it. With hair brushed, boots polished and a clean shirt I appeared at "Feltham's Tailors and Dressmakers of Quality".

On the pretext of needing to buy a civilian jacket, I boldly entered what I discovered was a rather smart shop. After being measured up by John who I took to be Mary's brother, her sister-in-law Jane entered the shop. I casually asked if it might be possible to have a word with Mary who I had met and who had mentioned she worked there. This was none too politely received. It was Jane who responded.

"She is far too busy to be chattering with the likes of you," she said. "She is working on a fine ball gown for the youngest of the Churchey sisters."

"I'm sorry?" I said.

"The family that lives in the manor-house we all call the Dogs," she replied.

"The Dogs? Why "The Dogs?" I asked.

"They have hounds' heads carved on their gate posts because they have them on their family crest."

"I see," I said, surprised.

"Yes," she said, "And I have to say they are proper gentry, not like some who just think they are, not to mention you lot with all your fancy foreign airs despite your "Revolution." and talk of Equality.

With that the door opened and in came Mary with a threaded needle in her mouth and part of the gown in her hands. She blushed at seeing me and started into earnest conversation with Jane about the instructions she had been given. I waited for a pause and said how glad I was to see her again and that my friend Pierre and I would so appreciate it if perhaps she had a friend and together they could walk around the town with us and tell us all about it since we were new.

Jane sighed and rolled her eyes and Mary looked nonplussed and taken aback by my forwardness. For a long moment I thought I had gone too far, but she surprised me by taking a deep breath and saying, "I see. But first please tell me, what's the name of your friend?"

"Pierre Courpon," I replied. "He's from Saint Domingue."

"Never heard of it. Some awful French colony based on slavery no doubt." she paused. "I thought it was disgusting the way those lads taunted him when you and your prancing generals came walking down the High Street. We are *not* all like that I can assure you. I'll have a word with my friend Catherine and her father about going for a walk with you both and let you know. Of course they might say no. I can't speak for either of them. Come back in a couple of days after I've had a chance to discuss it."

"You say your friend's name is Catherine. Could it be Catherine Doney? I asked.

And that was it. When I explained that I had got to know Catherine's father William because of my interest in clocks and that I had trained as a clockmaker before joining the Army, both she and Jane relaxed. It was of course out of the question that Mary and I go out straight away on our own, but we agreed that if William and his wife were happy for Catherine and Mary to walk out with Pierre and I, that would be decent and respectable and we might be able to arrange a walk on the next Sunday afternoon.

Pierre was embarrassed and angry when I first returned from Feltham's to say in excited tones that I had quite possibly arranged a walk for us with Mary Feltham and her friend Catherine Doney.

"Is she white?" he asked.

"Yes of course. I saw her briefly when I visited Mr Doney, the clock-maker. Rather a good-looking young lady I thought."

"And what do you think your Mr Doney will say if his daughter is to be seen out with a dusky Frenchman?" Pierre asked.

"I honestly don't know, but the whole reason we have got this chance is because Mary was disgusted by the way that local lad insulted you in the High Street." I replied.

"That doesn't mean her friend's father would like the whole town to know his daughter has been seen out walking with a *mulatto* like me. You know it would be impossible where I come from."

I could see his point and had to agree it was a long shot, also neither of us knew anything about Catherine. She might be just as against the idea as her father might be.

"And what about her mother? It won't just be up to father and daughter Alberto. In fact I think her mother might be the one who will be most against the whole idea." he said dolefully.

"Alright Pierre." I said. "We'll just have to wait. I'll tell you this though, Mary strikes me as someone sure of herself and sensible. I think she will already have been talking to Catherine about what happened and she would not have suggested the walk if she and Catherine hadn't reacted in the same way. I also think, though it was only a quick introduction I had, that you will find Catherine, well, rather nice."

And so it turned out. Small, dainty and excitable, Catherine was delighted that her friend Mary was offering her the chance to meet the mysterious young man they had watched walking down the High Street in his dashing and extravagant French uniform and who she had seen being so cruelly insulted because of his colour. She had already been imagining what his background might have been. Had he been brought over as a slave from Africa, or had he been born under the whip in some satanic French colony? She had so many questions to ask him.

It turned out my hunch was right. Both her father and mother had a high opinion of Mary and her judgement and agreed with her that we should be shown courtesy and that not only were most English people against slavery, they were against treating black or coloured people as inferior. When I heard that from Mary I just smiled and hoped it was true.

In the weeks and months that followed however things went very well. There were walks by the four of us out to the boundaries of the town, picnics on Windmill Hill and attendance at concerts in the theatre in South Street. Boye quickly became part of an impressive chamber group as well as a choir which the four of us joined. We took them out for supper in the Greyhound and there were brief encounters of just the two of us when Mary and I had a quick snack for lunch. I was smitten, totally. Her easy manner, quick wit, long dark hair and flashing eyes just overwhelmed me.

*****

She was endlessly curious and keen to learn more about the world and bemoaned her limited education and lack of travel.

"I have never been to Bath, let alone Bristol or London," she said. I quickly learnt that despite that she was very skilful at adapting the patterns and fashions she saw in ladies journals to make bespoke gowns and dresses and had built up, as her sister-in-law Jane was quick to tell me, quite a reputation attracting as much work as she could handle. "Particularly," as Jane proudly remarked, "From the better class of person around here."

She was keen to show me from those magazines what was happening in Bath where a dandy named Beau Brummel was leading a fashion revolution for men in clothing and hairstyles, putting aside the powdered wigs in favour of a carefully tousled Roman look. while the women were adopting rather more demure versions of the high-waisted breast-revealing classical style so popular in France.

"You will not catch English ladies showing off their nipples through thin cotton." She told me. I agreed earnestly and we both laughed. That was one of the best things about her. We both found so much to laugh about. It was a long time – if ever - I had laughed and enjoyed myself so much as I did just being with her.

Pierre and Catherine also were getting on well together. Naturally shy and reticent about expressing himself he found the way this small person bossed him about and teased him a delight and he relaxed and expressed himself as he never had in Norman Cross. She helped him along with his English and as a result of her relentless and sympathetic questioning I also learnt so much more about him.

As was the case with so many Saint Domingue *mulattos,* he was the son of a black slave mother and a white father, the manager of a large sugar plantation. This meant he was born free. As usual in cases like his, his father had a white, *creole*, island born wife. She bitterly resented his mother and him. His father, a harsh man, feared on the plantation, tried to be honest and a good father to Pierre and shield him from his wife's spite by sending him to the *Academie d'Education* in Le Cap as a boarder as soon as they would take him.

Reading between the lines of what he rather reticently said, it appeared he did well there and was then prepared for a career in the French Army on the island. After basic training however he was considered too lacking in self-confidence to be accepted for officer training for they trained *mulatto* officers to serve locally - and he was instead encouraged to seek a post with a senior officer as *ordonnance*. Like me he was told that could later lead to promotion as sergeant.

After serving two years as *ordonnance* to a colonel who was invalided out of the service and sent back to France, he was chosen by Rochambeau to be his *ordonnance*. From the start he found working for this self-obsessed, bizarre and erratic man who clearly held *mulattos* in contempt, hugely demanding and often depressing, but he had no choice but to make the best of it.

In Wincanton we found on many occasions when we planned to do something together Pierre would get a message that Rochambeau needed his presence, often for needlessly small tasks. He was of course well aware that he had no option but to obey.

*****

For many parolees - though frankly not for us - the most boring day of the week was Sunday for the pubs, shops and bars closed, the coaches did not run and most of the locals went off to church. Here the scene was very different from either France or Italy.

Where I came from attendance at Mass "on days of obligation" was something my Vaudois parents and I knew you dared not miss. In France the Revolution had seen the Catholic Church have its property confiscated, many priests killed and a rather absurd Cult of Reason installed. I had read articles about that when I was at school in Turin. Napoleon however had now made peace with the Pope and gave back the Church the use of some of its buildings, knowing that was what most people wanted. As I had seen him start doing in Italy, rather than fight the Church he worked to use it for his own ends.

In Wincanton we found the picture was very different. This little market town of less than two thousand people had a handsome Church of England parish Church, (the work of Nathaniel Ireson) a Methodist Church, a Congregationalist Church, a Baptist chapel, a group who called themselves Quakers and a small number of Catholics who met infrequently in private chapels when a priest visited. They all took their religion seriously and seemed to think that everyone should have freedom to worship as they chose and took that pretty much for granted.

I found that impressive, though when I discussed this with Boye he reminded me that the path to this stage had been painful. "The English have passed through a reformation, a civil war , a revolution, a regicide and a restoration before settling down to where they are now with a "constitutional monarchy".

So what should we do on a Sunday? In a sense we took the path of least resistance and with the encouragement of Mary, her brother and Jane and of Catherine and her parents we took to attending Sunday Matins with them at the parish church.

Boye and several of the other senior officers formed a musicians group to lead the singing and very good they were too. (Rochambeau got permission to travel with the Catholics when they set off for Mass.) The Protestant Church of England priest the Reverend John Radford welcomed us while knowing that we probably had no religion or were members of what he called "the Church of Rome." I really enjoyed the music and the singing and found the rich sonorous words of the Psalms and the English Book of Common Prayer calming and somehow inspiring.

*****

A religion of form however was not good enough for either Mary or Catherine. They took praying and reading the Scriptures very seriously. For them it also went with another passion. They were Abolutionists. Catherine in particular had a great pile of pamphlets written by a Thomas Clarkson including one on slavery in the French colonies. These she had collected and was keen to pass around. They both were particularly keen on an English gentleman and member of the British House of Commons, William Wilberforce who was leading an anti-slavery campaign. They both argued strongly that it was the duty of every Christian to be against slavery.

I was certainly against slavery as I knew Boye was too, but we thought it had to do with recognising basic human rights and had nothing to do with belief in God. Mary and Catherine disagreed with that saying we were all made in the image of God and all equally loved by God.

Once started on the subject they both got very heated, particularly about the trade in slaves from Africa to the United States. Both Pierre and I decided to keep rather quiet about what we knew and had seen when this subject came up and when Pierre was asked about Saint Domingue he just said that in the end slavery had been done away with there and things were probably much better now. It was not a subject either of us were ready to talk about.

Chapter 36
The Ironmonger Tragedy

The months were passing happily for the four of us when things suddenly went badly wrong for Catherine. She was employed as the assistant to a Mr Carpenter who ran an ironmongers at the top of South Street. There he sold a wide variety of metal goods including not only what one might expect, but oil for lubricating machinery and gunpowder for the yeomen militia's muskets and the farmers' shot guns.. These two ingredients he kept stored in barrels down in his distinctly dark cellar.

We had heard from her that he was not a good employer, in fact Catherine hated him. Married to the decidedly dominant and corpulent Mrs Polly Carpenter who ran a bake house on what everyone referred to as Polly Carpenter's Corner, he was a whining weasel of a man who Catherine found spent far too much time smiling at her, looking at her and finding any excuse to brush up against her.

On this particular day a farmer came in wanting to buy a can of oil. Immediately Carpenter said that they should both go down into the cellar to get it. He would carry the candle and Catherine could fill up the can from the barrel. Hating the thought of being caught down there with him she assured him she could do the job on her own and suggested the farmer could be persuaded to make other purchases if he stayed talking to him.

Down she went into the dark cellar with a candle, a can and a cup. Seeing the oil barrel she placed the candle on the next barrel which seemed full of a dark powder and proceeded to fill up the can with the cup. Carpenter then called out to her to hurry up for the farmer wanted to leave. She rushed upstairs and handed over the can of oil. As she did so she realised what she had done. She

239

had placed the candle in its candle stick on top of what was the open barrel of gunpowder. This meant if the candle gave a single sputter or spark, as it quite often did, the whole shop and everyone in it would be blown to bits. She went white, told Carpenter what she had done saying she would have to go straight down and bring the candle up again. Immediately Carpenter said, "No, no. I know just what to do."

With that he rushed to the door of the shop and on looking out he saw a young lad loitering outside the bake-house, a lad who he knew was "half sharp" and desperately poor. He called out to him and said that he could earn himself a sixpence if he just went down to the cellar and brought back the lighted candle he had forgotten down there. Catherine was appalled at the way Carpenter was ready to place the life of this lad at risk, and ran straight down the stairs, picked up the candle and ran back upstairs with it before blowing it out.

Carpenter tried to give her a "congratulatory" hug calling her a "brave girl." She kneed him hard and left the shop in tears shaking uncontrollably and never went back there again.

Sadly, the whole incident affected her deeply. We thought telling us all about it would help, but it did not. Always excitable and emotional her brave act brought her nothing but misery and fear as she relived being down in the dark with candle and gunpowder. She became depressed, stopped eating and sleeping and nothing could shake her out of it. Thin and weakened she soon refused to see Pierre and even Mary found it difficult to get through to her and when a fever swept through the town that winter she was gone. Pierre was devastated for I thought he was as deeply in love with her as I was with Mary. Life after that was very different.

We were all devastated. A beautiful, lively presence had now gone and Catherine's parents had lost their much loved and only child. Her mother Jessica, a quiet restrained woman had herself been laid low with the fever and like Catherine had taken to her bed. William had brought them both soup that evening and had persuaded Catherine to take a couple of spoonful's and saw that she had developed a high fever. When Jessica entered her room the next morning she found she had kicked off her blankets and was lying there cold.

Pierre said almost nothing and retreated into himself.

Rochambeau in a show of sympathy presented him with a bottle of whisky.

"This is very sad Courpon, "he said. "Terrible for the poor girl's parents. In my experience the best thing you can do to cope is to keep as busy as possible. Sitting around moping will just make it worse."

I do not know if he was right. Perhaps he was simply giving himself an excuse for providing no let-up in his demands for service.

To Boye and me he said, "Perhaps this is all just as well. He will be able to look back at his time with her without regrets. If it had gone on it could only have ended in pain, one way or another. Black and white relationships always do. Fine, so long as they are just for the pleasure. Also I'm sure people like him don't have the deep sensitivities of people like us. He'll soon get over it."

Somehow we both managed to say nothing. What would have been the point?

Mary and I visited Jessica and William together. Tears were shed by both women and memories revisited. I felt an intruder. William beckoned me to leave the women and follow him to his workshop. There on his bench was a fine brass carriage clock, almost finished, its spring and major cogs laid out.

"It was for her birthday." he said, and we silently held each other. There was then a knock on their front door and the Reverend John Radford, the curate, arrived. It seemed time for us to go.

Rumours about why Catherine had gone into such a decline after the gun-powder incident had been rife around the town for so many knew her. Carpenter gave out a garbled explanation about having been ready to go down with her himself when she had snatched the candle from him. His wife belligerently defended him saying to everyone who visited the bake-house that, "If you think about it, it was, I am afraid to say, the girl's fault. She should never have gone down into that cellar on her own. After all my husband did offer to go down with her. Yes, I just have to point out she could be rather thoughtless and silly, preening herself and thinking about her looks and mooning about her black boyfriend. After all her mistake nearly blew us all up."

Neither made any reference to the boy Carpenter had tried to use to retrieve the candle and who Catherine had saved from being placed at terrible risk.

I told Boye what Catherine had told us had really happened and his reaction was to train us hard in the choir and to arrange for the most beautiful singing to take place during her funeral. The service filled the parish church with a turnout of townspeople and parolees, many having to stand outside.

In the days that followed we did what we could to try and keep Pierre close and supported, inviting him to join us for walks or for drinks or meals. He came out with us a couple of times and on each occasion broke down.

A few days later we arranged to meet up with him at the Bear. He arrived there before us and was sitting alone in a corner, nursing a pint. No sooner had we joined him than he said, "Look, Alberto, you are doing your best and I appreciate that. And Mary, I know you have lost your best friend and I can see how that hurts." He looked silently down at his drink and then said, "I have lost the most precious person in my life, the only one I have ever felt really able to open up to. Now I have to face being alone again and yes I have to get on with serving Rochambeau."

Mary put a hand on his arm and said, "Pierre, I know. Catherine never loved anyone like she did you. I'm sure if it had not been for that fever she would have recovered from that dreadful incident and come back to you."

"We can't know that Mary." he replied, "And I will just have to live with the fact that I will never know. As for Rochambeau, perhaps he is right. Getting stuck into working for him, however menial, does give me something to do – polishing his bloody boots and all that. Listen. I will keep coming along with you both to choir and join you in church for her parent's sake, though I cannot see much of the hand of God in any of this. Apart from that, I think I need to be able to grieve on my own – when Rochambeau is prepared to give me some space to do it. Anyway, Alberto you and I see enough of each other – whether we like it or not!"

Chapter 37
Betrothed

So things changed. John and Jane became happy to see the two of us walking out together on our own and Mary and I simply had no doubts about each other. She was then twenty-one and I twenty-nine and the fact that we both came from such different worlds just added to the attraction we both felt. Soon after on a Sunday afternoon walk up Windmill Hill I proposed and without hesitation she said yes. It felt totally right.

"Alberto, I have no doubt about wanting to marry you and saying yes. I never thought any man could make me as happy as you do," she said.

"But?" I replied.

"But this is not going to be easy. Of course I have been thinking and your proposal comes as no surprise. I take it we need be ready to live either in England or in France depending on how this war goes, and I suppose depending on you still being tied to serving in your French Army."

"Typical," I said, "You have thought things through more fully than I. The quick answer is I agree. In the long term it is hard to know where we might settle, over here or over there and I think our freedom of choice in the matter may be decidedly limited, depending on what happens in the war. We will need to be ready to make the best of it whatever Fate or the Lord decides for us."

"Alberto do not take the Lord's name in vain. Oh yes I agree. So when will my French lessons start"

Here again Mary surprised me. She reminded me one of her friends was Elizabeth Clewett. I had met her father in the Masonic Lodge and he ran a small printing business in the town and produced all our masonic certificates. With his approval she had started to be seen out with a young naval officer, Louis Michel Duchemin. Again I had met him at the masonic meetings and he had come across as outgoing, intelligent and university educated, in fact more of an intellectual than most of the officers.

"Do you know he has been teaching Elizabeth French?" said Mary. "She says that despite the fact that he seems so very intellectual, she finds he is easy and patient and a really good teacher. She says he is thinking about setting up as a tutor to teach French language and literature here in England when the war is over – though don't mention that to anyone. Anyway, the trouble with you Alberto is that your English is so good we have never tried French, but if we get married and go to France I really must try and learn it, and as soon as I can."

"You think we might get together with Duchemin and his Elizabeth?

"I do" she replied. "I will see Elizabeth tomorrow and see what she thinks."

Which is exactly what she did. Louis Duchemin leapt at the chance of extending his practice of teaching to include Mary and the four of us met weekly. He had a quick and easy manner and was very good at explaining grammar and getting his pupils to remember rules. I concentrated on helping them with everyday conversation skills.

*****

That of course was the comparatively easy part. The rest was not so simple. John and Jane might appear happy enough, as they were when we went back to tell them about our betrothal, but what of her parents in Crediton? More to the point as Jane was quick to ask, "What do you think is going to be the legal status of your marriage given that Britain and France are at war? Also where do you expect to settle? In England or in France?" Again I spoke to my general and he said he would make some enquiries about the French situation, but that might take a few days. In the meantime he suggested we go and see the curate, the Reverend John Radford.

He lived in the Rectory, a large, rather grand house near the Parish Church with his wife and their three children. We made an appointment after Matins and turned up in the evening at six after roll-call. His maid opened the door to us and led us to his high ceilinged, book-lined study. He was I knew an Oxford graduate. Boye had explained to me that you could know that from the red silk hood he wore over his white surplice in church.

He had placed chairs in front of his desk for us and welcomed us warmly asking us how we were feeling after Catherine's funeral, a service which I thought he had carried out rather well. He spoke of having known her since childhood and of having prepared her for Confirmation when she was thirteen and of knowing her parents - William was the maker of their own clock - and of what a devastating loss it must be for them to lose their only child.

I had not been aware how well he knew Catherine and her family and now realised where she had learnt to take her religion so seriously for he struck me as a kind, thoughtful, sensitive man who believed and sought to practice what he preached. He then got to the point of our visit.

"So you would like to get married and you would like me to explain and help you understand your position. Normally it is my responsibility to check that couples who come to me wishing to enter the state of matrimony are legally entitled to do so. That means being of sound mind, being at least sixteen years old and of course not already married to someone else!

For you however Mr Bioletti, there is more to think about. You will have to get a magistrate to agree that you really are single and of reputable good character and are thus able to give reason for the magistrate to believe that you would not desert your wife and children."

I expressed myself amazed at this extra step. His reply was, "I am sorry to have to say this but this is because there have been several cases of Frenchmen declaring their wish to marry an English girl only to desert her and the children on embarkation for France after taking part in a prisoner exchange."

He went on to explain that while English law recognised marriages contracted in France, the French government did not recognise marriages contracted in England. This meant if a French citizen deserted his English wife the French courts would not acknowledge her claims for compensation, support or property and the deserted wife would have to rely on a very small subsistence allowance paid for by the British Government. We were both rather shocked by this, thanked him for his candour and left.

When Mary and I saw Boye he said, "I have spoken to other senior officers and what the curate has told you is true. It does not however close the door on your wish to get married. For a start Bioletti I would certainly be prepared to give evidence to a magistrate as regards your good character. I also have to say that the chances of us being able to be involved in a prisoner exchange before this war finally ends, seem to me, despite my wish it were otherwise and we could return to active duty, to be very slight. There is, and forgive me for saying so, Mary, in my opinion more of a chance that the Emperor will invade Britain.

At the same time Mary, I just cannot imagine whether that happens or not, that Alberto would turn into such a monster - cad I think you English call it - that he would abandon you and any children you might have on the quayside."

That at least was encouraging. Our next step then was to contact Messiter's office to arrange a hearing with him as the magistrate. We only saw his clerk who laboriously took notes on our case and assured us we would need to wait at least a month as a test of our seriousness before he would see us. We found that frustrating.

It was a tough time for all of us but at the same time it drew us even closer together which made what happened next seem inevitable. Despite Mary's Christian principles that physical union should be reserved for married life, our desire for each other was becoming too hot to handle for both of us. On another fine Sunday afternoon she pushed herself away and announced with the sort of candour I was getting used to "Alberto. We can't go on like this. I want you as much as I can see you want me. I love you and I have no doubt about your love and commitment to me. I know we will get married as soon as we can, but because of this magistrate hold-up we do not know when that will be. Things could drag on for months or change very fast. You may even have to go off with your general on some mad campaign. What I do know is I want you now."

"You mean?"

"Yes! Yes you silly Italian, I'm saying yes!"

So we did, very sensitively and gently for it was her first time, in a secluded glade by Windmill Hill on my spread out overcoat.

And of course we did it again and again and our passion for each other seemed to know no bounds. She looked wonderful and radiant despite the sadness she had known over the death of Catherine and it was not long before her brother John took me aside.

"Look Alberto, Jane and I are pretty certain about what is happening, and we think rather than the two of you having to find somewhere to have some privacy, you should simply come back here to our home and her room. As yet we have no children and there is no-one here to spread gossip. Let's just hope we can get your marriage organised as soon as possible." Who could ask for more?

Yes of course this was also a time when I also thought about Pauline Leclerc and the time I had with her in Port au Prince. When it came to giving and taking pleasure she was amazing and incredibly skilled, but with Mary it was so very different. Certainly I had fallen madly for Pauline, but she seemed incapable of reciprocating as far as deep emotion or talk or thought of love went, and she had quite kindly and considerately weaned me off having such thoughts about her by the time we had to move on. Although she saw herself as a sort of "liberated" free spirit, acting naturally, I now saw she was seriously missing something. Perhaps she felt that herself when she so extravagantly cut her hair off for Leclerc after finding it so easy to pleasure others. Love, commitment, the desire to have a family – for her these just were not there, and here in Wincanton I had been lucky enough to find them in Mary.

Back in the cottage in the High Street however, things were not easy. The pattern of bad nights that had been the worst element of our stay at Normans Cross started up again. While things had seemed much better after settling in Wincanton, they had never really stopped and now they increased. Intermittent shouts, nightmares and interrupted nights became something we had to put up with from each other.

Rochambeau however decided to consult the local doctor for in addition to his strange nocturnal walks - which he still denied knowledge of - he suffered from unpleasant digestive problems, in particular a frequent wish to defecate, the doctor called it *tenesmus*, which produced nothing but pain, cramping and involuntary straining as well as recurrent hot flushes. These he discussed endlessly with us and with Boye who also complained that he often slept badly and found little pleasure in food.

The doctor suggested they both visit the Horwood Well Spa on the edge of the town and start taking draughts of the mineral water. They did this for over a month and at the end of the "treatment" both pronounced it had been a great help. The owner, a Mr Gapper, then asked them to write a testimonial declaring how wonderful the treatment had been, and to my surprise, they both agreed. This was then printed up into a pamphlet which was circulated to advertise the spa.

There was however I noted one oddity, since this was meant to persuade an English audience. Rochambeau, with Boye following, despite having excellent English, insisted on writing the testimonials in French. For myself, having tasted the stuff, I thought the daily walk to get there was probably more helpful.

Quite apart from what I had seen of his appalling behaviour in Saint Domingue, Rochambeau always seemed to me an unstable person, subject to great swings in mood, never easy to get on with and generally self-obsessed to a peculiar degree. His constant need to dress up in his uniform and his boasting about his time in America when he had actually held a very junior position as aid-de-comp to his distinguished and accomplished father, struck me as being rooted in a sense of inferiority that seldom left him.

He let slip that he had never got on with his father who he intimated was always critical and who nearly dismissed him when he discovered he had made an American girl pregnant. I think his insecurity was also expressed in his extreme snobbishness and need to "play the general" and in the way he seemed to find it important to be able to look down on people of colour, including Pierre, who after all he had personally selected to be his ordonnance.

I think his general state of mind was also affected by the fact that In Wincanton he was never invited to dinner parties by the same hosts twice, particularly when he saw that Boye attracted more second invitations from the local gentry than he was able to accept. This clearly rankled and he started pub crawling, whoring and drinking heavily, though he also spent evenings in the cottage morosely drinking alone.

Chapter 38
A Sporting Occasion

I then noticed a sort of forced upturn in his mood, accompanied by gratuitous smiling. He seemed to be up to something. A few days later my fears were confirmed when he announced over breakfast, "By the way Boye I have arranged with Colonel d'Henin and Captain Linoi a day of real sport for tomorrow which I am sure you and of course you two *ordonnances* are going to enjoy."

"But I have arranged a game of chess for tomorrow with Colonel Delors," said Boye.

"Can't have that I'm afraid," said Rochambeau. "You'll have to give the gallant colonel your apologies. You've got all today to do that. No, I am afraid this is all organised. I told the others you were coming and everyone is expecting you to be there, besides, it is going to be a terrific day. There may be others and there will be some hounds".

"But what are we going to do?" said Boye.

"Have a cracking good walk out into the countryside and with luck flush out some game with the hounds for our table. You know Quantin? He's been training his hounds to go for rabbits and hare. Great way to get us some game."

There was no stopping him and he was so insistent it was clear that the position of all of us would become very difficult if we did not go along with him. In fact it could become impossible for all the other senior officers would back up and support his authority in order to maintain theirs.

The next day dawned. We all met at the bottom of Mill Street after the morning roll-call and set off up West Hill. It turned out to be a very pleasant day as regards weather and it did not take us long to reach the edge of the town and the stone which marked our boundary. On reaching it Rochambeau carried on as if he had not even seen it leaving little choice for the rest of us but to follow.

In front of us was farmland, rich green fields being grazed by cattle and in amongst them rabbits. Excitedly Rochambeau turned to Quantin.

"Wonderful. See that! Let the hounds loose." he said.

"Are you sure?" said Quantin, "What about the cattle. They will run off."

"Can't worry about that." Said Rochambeau. "Just do it."

"If you say so General", said Quantin and off they bounded baying as hounds do. They did go straight for the rabbits for they had been well trained, but in doing so they frightened the cattle who proceeded to flee down the field making a fair amount of noise, lowing and mooing with fright. That was enough to wake the farmer, Mr Josiah Pugsley as I later learnt, who had been engaged in a bucolic snooze unnoticed by us. He jumped up and rushed towards us, a big man of mature years

"Hey, you lot. Who do you think you are trespassing on my land with your bloody hounds causing my cattle to stampede? Yes, and I can see. You are some of those bloody Frenchies they have in Wincanton. Don't you know you have broken your parole coming out here? You are going to be for it."

By this time he had drawn himself up and was standing glowering at Rochambeau.

Without a second thought he reacted in the same way as he had when swaggering down the High Street stick in hand. He lashed out at Pugsley. The farmer who was carrying a good long cane immediately hit him back.

It was Rochambeau's time to scream only now he went berserk beating Pugsley to the ground with a flurry of blows and would have gone on if it had not been for Boye and the others restraining him. As this was happening four burly farmworkers appeared, took one look at their master on the ground and the largest man simply went up to Rochambeau and punched him hard in the face. Down he went shrieking and cursing. Menacingly with hoes and forks they all squared up to do the same to us. Somehow Boye succeeded in calming them down, saying we did not want a fight and it had all been a terrible mistake. Our general was not well.

Boye then came over to me and said, "Look after this chap and go back with his workers to his home and apologise. Apologise to him, apologise to them, be ready to grovel, and yes to his wife. Say our general has been taken ill with battle fatigue and that the rest of us are really sorry this has happened. I fear we are going to be for it this time."

Not surprisingly Pugsley took some calming down, but my genuinely expressed apologies started to get through. With a gentle and practiced hand Mrs Pugsley cleaned up and soothed down her husband before giving me a glass of her home-brewed ale and thanking me for my trouble in bringing him back to the house. Pugsley announced grimly that he would be down to see Messiter "within the hour."

By the time I got back to the end of Mill Street I found the town had gone very quiet, except that there were about two dozen of the yeomen out on the streets rather nervously brandishing their muskets. I asked one of them who I had met before, he was a barman at the Bear, what had happened. He was only too pleased to expand.

"Well Bioletti, your bloody General Rochambeau really has done for himself this time. He and a group of about eight others including one with three bloody hunting hounds, came walking down West View until they came to the George. People could hear Rochambeau shouting and swearing away in French. He then pushed into the George where a whole bunch of your lot were drinking and proceeded to harangue them about how badly parole prisoners were being treated and how he had been sworn at and assaulted by a common farmer who was not even a gentleman and then punched by a labourer."

"So where is he now?" I asked.

"He then told them to follow him up Mill Street." he replied. "Several went after him, all stirred up and shouting, "down with the beastly British" or words to that effect. I think he hoped to stir up a riot, and one of our men who had been drinking with them rushed up to Captain Messiter's office and told him there was "a sort of disturbance" in Mill Street.

"Sounds dramatic." I commented. "It certainly was," he continued, "He had the alarm bell rung and all the yeomen who were at work in the town put down their tools or whatever they were doing, grabbed their muskets and rushed down here. Under Captain Messiter's direction they surrounded the men who were

251

shouting and then went to secure the general who struggled like a man possessed. All the others then just stood there glowering. Captain Messiter, looking angrier than I have ever seen him, then ordered that General Rochambeau be locked up in the store-room of the Town Hall for the night and ordered all the parolees to disperse or he would read the Riot Act, which I am glad to say they did."

"And what happened to General Boye?" I asked.

"Captain Messiter told General Boye to get back to his lodgings and not to move out from them until he was summoned to do so."

I rushed back to our cottage to find both Boye and Pierre exhausted and very worried. Pierre put together some food and blankets for Rochambeau and set off to see if those guarding him would give them to him. He had hardly returned when there was a loud banging on our front door and there was a visibly angry Messiter accompanied by his company sergeant.

"Well, Boye, this really is a disgusting mess. What on earth has gone wrong with you and your General Rochambeau? After all I have done to make sure the two of you had a clean fresh start and were set up here in comfort. I really am amazed. I have just been talking to Farmer Pugsley who lost no time getting to my office to report a case of parole breaking and file a charge of assault and trespass. So just what have you to say?"

With that the two of them sat down, Boye signalling we get them something to drink. He then set out to explain that Rochambeau had organised the whole thing and that none of the party had known that he intended to break the parole boundary and that setting the hounds loose by the cattle had been Rochambeau's decision, and yes he had certainly assaulted Farmer Pugsley who had retaliated.

"I think you have to understand," Boye went on, "Our General Rochambeau seems to be going through a very bad time. He has not been in good health and his moods have been so extreme. Painful war-time experiences can do this to one you know and he certainly has had those. At times I think he can hardly be held responsible for what he does."

"And I understand," said Messiter, "That you are doing your best to make excuses for him, but we both know that this just won't do and I have to take steps to see that it never happens again and that all five hundred of you understand that disruptive, not to say criminal behaviour like this is not tolerated - whoever the perpetrator."

We all nodded and he paused. "General Boye, I must ask you not to leave this house. Courpon you are to take food down to Rochambeau and anything else he asks for. I am keeping him locked up until we have a meeting to settle this affair. My men will provide him with a proper bed. I shall be consulting with others and telling you what the Transport Board decision as regards your future is after I see you all in my offices at ten a.m. in three days that is on Thursday 14th July. One other thing. I wish to see you Bioletti, in my office tomorrow straight after your morning roll-call." With that he got up and left.

After he had gone the three of us sat down and Boye looked grave. "I certainly can understand Messiter's anger. This whole debacle was an insanity, a provocation. I wonder what he has in mind. What are his options? I think they are to return the four of us to Norman Cross and confinement there or possibly to confine us with the prisoners who have just completed this new prison camp on Dartmoor."

I then said. "Excuse me sir. What about Verdun?"

"Yes Bioletti. Verdun. We know the British are terrified Napoleon might take out reprisals on those he is holding in Verdun. If it were to come to Napoleon's attention senior prisoners of war over here were being given a hard time the English fear he might restrict privileges, reduce the parole area, increase rents, that sort of thing. This is because so many of the British in France are either their precious nobility or gentry. Still they held us in close confinement at Normans Cross without provoking a French reaction, so I think they might decide to do that again."

The thought really upset me. What would happen to Mary and our plans? Boye then said, "I can see what you are thinking Bioletti. There are however two things he has done which might give us grounds for some sort of hope. The first is that he appears to have accepted my explanation of what happened today and has not arrested and confined any of us, save poor Rochambeau, including the others who were with us. He could have locked the whole lot of us up. The second point Bioletti is that he wishes to see you tomorrow alone. I wonder why."

The next morning, after consulting Boye as to whether I should wear uniform or civilian dress – he suggested civilian - I presented myself at Messiter's offices by the Town Hall and was ushered in by his clerk to stand in front of his desk. He was already examining papers.

"Ah, Bioletti," he said, "I see here you have put in a request to be married to a Miss Mary Feltham."

"Yes sir. We were hoping to get married as soon as possible, but have been told to wait for an appointment to see you in about a month."

"That is just to put off frivolous requests – which I can assure you often happen."

"Yes sir."

"I see here that Miss Feltham who is working here with her brother and sister-in-law in their tailoring and dressmaking business, actually comes from Crediton in Devonshire?"

"Yes sir. Her family live there and her father owns and runs a similar business to Feltham's here.

"I see. Obviously you have not visited Crediton?"

"Obviously not sir! That would be to break parole. But we hope that soon we could afford to invite Mary's parents to visit here so that I can make their acquaintance and obtain their consent."

"So are they happy with this, er betrothal of yours?

"I do hope so sir. I understand Mary's brother has written recommending me and saying we are well suited, for which I am very grateful."

"I see." said Messiter, "Look Bioletti, I have been making enquiries about you and this young lady and hear she is of excellent character and considerable skill as a dressmaker. I also have heard many good things about you, both from your general who I have got to know quite well and admire, and from others in the town. In my positon it is important to note these things. I also hear you have been attending the French Lodge.

"Yes sir." I said.

"You may tell your general that I completely accept the accuracy of his account of what happened yesterday and recognise the difficulty all of you would have if you tried to disobey the wishes of so senior an officer as General Rochambeau. I also wish to pass on the thanks of Farmer Pugsley to you for the way you supported him, apologised and helped him back to his home. At this time until I have met with my colleagues that is all I can say.

My thanks for attending this meeting."

Dazed I left his office and went straight to see Mary and John telling them all that had happened.

"What do you think he has in mind?" asked John. We discussed the Norman Cross and Dartmoor options with foreboding and were at a loss to think of anything else, when Mary said, "Well this is just an idea, but what if he decided to separate the two generals and send you to different places? After all Boye seems to have done nothing wrong on his own. It is simply that his reputation has been tarnished because he has felt he has to be loyal to Rochambeau."

"Which different places?" said John.

"I don't know," said Mary. "But perhaps one of them could be Crediton."

We sat stunned as the possibilities sank in.

"The trouble with you Mary," I said, "Is that you are just so brilliant. Next you will be suggesting you know of a suitable property to put us up in."

"Well yes." She replied. "I can think of a few."

The next step was for her to put on her smartest outfit and set off for Messiter's office and ask to see him. Expecting she might have to wait until the next day or so she was surprised to be ushered straight in. He asked her to sit down and listened very carefully to what she had to say. He confided that he had indeed been contemplating separating the Generals and was very interested to hear more about Crediton, telling her that he knew little about it except that it had a Board Agent and already held some sixty paroled naval officers who had been taken after the Battle of Trafalgar. He asked no more of her except to hear her confirm her wish to marry me.

Mary reported that he then said, "Having seen you today Miss Feltham, I feel much better about sorting this affair out in a way that could work out reasonably well. I make no promises but would appreciate your coming to the meeting on Thursday when I shall be seeing all the others and announcing our decisions." Surprised and pleased she thanked him and rushed back to tell us.

The day of the meeting arrived. Present were Boye, Pierre, Mary and I, together with Messiter, his clerk to take notes and two yeomen who arrived with Rochambeau. He looked gaunt and crumpled as if he had not slept for days.

Messiter opened the meeting by welcoming Mary and the rest of us and went on to say. "I am going to start by setting out what we intend doing. I shall then give you an opportunity to express your opinions before issuing a final decision. First, I see no point in going over the miserable events that have led up to this meeting except to say that my decisions are based on making any repetition of them either here or anywhere else as unlikely as possible. The first point I need emphasise is that you two generals have between you caused more disruption and trouble for the Transport Board than any other officers in the entire war to date. Think about that. It is not a record to be proud of. It is also my conclusion that this is mainly the fault of one of you.

Having considered alternatives I have decided that you, General Rochambeau should be moved to Moreton Hampstead in Devonshire, accompanied by your orderly Courpon where again you will be provided with accommodation suitable to your rank. This will be after you have signed fresh parole papers declaring that you will accept the authority of the Agent, abstain from offensive behaviour there and not seek to escape on pain of being sent to Dartmoor.

For you General Boye, my decision is that you be sent to Crediton with Bioletti and his betrothed Mary Feltham where you will be provided with suitable accommodation as the local Agent shall decide. I have also made other enquiries and it appears the Grand Master of your Lodge is wanting to enrol you Bioletti, at a special meeting tomorrow night before you leave. I have also spoken to our curate the Reverend Mr Radford and he is happy to marry you both on Saturday. The Transport Board will be providing both parties with coaches to go respectively to Moreton Hampstead and Crediton on Monday with all your belongings, it being my opinion that it is of the utmost importance that all the parolees here see that our response to disruption is swift, efficient and fair. I want the whole matter to be over as soon as possible. Have any of you anything to say?"

Rochambeau mumbled that he could not see why the threat of Dartmoor and rewritten parole only applied to one person. Messiter said he declined to answer that. "That being all then my orders stand as you have heard them. Good day, and for the betrothed couple my best wishes for your future happiness."

And so it ended. The speed at which everything then happened was overwhelming. The ceremony in the Lodge I found deeply moving. William Doney, Louis Duchemin, John Feltham, my general Boye, and to my great surprise Rochambeau were all there and signed my certificate. Our wedding the next day was unforgettable and very happy despite being so rushed. Mary found the most beautiful gown in Felthams which Jane fitted for her. Elizabeth Clewett was her bridesmaid and Boye played his violin most beautifully. He also conducted his choir in a rousing anthem for the last time. John Radford read St Paul's chapter on charity with perfect expression. I was only sorry there was no-one from my side of the family to be there or even to know it was taking place. Of course I chose Pierre to follow the English custom of having a best man and the church was packed with Feltham friends and parolees.

The one who had done worst out of all this was of course poor Pierre. We had lived and worked together through war in Saint Domingue, capture and time as parolees in England, and in the course of less than a year he had lost the love of his life and the companionship of working with a friend. He was now left working for a difficult and unstable superior in a new place where he knew no-one. Of course we promised to write and keep in touch, but we knew that would be expensive and not the same. So it was that our time in Wincanton suddenly came to an end.

Chapter 39
Deep in Devonshire

Arrive 6 p.m. Wednesday 19ᵗʰ July 1807
Depart 8 .a.m. Thursday 2ⁿᵈ March 1811

Two coaches were drawn up in front of our cottage on Sunday morning, one for Rochambeau and Pierre and one for Boye, Mary and I and we spent the day sorting, packing and preparing for our journey. We were told that in addition to the coachmen two soldiers would be escorting us.

"That is not just to stop us making a dash for the coast. The English are having quite a problem with highwaymen", Boye told us.

Messiter also provided him with a map and notes about the journey for none of us except Mary knew anything of the whereabouts of either Crediton or Moretonhampstead. She told us they are Devonshire market towns and the map showed Crediton to be some miles North of Exeter and Moretonhampstead as being right on Dartmoor. Messiter's note also stated that he expected us to leave Wincanton at 5.30 a.m. on Monday. No doubt he did not want our departure to attract a crowd of parolees and he wished to see his troublesome generals gone as soon as possible.

Mary had a worry of her own. "You realise we are going to be turning up in Crediton unannounced. There has been no time since Messiter made his decision for a letter to get to them." she said to me.

"You mean to prepare your family for our sudden arrival, let alone that you will be turning up with an Italian husband." I replied.

"Exactly. My poor mother may be quite put out at having

missed our wedding and my father may be angry because we went ahead without consulting him. Also, what will the neighbours say?" she smiled ruefully.

"I think their Transport Board Agent will just have to put us up in an inn until he's able to sort things out with proper accommodation." I said.

The day rushed past with many friends turning up bearing wedding presents. There was everything from blankets to kitchen utensils and crockery to the point that we were worried our coach would be overloaded. Boye had no more than a couple of trunks and his violin and encouraged us to fit in as much as we could.

That evening John and Jane prepared a final meal for us and Pierre joined us while the two generals were entertained by the senior officers in the Greyhound. Jane also presented Mary with a beautiful set of baby clothes - delivered without comment. Our second night as man and wife was again celebrated in Mary's room.

At five the next morning our two soldier escorts, a corporal and a young private, knocked at the door and with ready smiles helped us carry the last of our possessions to the coach. The corporal was a thin, wiry, streetwise Londoner experienced in escort work who turned out to have a quick, sardonic wit which he employed constantly and which we all came to appreciate. When we got to our coaches we found a bleary eyed Rochambeau fussing around giving last minute orders to Pierre. It was taken for granted the generals would travel in one coach and the three of us in the other.

At that point a third carriage pulled up in the High Street and Messiter got out. He carried two sealed document folders. One he gave to the corporal and to my surprise then turned to Mary.

"Mrs Bioletti," he said, "Here are the documents relating to the case of General Boye and your husband which I would like you to give to the Transport Board Agent, a Mr. Ponsford I believe, when you arrive in Crediton."

"Of course sir. I will do so as soon as we arrive." she replied, "I know Mr Ponsford. He's a long standing customer of my father's. I've also made a gown for his daughter. He's a well-known and respected gentleman."

"Very good." he said, "Please also express my apologies to him and to your parents for having sprung your presence upon them without any preliminary warning. The letters refer to the circumstances involved, but I am sure you will be able to explain why this has all happened well enough."

With that he shook hands with both generals wishing them a good journey, gave a grim smile to Pierre and me, acknowledged the salutes of the two soldiers and climbed back into his carriage. By this time our coachmen had our horses harnessed and were ready to pull away at precisely five thirty by the Town Hall clock.

*****

Our journey went ahead that day without incident, it being beautiful July summer weather. We passed by rich Somerset farmland with cattle, sheep, wheat and barley to be seen around Langport and the orchards of cider apples hanging heavy on the trees around Taunton. There we spent the night in a large and comfortable inn.

The next day the heavens opened, rain fell and the road turned immediately to mud. Everyone but the coachmen sought shelter crammed inside, including our two jolly escorts until our coachman – we were at that point in the lead - brought our coach to a halt and shouted, "You men inside, show yourselves. We have gentlemen of the road ahead."

Our corporal grabbed his Brown Bess musket and jumped out, but before doing so he passed me his pistol – as we had already discussed he would do if this situation arose. Sure enough across the road some distance ahead we could see a rope strung between two trees and three scraggy figures on horseback facing us. They wore large three cornered hats and had kerchiefs tied across their faces.

"Regulation highwaymen dress." joked the corporal. All three brandished pistols. I clambered out and stood at the side of the coach as did Pierre from the coach behind looking relaxed yet aggressive, our pistols held nonchalantly. With that Boye and Rochambeau jumped out also armed with the pistols they too had been given. Suddenly our brave robbers found themselves facing six armed men, four with pistols, two with muskets and in full army uniform.

That was enough for them. They simply slashed their rope barrier and galloped off as fast as their rangy nags would take them. One of our number then raised and fired his pistol at the

261

retreating figures. It was of course Rochambeau. There was a loud click.

"So sorry sir," said the corporal. "But the only arms that are actually loaded are our muskets. Our job is not to kill highwaymen, or let you hold us up with pistols, but to deliver you French gentlemen safely." We all agreed, laughed and handed the pistols back.

On we travelled with a break for lunch at Tiverton until we arrived in Crediton at six in the evening. There we went straight to the largest inn and following Messiter's instructions, booked in for the night and had a final drink together in the bar. Rochambeau and Pierre then set off in their coach with the escorts for they were to go on and spend the night in Exeter before travelling to Dartmoor and Moretonhampstead the next day. Farewells were quickly said, with promises to Pierre repeated that we would keep in touch and off they went with a wave of the hat from Rochambeau.

*****

So here we were in Crediton. First impressions were of a larger and more prosperous town than Wincanton with a handsome High Street and the large and imposing cathedral sized Church of the Holy Cross. The hour was too late for us to seek out Ponsford the Agent, but Mary was naturally keen to see her parents as soon as possible, their shop being close by in the High Street. Boye suggested that he stay and have supper at the inn while the two of us visited her family. This we then did.

As in Wincanton the Felthams lived comfortably above and behind their tailoring business. They had of course heard about me and Mary had written that I had proposed and that she had agreed. I had also written to them assuring them of my honourable intentions and wish that we could marry, but that we had to wait for the approval of a magistrate. I also knew John had written to them about me and the letters he had sent must have been re-assuring for they had written back saying that they hoped to come to Wincanton for our wedding once permission came through, understanding that I could not go to Crediton to meet them.

Coach travel however for private citizens was extremely expensive so it was not surprising that we had not yet had a chance to meet. Certainly the turn of fortune which had placed us married and with them in Crediton was something no-one could have predicted. It was thus with feelings of some trepidation mixed with anticipation that we stood knocking at their door that evening.

It was her mother Sarah who came, took a long look at both of us and embraced her daughter.

"Come in," she said. "For a start you both look very well, and yes Mary, I can see the ring. So the great deed is done! Come in both of you and you can tell your story to your father and me."

Immediately I could see where so much of Mary's personality had come from. No hysteria, fainting or fuss, but a sensible calmness and straightforwardness that I immediately warmed to.

"A surprise for you David." She said, "Our little daughter is home with her Alberto, and it seems they are already married!"

Her father got out of his chair putting his paper aside and, looking completely amazed, shook my hand while looking me up and down quite sternly and intently. He then turned and kissed Mary. "Come, both of you. Sit down and tell us all about it and just what has happened to bring you here."

Again I was impressed by his no-nonsense approach as for the next two hours we sat and talked and responded to their questions. I explained my position as orderly to General Boye and Boye's position as regards Rochambeau, how Rochambeau's behaviour had brought everything to a head and how skilfully Messiter had chosen to handle the whole affair. Finally Mary described how we were now expected to live here in Crediton with Boye for an indefinite period.

"I look forward to meeting this General Boye. He sounds like a fine man and you obviously both like and respect him." said her father. "I think we should all go together to see Ponsford tomorrow. There is much to think about and work out."

And so there was. Ponsford like Messiter was a local solicitor, but Crediton, unlike Wincanton, only had some sixty parolees living in the town and none as high ranking as Boye. He agreed with Mary's father that Mary and I move into the Feltham home and Boye remain in the inn until a suitable property could be organised. Here Sarah's father helped again, knowing a friend with a good sized reasonably furnished cottage that was up for rent where Boye could have space enough for himself and we could live comfortably as a family. We all moved in there ten days later.

From the start these new domestic arrangements worked marvellously well. The relief of not having Rochambeau around after all the years of enforced closeness was enormous. We had been living without any choice but to put up with him and to do his bidding. Now I could see the relief for Boye was as great as it was for Mary and me. We also had time to discuss and agree with him what my duties were and what was needed. The one thing we did miss a bit was Rochambeau's gold. Boye while not abandoned by his family, did not, like Rochambeau, receive regular and substantial payments from his family in France. Instead we were more dependent on the allowance for senior officers the Transport Board paid him and the smaller allowance they paid me. This covered the cottage rent and almost enough to feed us, but no more. This meant it was clear that I would need to do what I could to make a living and Boye declared that he was very happy with that. It was also agreed that Boye eat the main meal of the day with us. Mary then came up with an interesting suggestion.

"General, you know that when we were in Wincanton I started to have French lessons with Monsieur Duchemin.

"Yes Madame Bioletti I do, and he told me you were proving a quick pupil." He replied.

"Well, I did that because now I am married to a soldier of France it is quite likely we might at some time need to live in France. Am I right?

"Indeed, but no-one can say when that might be or for how long." He replied.

"I know. But I think I really must learn to speak French. You speak excellent English, in fact much better English than I do. Yours is the English of an educated man. I wish I could speak like that in French. What would you say if I asked that while you are here with us and particularly when we eat and talk together, all our conversation should be in French?"

I wondered how he would react, but he laughed out loud. "I think that is a wonderful idea Madame, provided your husband is happy with it. What do you say Alberto?"

"I think that would be excellent sir. What could be more important for Mary if we were to return to France and I was to go off to serve as your *ordonnance* on active duty than that she be able to understand France and to work and make friends using French."

"Well said." he replied, "And when we are here without others present, please, both of you, let's not be so formal. Sir in English or Monsieur when using French is quite enough rather than General. It will also give me the greatest pleasure to be able to converse with both of you in French. And yes Madame, I will happily help you to say things in the correct way."

And so things progressed. Our meal-time discussions were lively and wide-ranging and soon we suggested he use Mary rather than Madame when we were alone for he usually referred to me as Alberto. At the same time Mary and I never felt it would be quite right to call him by his first name and he never suggested it. I was after all still serving as his *ordonnance*. Again while he clearly appreciated Mary as attractive and intelligent, his behaviour towards her never gave rise to unease for either of us despite us all living so closely together. The fact that we did not have to constantly take account of Rochambeau's prickly sense of social decorum was also a great relief.

It did not take long for Boye to be in constant demand from the local gentry as he was the most senior officer among the parolees. As in Wincanton his social life quickly built up with many repeat invitations to dinners, balls and other social events. Again his musical talents were much appreciated. He joined a chamber music group and we all joined the local church choir and the local classical choir. This also contained French officers who soon had him training and conducting them. Again we saw him being attracted to - but in the end rejected by - some of Devonshire's most eligible young ladies.

At first Mary spent part of her time working in Feltham's and I cast around for work. The one clockmaker in the town, was very suspicious of me and clearly terrified of a potential competitor. Unlike Wincanton which had several clockmakers and had developed quite a reputation for clocks and barometers based on its coach trade customers, Crediton was comparatively isolated. I had better luck getting some work with a local barber, but it was part-time and poorly paid. It was then that I cast my mind back to Norman Cross and the bagatelle tables I had seen and made there.

On visiting local pubs I found that bagatelle was becoming very popular, but many had no table or very poor ones. Our cottage had a good size work-shop at the back and I set about making bagatelle tables which I sold quickly and profitably. I also found I really loved working with wood and producing tables of high quality that could withstand the demands of pub usage.

So life in Crediton progressed. Mary and I could not have been happier and within seven months on the 8th of February 1808 at 7.15 a.m. she gave birth to our first child Jacques, (Boye's first name) James to his English relatives. Two year later, also in February, she gave birth to a baby girl who we named Cecillia after the patron saint of music. In fact music suffused our lives with Mary and I singing in choirs and around the house and the sounds of Boye practicing on his violin drifting down from his room. Unsurprisingly singing was also something our children quickly took to.

Again Boye and I joined the local masonic lodge which proved a good way to get to know the other parolees and many men in the town. I progressed to the third degree which gave me some satisfaction.

Letters went back and forth from Wincanton from John and Jane. We heard that Elizabeth Clewett and Louis Duchemin had got married, that a depressed parolee had committed suicide, that a rear admiral had died and been given a grand funeral and that the group of young midshipmen who had nearly starved had attempted a mass escape, but had been caught.

*****

There were also letters from Pierre. Rochambeau had again caused a stir in Moretonhampstead by swaggering around in his uniform with poor Pierre in tow. Again Pierre's colour was often commented on as he walked past the locals. He did however mention that a young girl named Suzanna had shown him some sympathy and friendship. Six months later we received a letter telling us that he and Suzanna Parker were to be married. He wondered if any of us could attend the service.

It was of course impossible for either Boye or I to go without breaking parole, but Mary and her mother decided to take the trip which meant a coach into Exeter and then a second one to Moretonhampstead. It was expensive but much appreciated. It turned out that Suzanna started as Rochambeau's chamber maid, but was promoted by him to being cook and housekeeper. Mary described her as "Sweet and gentle, but I fear hardly literate, still she and Pierre seem devoted to each other and it was lovely to see him looking so happy."

Mary also said that Rochambeau paid for a reception meal at the Mortenhampstead Inn for the Parker family (who she said ran a sweet shop) and of course Mary and her mother. She described how Rochambeau came in, proposed a toast to bride and groom, gave a surprisingly gracious speech and then withdrew. Clearly he did not think the assembled company were the sort of people he was prepared to share a table with. Still, he had shown some generosity for once.

And so it was our lives in Crediton continued. I knew I had never experienced such deep happiness. Mary and I shared everything and I felt enormously proud of her as she grew in confidence in everything she did. We were also extremely lucky that both our children flourished for around us so many did not. I had never thought about small children before, but found helping them take their first steps, playing with them, talking and reading to them gave me a new and deep sense of satisfaction. We knew of course that such straightforward happiness could not last. Something would happen which would really test us. Still it was hard to believe that by March 1811 we had been living in Crediton for three years and eight months.

I suppose as someone who had started life training as a clockmaker I obsessed about the passing of time and the use of time, and the inexorable nature of time, how it never stands still and how we need to prepare for the next shift in time.

To be prepared for such a shift and to be ready to again take up military service it was vital Boye and I kept in training. To do this for three days a week, joined by a good number of the other parolees, we did a one hour forced march from the centre of the town, out to a parole milestone and back. The forced march was the key to Napoleon's success, employed over and over with devastating effect. It simply meant having an army trained and fit enough to march at pretty well double the speed of its enemies. This meant his troops could turn up at the right place for what was the wrong time for his opponents. We assembled at ten to six and were back home ready for breakfast by seven.

On the morning of the first of March 1811 we arrived back at our cottage to find a splendidly dressed redcoat sergeant waiting for us. He saluted Boye with exaggerated punctiliousness.

"Sir! Are you General Boye?

"I am," he replied.

"And are you French private Bioletti?" he said.

"I certainly am," I replied.

"Well sir, I have good news for you both. Discussions have been taking place at the highest level between your government and ours, and it has been agreed that you will both be taking part in a prisoner exchange and will shortly be returned to France. This also means that responsibility for you now changes from the Naval Transport Board and its Agents to the Army. "

This hit us as a bolt from the blue for there had been no rumours or particular reasons evident why this might happen. Boye indicated to the sergeant that he should come inside and explain what the British Army had in mind over a cup of tea. Mary joined us at the table carrying Cellicia. It was the first time I had ever seen her look terrified.

"The plan is this sir," said the Sergeant. "My orders have been to speak to you first before informing the other prisoners on parole here in Crediton who are on my list.

"Are you saying they are not all on your list?" asked Boye.

"No sir. All I know is that those who were taken at Trafalgar are not, just those who came earlier. You, together with private Bioletti, his wife and children, will be transported by coach to Moretonhamstead on Dartmoor. There you will be joined by General Rochambeau, his orderly and his wife. You will then all spend the night at the Princetown Inn - which is by Dartmoor Prisoner of War Camp - before proceeding in your coach down to Plymouth. There you will embark on a cartel boat for the French port of Morlaix. In Plymouth you will also be joined by some one hundred other prisoners from Dartmoor who will carry out the journey on foot."

He gave us what he no doubt imagined was a magnanimous smile.

"I see." Said Boye, "Well, thank you Sergeant for coming to us first and for making the plan so clear. Can you tell me if you have any dates for this operation in mind?"

"Yes sir. As I think you may be aware when these prisoner transfers come through the policy is always to expedite them as soon as possible to avoid complications arising on either side. We

British are particularly aware the French authorities, no doubt acting under the orders of your Emperor, are quite capable of changing their minds at the last minute and blocking the return of British prisoners from France and the return of French prisoners from here."

At this Boye just took in a breath and looked up. The sergeant then continued, "For this reason we have booked a carriage and two military escorts to collect you in twenty-four hours. This should allow for your party to have a reasonably comfortable journey to Plymouth in time to catch the cartel ship booked to sail on the eighth. You should then arrive in France on the ninth.

"That march for the Dartmoor prisoners sounds tough. How fit and ready will they be for such an ordeal?" asked Boye.

"Well sir, clearly it would by quite impractical to take all the prisoners to Plymouth by coach and we are talking about serving soldiers who should all be ready and willing to undertake the march and we think a week to get to Plymouth should not be difficult. In fact I have done the journey in three days myself."

He got up and again Boye thanked him and he left. We looked at each other stunned.

"Well," said Mary after a moment when we all sat there lost in our own thoughts, "We always knew this might happen and when it did there would not be much we could do about it. In fact this is not such a bad time. Jacques is now three and Cecillia eighteen months. We are lucky they are both fit and thriving and both of us are still young and fit. In addition thanks to you Monsieur, I am tolerably fluent in French and feel quite ready to take on Paris."

I rushed around the table to give her a hug, quite overwhelmed by the courage she was showing.

"Mary, you are quite remarkable." said Boye. Mary then rushed off with the children to break the news to her parents while Boye and I ate some re-warmed porridge, an English breakfast habit we had both picked up.

"Problem is," said Boye, "That sergeant was quite right about Napoleon being difficult about prisoner exchanges. It is almost as if he feels anyone who has been taken prisoner will have lost his loyalty and his fighting spirit."

"Do you think he is right?" I asked.

"Sometimes." He replied. "I can't see that Louis Duchemin taking up his sword for the Empire again. As for me after what you and I have seen and been through in Saint Domingue I want to wipe the memory of that away by being able to take part in a proper battle fighting for France, whatever the outcome." I nodded in agreement. I knew just what he meant and felt much the same.

Chapter 40
Over the Moor

22nd February 8th March 1811

Coming to terms with what was about to happen was a real shock for us all, but particularly for Mary's parents who could have no idea when they might see her or their grandchildren again as we set off to join Britain's enemy. They faced the day by closing their shop and doing all they could to look after the children and help us pack. Most of our presents we left with them knowing there would be no return.

Boye took me aside. "You realise of course Alberto, this means falling in with Rochambeau until we get to France and hear what plans the Army and possibly Napoleon has for us. About that of course I have no idea. One thing I can be sure will happen is that as soon as Rochambeau starts to prepare for going back home he will again expect us to be dressed in our uniforms, so you had better get all that ready. Also with six adults, two children, two escorts and the coachmen the British Army will need to have organised our travel in two coaches."

"Yes, sir," I replied, "And I am sure Rochambeau will not wish to share a coach with our wives or the children. It will be back to full separation by rank."

"Exactly. That is how it has to be. Still let us all enjoy the first part of our journey to Moretonhampstead."

A surprising number of people turned up to wave us off the next morning. There were choir members, musicians, members of the Lodge, old friends of Mary's and Feltham relatives and some of those parole officers bitterly disappointed to hear they were not on the sergeant's list. Among those who came to bid farewell were some young women from the choirs and the grander social circle who embarrassed those who came with them by breaking down and weeping, so displaying a sensitivity of feeling towards Boye that was greater than I had realised was around. It clearly touched him.

That morning also brought a not unpleasant surprise. Knocking at the door early to help us load the coach were the same two escorts who had brought us to Crediton almost four years earlier.

"Glad to see you mate," said the corporal. "So you are off to get shot at again. Perhaps by some jolly redcoats?"

"You never can tell. It could be Germans or Russians." I replied.

"Or Italians. I hear Old Boney has been busy again in Italy. Seems your lot don't all like being "liberated.""

"True. And what about you? I thought you might be out in sunny Spain with Wellesley by now."

"Not if I can help it." He retorted. "I've had my fill of battlefields."

"Where was that?"

"Bergen in Holland. Abercromby was commanding under the Duke of York. We were supposed to be allied with the Russians against the Dutch and you French. What a shambles. Our officers could not even agree with the Russians as to what the time was. Lucky to get out of it alive – though I took a shot in the shoulder."

"So now?" I asked.

"Signed up for this special escort service. We are sent all over the country moving our bigwigs and your senior officers about. It's safe, interesting and fun."

"Even with highwaymen?"

"Especially with highwaymen. Had to fire my Brown Bess a couple of months ago at a gang outside Shepton Mallet. Winged one of them and watched him swing after his trial."

*****

Going via Exeter where we changed horses, we set off across the moor to reach Moretonhampstead by late afternoon. The roads remained good and the children behaved.

On arrival our corporal directed the coachman to go straight to Court Street where Rochambeau had rather a smart residence. A coach without horses was already parked and packed for the next day's journey stood outside.

Rochambeau came out first to greet Boye as if he were a long lost friend, giving the rest of us little more than a curt nod, slight smile and the children no attention at all. I noted he had aged and spread. Pierre introduced me to Suzanna who was more comfortably sized than I had imagined and we were ushered through to the kitchen before being presented with a large Devon "tea" consisting of far more food than we could possibly eat. That of course was after the children had been settled upstairs for the night.

Boye and Rochambeau remained in the front "parlour" where dinner was served to them by Pierre. I was surprised how much this treating us as inconsequential servants rankled after the atmosphere of our relaxed home in Crediton. Still Pierre and Suzanna had clearly done everything they could to make us welcome and prepare for us. Like us they had only had a day's notice and had spent it packing. I asked Pierre how he was managing his general.

"Well, he is fifty-six now you know, so he is definitely slowing down. He seems to have stopped whoring, though we can never be certain about that when he goes out. Yes. And of course we had to persuade him not to take too much interest in my wife." Suzanna smiled grimly.

"And the nights?" I asked.

"Greatly improved." He replied. "He only gets up and stamps about shouting in his sleep infrequently. He still gets through a lot of drink, but that is hardly a problem. His great interest now has become maps, poring over old maps, and if possible, maps of the United States. He says when he gets home that is what he is going to do."

"Collect maps?"

"Yes. It seems his father brought back quite a collection after his service with President Washington and there is much to be done cataloguing them and that sort of thing."

"And you two?" I asked.

"He wants us to come back," said Suzanna proudly, "To his family chateau at a place called Vendome and continue as his servants with me as his housekeeper and Pierre as his valet."

"And before you say anything else Alberto we have thought hard and are quite happy with that." Pierre burst out. "We have got used to his funny ways. We are not worked too hard and we think life in his chateau should be good."

"Mary we are not like you and Alberto." added Suzanna, "We know our place and we are not unhappy with it. Service in France would give us a much better life than anything we could expect here."

"But enough of all that," said Pierre. "Tell us more about your lives in Crediton. Also, I must warn you Mary, I think we are in for a very tough and bumpy ride across the moor, and have you heard, tomorrow we spend the night outside Dartmoor Camp in Princetown in an inn called *The Plume of Feathers.*"

And so we chatted on. Mary and I did a lot of nodding, smiling and keeping our mouths shut until we were alone that night.

"Well, she's right. We are not the same." Mary declared. "I have spent my life regretting that I was not able as a girl to go to Queen Elizabeth's Grammar School – yes Queen *Elizabeth's* Grammar School in Crediton. They say she spoke several languages and was the equal of any man."

"So what happened instead?" I asked.

"I had to make do with that stupid ferocious dame's school where we were slapped and you were taught to read and sew and know your place even though I felt I was cleverer than my brother. Also it made me mad that I could never go to the balls some of the silly, stupid girls I had to serve in our shop were going to. Yes, and I swooned over some of the smooth young gentlemen who came in to be fitted with a suit by my father before they went off to Oxford.

"I've seen some of them." I added.

"I also know that breaking through that barrier, unless one makes a huge amount of money and are quite brilliantly clever, is very, very difficult for a man, and impossible for a woman."

"Again you are right." I said. "It was my unhappiness with the way my family and I were treated that led me to join the French Army of Italy in the first place. What I did not think about was how much worse things are if you start thinking for yourself and want to get on if you are a woman."

"Thanks," she said. "You are pretty good, but you don't always see it." With that she turned over and fell asleep.

*****

What really surprised me was the way Pierre was able to accept and live not only with Rochambeau's relentless snobbishness and assertion of social superiority, but the terrible things he had ordered in Saint Domingue and what we knew was his attitude towards people of colour, but that was something I did not want to discuss with Mary just then.

After the usual interruptions to our night which go with life when a baby is around, I donned my uniform for the first time in years and we ate breakfast with our hosts and prepared to set off. As expected by Rochambeau we were all in uniform making quite a colourful sight and provoking joking remarks from our escorts. Here there was no farewell party except from Suzanna's parents doffing their hats and keeping their distance looking awed at our finery. Sadly it was a miserable, blustery, drizzling day.

The road to Dartmoor was no more than a rough track so our coach shook and tilted and the horses strained to keep going with the coachman frequently resorting to the lash. The journey to Princetown was only fourteen miles, but it took us four hours travel with a break for the horses to recover so we arrived in the middle of the afternoon.

Princetown is a gloomy little village with a single rather gloomy inn surrounded by houses for the camp staff, a dreary looking church and pretty well nothing else. The whole town and the inn was full of redcoats who we learnt would be escorting over one hundred prisoners to Plymouth for the ship to France. It was here we learnt for the first time that this prisoner exchange applied to those who had served in Saint Domingue. When Rochambeau heard that he was delighted and saw an opportunity to make an impression.

No sooner had I seen the family settled in the inn than I was called to see the generals who were seated by the fire in a small side room.

"Ah, Bioletti," he said. "Good to see you and your lovely wife. Breeding too! I hear from General Boye that you have been taking good care of him in Crediton."

"Thank you sir." I replied. "It has been a real pleasure."

"As I am sure it was in Wincanton. I have just heard that tomorrow, when we set off in our coach for Plymouth, all our officers and men who served in Saint Domingue will be setting off to march there. I hope they will be properly treated by all these redcoats. I've been thinking that in order to encourage them to behave in a civilised manner we might arrange a dinner tonight for their officers and also invite the Agent in charge of the camp, a Captain Cosgrove of the Royal Navy I believe."

I looked at Boye. "Yes," he said. "And I suggested to General Rochambeau that if he wishes to do that you should go with our corporal escort over to the prison and deliver an invitation at the gate."

And so I found myself accompanied by my redcoat friend walking under the great arch and up to the gate of Dartmoor Prison wearing my French uniform of blue jacket, white breeches, high boots etc. It made quite an impression on the soldiers and turnkeys standing about

Dartmoor Prisoner of War Camp was a huge establishment constructed of granite with a high circular perimeter wall enclosing, like Norman Cross, a series of barrack blocks and adjoining yards. It looked more like a prison or medieval fortress than anything else with each barrack block having four stories of cells. The whole place looked extremely forbidding and was much larger than Norman Cross. My friend the corporal, really enjoying himself, persuaded the sentry at the gate to let us though to see the Agent's secretary, but for him that was not enough.

"Mr Secretary, how good of you to see us. As you see I have here my French friend who has a very special invitation to deliver to Captain Cosgrove. I understand he is in his office. Do you think it might be possible for him to receive this invitation in person?"

"What's it about?" the secretary replied suspiciously.

"Well, no doubt you know a consignment of prisoners are to be escorted on a march to Plymouth starting tomorrow."

"Yes. What of it?"

"And they are all prisoners who served France in Saint Domingue."

"So I have been given to understand." said the secretary.

"Well, I have just brought the man who was their commander in Saint Domingue, General Rochambeau, here from Moretonhampstead where he has been living on parole. Yes. And do you know he is I believe the most senior French prisoner we are holding! What's more it's my job to escort him down to Plymouth and see him safely on his way back to France.

"What of it?" said the secretary stolidly.

"The invitation is for Captain Cosgrove to join him tonight at the Plume for dinner. So, do you think he might see this man?"

"I will find out." replied the secretary and that was how I found myself saluting Captain Cosgrove and handing over Rochambeau's invitation. He received it without saying a word, read it and sat down to write a reply which he then passed on to me. Suddenly he smiled.

"Very decent of your General. I look forward to meeting him. It should be an interesting evening. My last posting before I came here was off the coast of Saint Domingue blockading you French."

The dinner was quite a stilted affair with Cosgrove arriving in dark civilian attire, but Rochambeau and Boye dressed as if to go on parade in the full splendour of their uniforms with medals, sashes, the works. It certainly made an unforgettable impression, though if the quiet smiles of the three English officers who were also present were anything to go by, not quite what Rochambeau wanted. I knew the English well enough to know that.

Yet again Rochambeau steered away from talk of Saint Domingue and retold his American exploits. Pierre and I were of course present in our role as servants and waiters, serving the Dartmoor roast mutton, spooning the mint sauce as directed and standing behind the chairs of our generals keeping glasses filled. Suzanna and Mary were only too glad to have an early night on their own.

Glad to see the back of that depressing place we set off the next morning. It was again a bumpy ride and Cecillia threw up over my uniform as we drove across the moor to Tavistock. It was a relief that there the road improved markedly. In Plymouth we could see several of the dreary prison hulks on which so many of our countrymen were wasting away and where we could easily have ended up.

Our last night was spent in a rather scruffy inn interrupted by the singing of the jolly jack tars downstairs in the bar. We knew that we would be travelling on an ordinary cartel ship, but to our surprise our corporal announced in passing that moored alongside the ship assigned to take us was none other than the "Billy Ruffian" as the *Bellerephon* was commonly called by the English. She was currently on blockade duty in the Channel and was picking up supplies.

In the morning Pierre and I saw to it the four of us were ready to go aboard in full uniformed splendour while making sure Mary, Suzanna and the children were well wrapped up for a chilly crossing. I was able to show Mary that alongside our cartel ship was the same ship that had both nearly killed me with its ferocious broadside and then saved me after the sinking of the *Surveillante* off Saint Domingue. We walked up and down alongside it before going aboard our much more modest ship. Yet again the *Bellerephon* gleamed with its scrubbed decks, paintwork and brass. Several tars waved and laughed as they saw us go aboard in our French uniforms.

No sooner were we aboard than we were joined by the Dartmoor prisoners who came marching down to the dock with their redcoat escorts singing the *Marseillaise*. Many of the men looked thin and exhausted, but all were wreathed in smiles at the prospect of going home after nearly eight years of captivity. Midmorning we set sail full of trepidation and excitement.

Bioletti from France to Russia
- 1812 to 1814 -

Chapter 41
The Paris and Empire of Napoleon

9th March 1811

Mercifully for Mary and the children our cross channel voyage was calm. We arrived at the French coast on a fine clear morning to be met by a small unarmed French schooner. This then led us in up the river for us to dock in Morlaix harbour. Relatively small this former base for privateers and pirates had become a fishing and trading port and was not used as a French naval base. Word that a sizeable consignment of prisoners were expected from England on a cartel ship had attracted quite a crowd.

Waiting for us on the quayside were drawn up a series of coaches which had brought a number of smartly dressed English families, no doubt from Verdun. There was also a party of English soldiers under French guard. These were of course all waiting to come on board to be repatriated to England.

On arrival French Army officers came on board with lists and papers to be checked by the English and the French troops from Dartmoor disembarked to be processed. The French officers also brought with them a mailbag with letters to be distributed. Among these were letters for both Rochambeau and Boye. The letter for Boye looked highly official and carried the monogram of the Emperor. That for Rochambeau looked more personal.

On opening his post Boye had a pleasant surprise. It contained Napoleon's confirmation of his 1804 promotion to Brigade General recommended by Rochambeau in 1803. It also contained the news that he had been awarded *Chevalier* of the *Legion d'honneur* by

Napoleon for the work he had done in Saint Domingue. This, the citation stated, was for first commanding the fighting against the English and then negotiating their withdrawal from the island. This had happened when he had actually been working under the command of Louverture – before the Leclerc invasion. The Legion carried a pension and showed that he was still appreciated by Napoleon. The letters went on to say that his next posting would be decided when he visited Army headquarters in Paris.

Rochambeau stormed over to speak to Boye after reading his post to say it was a letter from his wife welcoming him home to his chateau at Thore-la-Rochette near Vendome and saying that his son was serving in the Army in Belgium and she was currently indisposed but had sent a carriage for him. This was the first time I had heard him mention his wife or his son.

At the quayside we could see a very grand coach drawn up apart from all the others with four fine horses and a liveried footman. It was of course the Rochambeau coach.

On disembarking we said brief farewells and Rochambeau with Pierre and his wife went off in the grand coach. They of course were seated outside at the back, he morosely alone inside. That was to be the last time we would see them. We had spoken on the crossing and they seemed happy and excited at the thought of their new life in service at his chateau.

Boye then told us that Rochambeau was very upset that there had been no official or family welcome home for him and he had soon learnt, as he had suspected, that Napoleon had made very critical remarks about him and had blamed the failure of the Saint Domingue campaign on him. It was his failure to defeat Dessalines, not his brutality that had been criticised. Napoleon did not forgive failure, particularly if it might be laid at his door. On getting back to France we soon discovered that the whole Saint Domingue campaign was a defeat that was simply not talked about.

*****

Boye, Mary and I had of course discussed our future and since he at 45 and I at 33 were both serving soldiers of the French Army I would remain Boye's *ordonnance*. He would then find a suitable property in Paris where we could have a ground-floor apartment suitable for us and the children with Mary running the household overall and an establishment suitable for a general upstairs for him.

Boye was able to hire one of the coaches and it took us six days to travel from Morlaix to Paris with the road passing through Rennes. Travelling as we were with two small children we were all very glad to reach the city. As we drew near both Boye and I sat outside at the back so we could get a good view. He had not visited Paris since he was a young student and I had never seen it. It seemed huge and widely spread out. He put us up in a modest hotel near the centre and the next day we went in search of a suitable property for him to rent or buy. With the help of an agent we were lucky in quickly finding what he wanted at 8 Rue de Grenelle close to the fashionable, but not too expensive, San Germaine area. We could move in immediately and he had an option to buy.

That evening, the 19th of March, we found people were pouring out onto the streets and talking to each other excitedly. It had just been announced in all the papers that the Princess Marie-Louise, Napoleon's new twenty year old Austrian wife, was about to give birth. Work stopped early and it seemed the whole city was in a state of febrile excitement as crowds gathered around the Tuileries Palace. Extra editions of the papers were being printed with newsvendors shouting themselves hoarse.

Then nothing happened. The night hours passed and sombre rumours started to circulate that things were not going well. Still people continued to stand about. Next morning suddenly a canon shot rang out from the *Invalides* and the whole city stopped and waited in complete silence. A minute later another gun fired and this continued at one minute intervals until two hundred shots had echoed around the city. Everyone was cheering deliriously and the news was announced that the King of Rome had been born. This the papers explained was the title given to the heir of the Holy Roman Emperor. It meant the Emperor had a baby boy and had established a dynasty. Perhaps a dynasty to reign France and Europe for a thousand years?

As soon as we were installed in our new home Boye and I reported to Army headquarters where I was extremely glad to receive my back-pay for the time I had been in England as no doubt he did too. He was informed that he would be appointed chief of staff to a new 9th Army corps. under the command of

Marshal Claude Victor Perrin, Duke of Belluno who was currently on active duty in Spain. On being interviewed by the senior marshal in charge he was told he had no need to report for duty for another month and should take advantage of this time while he could.

Boye was naturally keen to go and visit his parents and extended family in and around Caussade, a small town a few miles north of Toulouse in Southern France and he prepared to set off almost immediately.

The night before he left Mary cooked us a fine meal and we all sat down to eat it together and drink a toast to the King of Rome.

I then asked him, "Tell me sir, what do you know about this Duke of Belluno?"

"Good question Alberto." he replied, "How things have changed. Marshal Claude Victor-Perrin, known by everyone as Victor, joined the Army as a musician with the rank of private and he served as such for ten years. He then left the army, married and became a grocer. Come the Revolution and he first joined the National Guard as I did, and then was in the Revolutionary Army in Italy where he joined Captain Napoleon in the siege of Toulon when the English tried to capture it. There his skill and bravery earned him promotion and he has subsequently risen to become a Marshal of France!"

We were amazed. He then continued, "He has fought in Italy, Austria, Germany and is presently in Spain. I hear he is a good, capable officer who has risen right through the ranks. Now Napoleon is rewarding men like him with these fancy royal sounding titles, Duke of this and Prince of that and of course for himself Emperor. I find it all quite odd. Is Marshal of France which he earned on the battlefield not enough? At the same time, Napoleon uses these labels and titles because I suppose he sees people still like them and want them as they do miracles, superstitions and the Church".

The next day he set off in a hired carriage saying he hoped to return a week before we needed to report for duty.

*****

Paris was by far the largest city I had ever seen and Mary and I both found it captivating. To find out about it we bought a street map and avidly read the daily papers. These quickly showed that though they were scurrilous and gossipy and made for an amusing read, they were under much tighter political control than English papers for critical articles or comments about the Emperor or his policies simply did not exist.

Mary advertised with a card in some local shops for a maid used to caring for children so we could go out and about while we had the chance. We found walking in the streets with the children was hardly an option for the streets in our area were narrow with a channel down the middle for sewage and the rest was clogged with mud and horse manure. To walk in them required high boots and at the end of each walk a real session scraping off the mud or you could pay a few small coins to a *decrotteur* to do it for you.

The only alternative to walking was for us to take a *fiacre*, a one horse carriage which cost one franc for a journey plus an expected tip for the driver. One could also hire these for the day and we did this several times, asking the drivers to take us on tours of the main sights of Paris.

We drove up and down the main boulevardes, around the *Arc de Triomphe,* which at that stage was a full sized temporary model made of cardboard. We also admired the huge *Vendome Column* which had just been completed and was made from the iron canon of the recently defeated Austrians and Russians. We also admired the Seine snaking through the city and the three grand new bridges that Napoleon had built to augment the older six.

Especially fascinating for us after our provincial lives in Somerset and Devonshire was to visit the much frequented *Palais Royale*. This was a very grand shopping mall where dressed in our best we could promenade with the richest in the land and gaze into the windows of their shops selling jewellery, hats, perfumes, paintings, in fact anything the rich and discerning or the rich and vulgar could want. We also walked past the top restaurants and read their incredibly long, complicated and expensive menus.

More within our means were the cafes under the *Palais Royale* where you could eat a good full meal and enjoy a show for as little as half a franc for the two of us. Another discovery was the Tivoli Pleasure Gardens where for a small entrance fee of twenty sous we could come with our children, buy ice-creams and promenade in the garden along with all social classes. There we could watch acrobats and jugglers, listen to musicians and in the evenings see firework displays.

The city with all its wealth, grandeur and bustle was quite remarkably safe and peaceful, though one was aware there was a strong plain-clothes police force keeping an eye on what was going on in public places. It was also noticeable that there were few young men about who were not in Army uniform, conscription being in force.

Mary was keen to know about places of Protestant worship and we discovered Napoleon had allowed three Calvinist and one Lutheran church to open. Many Catholic churches and convents had been pillaged during the Revolution but with his Concordat with the Pope, some were now re-opened. We visited a French speaking Calvinist church which reminded me of the Waldensian worship I had known as a child. Mary found it very plain and rather "foreign" which was not surprising.

*****

I was particularly keen to take Mary to the Louvre, the former royal palace now an art gallery open to the public and known inevitably as the Napoleon Gallery. We visited several times. There alongside the huge contemporary exhibitions of the Paris Salon that took place in one of its wings, I was able to show her the galleries filled with the great art works I had helped pack up to send from Italy. I was amazed to see just how extensive this collection of "requisitioned" works was.

There was also a collection of works glorifying Napoleon and the Empire such as the huge paintings of his recent marriage to Princess Marie-Louise of Austria, one showing the elaborate carriage procession and one of the ecclesiastical marriage service. Then there was the amazing painting of Napoleon crowning himself Emperor by Jacques Louis David and the wonderful if fanciful picture by the same artist of him astride a prancing stallion with flowing cloak while crossing the Alps.

There were also many portraits of his family, his marshals, his battles and of course - looking particularly beautiful and demure - a portrait of Pauline. That was one I did not draw Mary's attention to though she mentioned how pretty she thought she looked. A by-stander who was also admiring it then chipped in and said, "Don't you know the famous Pauline commissioned the great Italian sculptor Canova to carve a statue of her in marble. It is entitled Venus Victorious and she insisted on posing for it –

would you believe - in the nude."

"Is it on show here then?" asked Mary.

"Oh no," he replied. "They say the Italian Prince Borghese she married has said, once it was completed, he would not allow anyone to see it but himself, not even Canova. He keeps it in his palazzo in a special room in Rome."

*****

With this and many other visits and outings to the sights of Paris Mary and I had a very happy and relaxed time. What is more once Boye came home we could see that we were able to have quite an unusual and privileged way of life. Boye had become so used to sharing a table and talking in an open and trusting way to both Mary and I during our years together in Crediton that he wished to see it continue. I was well aware it could all have come to an end when we reached Paris, but to his credit it did not.

On his return from seeing his parents he suggested that if he had an evening at home he would like us to plan having our evening meal together, but if, as was expected of a man of his rank, he invited guests to dinner, then I would serve as his *ordonnance* at the table and Mary would appear as my wife and his English housekeeper. We were very happy with this arrangement knowing anything else would be misunderstood and cause us all difficulties for despite the Revolution the class barriers between the middle-class educated *bourgeoisie* and those regarded as *petite-bourgeoisie* or lower were much the same as in England. In fact as Napoleon embraced the idea of Empire they were again treated as very important and pretty well unbridgeable.

As regards Mary's talents Boye was quick to say on his return, "Mary, if, as I think it is likely, Alberto and I will soon be off on some campaign, there should be some good opportunities for you to use your dressmaking and seamstress skills here. There is a "new aristocracy" in town made up of all those who have been promoted by Napoleon and those who have become rich supplying the state and the Army. Their women all need dressing and there must be several thousand of them. I suggest you advertise yourself as "the English Dressmaker" for with so many *aristos* now coming back from England, English fashion has become quite fashionable here."

"Sir, I am amazed." Mary responded, "I thought the French

regard themselves as the leaders of all the arts of civilisation, particularly when it comes to fashion."

"Yes Mary, I am sure we do, but I have bought a little present for you, a copy of the latest edition of the *Journal des Dames et des Modes*. Look carefully and see for yourself." Mary thanked him, quite overcome. "Oh yes," he continued, "Funny isn't it when the English are the ones we are so often at war with. Our two nations have such an odd relationship of mutual regard, distrust and envy. They say Napoleon did not like the immodest breast-revealing fashions so popular during and just after the Revolution, like those worn by his sister, and that he prefers the modesty of English dress."

We then discussed ways of advertising Mary's dressmaking and seamstress services and Boye volunteered to draw attention to what she did when he entertained. We also agreed that to run the house properly Mary would need a maid to help her in the kitchen and with the housework and if Mary was to work she would need the woman child-carer to work full time.

*****

The next day he and I turned up at our regimental depot at Versailles. He was immediately immersed in meetings and I reported to the regimental sergeant major. He was in charge of equipment and supplies and he immediately informed me that both Boye's uniform and mine were not up to date. While we had been in Saint Domingue and in England the new versions of both had become more elaborate with more gold braid so I needed to draw a new uniform for myself and organise getting a new set made for my general by a military tailor.

I was then told that if I was preparing the travel needs of a brigade general he would need a carriage for his uniforms, books, notes and personal effects, a coachman, at least four carriage horses and four saddle horses and some pack horses or mules. We would be expected to travel with a coach and it was expected that both he and I would be mounted on horseback so I could deliver his orders to his officers. The overall care of all this was my responsibility. Getting this organised of course took quite some time. I also knew I had a lot to learn for I had ridden little since I had been in Egypt where the heat and lack of fodder had killed most horses and the only person to have a carriage was Napoleon, so I quickly procured a good horse and took to riding daily. So did Boye.

Chapter 42
Preparations and Rumours

Militarily March 1811 to January 1812 turned out for us to be a period of rumours and military training and the procurement of what we might need for some as yet unidentified military campaign for there was nothing specific about what to expect in the military newspaper. In late December however, Marshal Perrin, our Victor, returned to Paris from Spain and he and Boye spent long working meetings together and it seemed got on well with each other and I wondered if Napoleon's plan might be to lead us on a Spanish campaign.

For Mary and I then this was the grandest living we had ever had. Boye had the pay and allowances of a decorated General of Brigade and he arranged that I be paid as a sergeant. Now we could "glory" in being part of the finest army in the world living in the most splendid, lively and fashionable capital, not only of France but of its great new pan-European Empire.

Boye organised many dinner parties entertaining the officers he worked with together with their ladies. These were quite grand affairs often using outside caterers so not all the work of cooking fell on Mary and the maid. As housekeeper she would appear, greeting guests, supervising service and looking extremely fetching in an elegant outfit she had made in the latest fashion while I proudly served the party at table in my uniform.

A memorable occasion which stood out was the one where he invited his commanding officer, Marshall Claude Victor Perrin to dinner. The same age as Boye and with a carefully coiffed and tousled head of hair he appeared looking very splendid with the high collar, silk sash, and gold oak leaf embroidered tunic together with the medals his rank and service had earned. He also came with his Dutch wife Julie Vosch van Avesaet who he had met while commanding the Army in the Batavian (Dutch) Republic. She was his second wife for he had divorced his first, something difficult to do in England and impossible in Italy, but acceptable under the new Code Napoleon.

Often these evenings would take a musical turn with singing and violins being brought out and this evening was no exception for Victor, with his bandsman background, enjoyed an opportunity to again play an instrument. His wife, as a fellow foreigner among the French, quietly got talking to Mary.

Conversation that night moved on to gossip about the Emperor and his court and speculation about what might happen next militarily. No-one knew and there were many wild rumours flying about. Knowing that Victor had recently been recalled from Spain where he had been in action against the English General Arthur Wellesley, the other guests were keen to quiz him about this.

"He is extremely skilful." He said, "Despite being starved of men by his government, he has been causing us real trouble in both Portugal and Spain. He has developed some very clever tactics that make the most of what he has, and he is getting the Spanish people on his side for unlike us he does not impoverish them foraging for food, but buys and imports supplies for his men. The Emperor knows he needs to face him on the battle-field if we are to hold on to Spain."

Other options were discussed. Would we be sent to Russia or Turkey? What about being sent again to Egypt or overland to India? I noted however that no-one suggested Saint Domingue which I heard General Dessalines had declared the Independent Republic of Haiti.

After this dinner Julie brought her custom and gossip to Mary, as did the wives of other officers who came to our dinners. Soon she had as much dressmaking work as she could handle. Her French became good and her pleasant self-confident air and her foreign Englishness made her obviously well liked.

The children took to their new nurse and were growing up bi-lingual from the start and we hoped to place them in a local school as soon as they were old enough.

All this went on until by February 1812 the amount of frenetic military planning, recruitment of new conscripts, the organisation of supplies and the setting up of training exercises made it obvious that our Emperor was planning something big.

*****

Boye was often out entertaining and being entertained, still we continued to have our dinners together more or less once a week. It was at the end of one of these meals that Mary asked the question that had been bothering us.

"Sir, forgive me as an ignorant Englishwoman, but now that it seems the Emperor has subdued nearly the whole of Europe so that France, as everyone is constantly telling me, is bigger, greater and more powerful than it has ever been, what are the dangers it is still facing?"

"I suppose Mary what you really want to know is where are Alberto and I likely to be sent to fight next." he replied. "The quick answer to that is I do not know yet for certain for there are still different possibilities. The long answer is one option is becoming more probable. This will make more sense if - in the strictest confidence of course - I explain how I see things using a map." And with that he left the table to collect one which he spread out in front of us.

"As you already know the English have us under a naval blockade and twice Napoleon has thought about invading England, only to give up the idea. The Royal Navy as we learnt from the *Bellerephon* is just too good at blowing us out of the water. As a result of this England has this huge empire and it also imports and makes all types of goods in its new factories far better and cheaper than anyone else can do - so it just gets richer and richer."

"Like cotton materials." Said Mary.

"Yes, cotton cloth, finished garments, sugar, coffee and much else besides. This trade makes us and any country that trades with them dependent on them."

"Your Emperor can't like that. So can anything be done to stop this?" she asked.

"Our Emperor thinks so. He has forbidden France and all countries under French control, like Spain, the German states, Poland, Switzerland and Italy from buying or selling anything from the British while running Europe as a common trading

293

market. He calls this the Continental System. He also threatens our neighbours, Austria, Russia and the Scandinavian countries with war if they trade with Britain. He hopes this will bankrupt Britain so he can then defeat and "liberate" it."

"How kind of him," said Mary.

"And is this working?" I asked.

"Yes and no." he replied. "Yes in that Austria is not trading with Britain, but no for Britain confiscates or sinks the ships of any country it catches trading with France. Also many countries, including France, say they desperately need British goods, so there is a lot of smuggling going on. Oh yes into France. What do you think all those boats were doing in Morlaix? But also into Sweden and Denmark, Germany and most importantly Russia."

"Why do you say most importantly Russia?" I asked.

"This is where you need to look at the map." he said. "If you run your finger down the whole of the Western border of Russia I can tell you that all the way from Riga in Lithuania in the North to Georgia in the South Russia has been steadily or violently expanding westwards. In fact France went to war with Russia over this and defeated them in 1806 when Napoleon set up the Grand Duchy of Poland."

"So while we have been in England what has Napoleon been doing about all this?" I asked.

"Well, after that war he has been having this love-hate affair with Russia and Tsar Alexander which has divided opinion both inside Russia and inside France. The Russian aristocrats love French culture, but hate Napoleon and feel humiliated by their defeat, and the French liberals and revolutionaries hate Russia's slave-like serfdom, as do Russia's new middle class who rather admire Napoleon. So you see it gets complicated. Then take the Poles. They have imbibed our Revolutionary ideas, see Napoleon as their liberator and want autonomy for themselves while Russia simply wishes to absorb Poland into its empire as it has been at some times in the past."

"Would Napoleon let that happen?" I asked

"You might think not because the Poles are his ardent supporters, but I have heard it discussed that a couple of years ago he thought of ditching them for an alliance with Russia against Britain. He even contemplated marrying a Russian princess and spent a lot of time with the Tsar at Tilsit. This all happened when we were in England."

"And what is stopping him?" asked Mary.

"The old enemy," he replied. "Britain. Napoleon has told the Tsar he would never make war on Russia unless he finds Russia is continuing to trade with Britain, so breaking the Continental System."

"Has the Tsar done so?" I asked.

"It appears so. Russia is pretty backward and it cannot run its economy without imported British goods. The Tsar has also fallen out of love with any revolutionary ideas for reform he used to have and has been very annoyed by Napoleon marrying an Austrian princess and supporting the Poles. His officers and nobles hated him getting cosy with Napoleon at Tilsit so he needs to satisfy their wounded pride. Possibly because of that he has now done something else."

"What!" we asked in chorus.

"Our latest intelligence reports are that the Tsar has moved some 400,000 troops into his Eastern European border regions."

"That is a vast army!" I said incredulously, "That's ten times bigger than the armies we have fought in. But does it threaten France?"

"Certainly. As things stand our troops control the German speaking states, but many of them have taken to revolutionary ideas and like the Italians before them as you know Alberto, they do not appreciate being "liberated" by the French and are on the edge of revolt. Russia could back them against us."

"So Russia is a threat to France, Germany is unstable and I guess so is Italy. Are there any other flash-points?" asked Mary.

"Yes. Britain again." he replied, "Just when France thought it had seen off revolts in Portugal and Spain Britain has come in on the side of the locals sending in this General Arthur Wellesley who as Marshall Victor said has been doing rather well down there, so Napoleon feels he should get down to Spain and sort out Wellesley himself."

"I have been imagining that might be his plan, but what about Russia?" I asked.

"Exactly." he replied. "The Russian threat is so big the talk is that Napoleon is planning something to frighten or bully the

Russians into accepting the Continental System first before he deals with Wellesley."

"How?" I asked.

"By sending into Germany and assembling there an even bigger army than the Russians have massed."

"With the intention of actually attacking Russia?" asked Mary.

"I do hope not. I think he and many of us senior officers would be much happier to see Russia as an ally rather than an enemy, but we shall have to see." he said. That of course filled us with a sense of foreboding for if threat turned to war with such huge armies involved who could say what might happen.

Chapter 43
Prepare to go North

Both Boye and I then had earnest conversations about our training and readiness. I knew from the men at the depot that skirmishers had been recognised as being more important than when I was in Italy and Egypt. They were now called *voltiguers,* and given a higher rate of pay than other soldiers and distinguished themselves by wearing yellow-red or yellow-green epaulettes – epaulettes usually being reserved for officers. Their duties however remained much the same, showing initiative and working in small groups scouting, gathering intelligence, sharp shooting as snipers and highly trained for hand to hand combat.

I asked Boye if I could be temporarily assigned to the *voltiguer* company in our regiment for a month of training as such an important part of my role was to act as his body-guard and he agreed. He also decided to lead the men on some long training marches to build up his own fitness.

"From what I hear about the Polish lands where we may find ourselves, they are huge areas, burning in summer, freezing in winter. We will need to be fit for certain." he said.

I really took to the *voltiguer* training led by an excellent sergeant. All the men were chosen for short stature, intelligence and at least two years of exemplary service. This gave the company quite a competitive elite mentality and the hand to hand combat sessions were pretty demanding and brought out that side of me I rather enjoyed rediscovering. I also felt at 33 I had never been fitter or stronger.

That was more than I could say for so many of the young conscripts. These of course were not *voltiguers* but were doing their basic infantry training around us for the first time. In love with their uniforms and keen to be drilled these provincial boys of 18 now seemed to me pitifully soft and so very young.

It was also a surprise when I came across the newly recognised and recruited 29th Regiment of the Line to discover it was mainly made up of survivors of the Saint Domingue campaign who had been held in the hulks or we had seen embarking from Dartmoor. Like me they were mostly keen to prove themselves. They did not however seem that well or fit.

I also found it surprising that in the ten years since Italy and Egypt we were still issued with the same old muskets with their slow load and indifferent accuracy. What was more the buttoned up white breeches they all wore, though good at showing off the legs on parade, actually became very uncomfortable around the knee on a march reducing circulation, and the square toed shoes, not boots, they were issued did not look tough enough to stand up to a campaign.

Huge convoys of wagons pulled by four horses were being assembled loaded with grain, other foods, ammunition and equipment and in January 1812 these started to be sent off "north" while from then on troops from different regiments based in different places in the Empire started to come through Paris and follow after them. Excitement was mounting but still no definite word was given as to where we were all going except Northern Germany so the rumours about why and who the enemy might be continued.

By this time I had organised our carriage and had chosen a coachman. He was a pleasant young man from Alsace who adored and had been brought up with horses. I also had an interesting conversation with the sergeant-major.

"I wonder why everything about this campaign has been left so late." I said to him. "We could have gone several months sooner."

"Just think for a moment." he said. "With Northern Germany and Poland as your destination, how are you going to feed your horses?"

"With bales of fodder we get on the way either from those convoys or buying up local stores." I replied. He then pointed out that with the huge numbers involved and thousands of horses to feed as we went north we would inevitably find fodder would run out. That meant when we reached Northern Europe to feed our horses we would have to wait to get freshly harvested hay and oats and that would not be available until the end of June. That certainly was a sobering thought.

"What's more," he added. "If you feed them hay and oats which is still green their bellies blow up and they get very sick. I have to say, when it comes to caring for horses so many of these young conscripts are a disaster."

*****

The order for the 9th Corps to set off under the command of Victor came through in April with little warning, but since we knew it was coming we were ready. What was a surprise was our being told that our role would be that of rear-guard reserve corps.

"Don't think that will mean in any way an easy ride." Boye told me. "Napoleon keeps his reserves either to relieve a corps that has got into difficulties, or to give the knock-out blow when the outcome of a battle is not yet clear. It can also mean a lot of escorting equipment, provisions, columns of wounded and seeing fresh horses are delivered to the front. That could all turn out to be pretty demanding."

Farewells were said with Boye telling Mary that Napoleon estimated it would all be over and we would be back in about two or three months at most. She gave a wry smile as she waved and I felt quite overwhelmed. Boye and I felt so strongly that the only way to exorcise some of the disgust and guilt we felt about Saint Domingue was to fight in a proper battle that we could take some pride in. At the same time I feared that I might never see her and our children again, particularly when I remembered how few had survived the three campaigns I had already served in.

*****

Moving our Army and all the allied troops joining us was a huge logistical task. Basically the Army was divided into Corps, ours was the 9th and contained some 40,000 men. Each corps contained four divisions of around 10,000 infantry with supporting cavalry and artillery. Each division was divided into two brigades with two regiments. Each regiment was given an exact route, with stopping places for food and overnight accommodation. It was impressive how this worked while we passed through France and Southern Germany.

The troops marched on average around fourteen miles a day and were rewarded with a meal of bread and meat, wine or beer and somewhere to sleep each night. There was also fodder provided for our horses so there was little need for foraging parties to be sent out as I had seen used in Italy and Egypt so the children of the peasants we passed waved excitedly to us and their parents gave friendly smiles.

Morale amongst the ranks of conscripts was high for they all thought marching to war a great adventure. They were after all soldiers of the "greatest military genius in history." Our destination was the city of Dresden, but apart from going through the city of Frankfurt, we passed though rich and fertile countryside. The whole journey was 650 miles.

Dresden is not far from Poland and we arrived there on the 16th of May to discover that Napoleon, travelling in a grand convoy of coaches accompanied only by cavalry, had done the journey far faster than we. In fact he had brought almost his whole court together with his queen Marie Louise. Boye accompanying Victor came back from some of the events laid on there almost speechless with amazement.

Napoleon had apparently been greeted on his route at Mainz and Wurzburg by the local princes and dukes behaving like vassals, but at Dresden he was greeted by the King and Queen of Saxony and other royalty and had taken over the royal palace. Next morning they, together with all his courtiers and the German Princes for miles around, had attended High Mass in the Cathedral. The next day they were joined by the Emperor of Austria and his queen (mother of Marie Louise) and the King and Crown Prince of Prussia. In all this Napoleon played the grand Emperor and made much of greeting and speaking in a friendly way to the Russian ambassador.

There was also a bizarre daily ceremony in which all these high and mighty ones were invited to stand and witness the *toilette* of Marie Louise. In this she sat with her spectacular collection of jewels laid out before her so she could make her choice of which to wear while chatting nonchalantly to the assembled company. The days then continued with balls, banquets and hunting parties until Napoleon finally left Marie Louise for the front after thirteen days.

The purpose of all this theatre of excess was of course to

make sure the Tsar and the Russians knew just what a vast and unconquerable army and what a powerful political bloc he had ranged against him, but if its purpose was to get the Tsar to agree to a treaty, there was no sign of one.

*****

We, as part of this "unconquerable army" now had a journey of 400 miles ahead of us to reach our goal outside Danzig. Basically this meant the men marching right across Poland via the city of Poznan.

Moving into Poland was immediately a sobering experience. There was almost no-one there. The landscape was flat and treeless and it just went on and on. We also had to skirt wetlands and were surprised to see great flocks of storks. When eventually the rough track we had to use as a road led us to a village, we found it consisted of a small number of poorly built wooden structures and the people who came out of them seemed incredibly poor, thin and dirty. Many of them were Jews and they could only speak to us in Polish and a little German. They sought to sell us some food at what we took to be exorbitant prices. The fact was they had very little to sell. Instead of meat and bread all we had was buck-wheat gruel, some bad vodka and a foul drink made of fermented bread. Most seriously there was very little fodder available for our horses. Our coachman was not happy. On we went to Posnan.

This small medieval city we found was totally overwhelmed by our arrival for there were two other corps already there making well over 100,000 troops, all now short of food for the men and fodder for their animals. There we found Napoleon had preceded us and heard he had been very angry when he discovered that all his plans for provisioning the army had, under General Dumas, broken down.

As I knew from experience Napoleon's tactics were based on foraging, speed, and surprise. Here there was very little food to forage, the distances were so great there was no point in subjecting troops to forced marches that would exhaust them, and the flat countryside gave little opportunity for surprise tactics. Such tactics were also not much good with such a huge and unwieldy army which was only about half French supported by Poles,

Italians, Germans, Swiss and Spanish. At Dresden, no doubt to terrify the Russians, the total of our numbers was advertised to be 690,000.

On we marched north often finding that others had preceeded us leaving nothing behind. Despite the Poles having many regiments on our side, we came across villages which our troops had totally destroyed. Very depressing. The words of the sergeant major in Paris came back to me as we stripped the fields of their partly grown crops for ourselves and our horses with the result he had predicted. The choice was to see our horses starve or blow up and die. Could things get worse? Oh yes. Several of our young men started to die and some deserted. Did they really think they could walk back to France on their own? Finally in a poor state and having lost several horses and quite a few men we limpted into a camp outside Danzig in the first week of June. A shot had yet to be fired.

Chapter 44
Over the Niemen

Soldiers! The Second Polish War has begun. The first ended at Friedland and Tilsit. At Tilsit Russia swore an eternal alliance with France and war on England. She is now violating her promises.

So started the proclamation Napoleon issued to us all on the 24th of June 1814.

Let us cross the Nieman! Let us take the war onto her territory... and put an end that arrogant influence which Russia has been exerting on the affairs of Europe.

This proclamation provoked among us enthusiastic shouts of *"Vive l'Empereur!"* and we could hear this cry being taken up right across the whole Army. At last battle was about to commence. Clearly what Napoleon was looking for was to be able to take on the Russian Army in a single decisive engagement which could then defeat the Tsar and give him the treaty he wanted. If that happened after crossing the Nieman there would be no need for us to go further into Russia. It had been widely advertised so the Russians could be intimidated that our army was over 600,000 strong with 185,000 horses. Even if these numbers were rather inflated, for I am sure other corps had lost men as we already had, it was clear our numbers were huge.

That night the *voltiguers* crossed the Niemen silently in light skiffs ready to protect the sappers as they put several pontoon bridges in place. Despite being in reserve our corps spent the evening cleaning and polishing uniforms and grooming our horses for the next morning so we were ready to go into action if ordered to do so. It certainly was a stirring sight as the huge army of three corps advanced as if going on some gigantic military parade. They, marched out in columns complete with military bands playing under the eyes of Napoleon seated prominently on horseback. More cries of *"Vive l'Empereur!"* as they marched past to the pontoon bridges and so over the Niemen. It was a beautiful, warm, clear morning and the sun shone. The fine horses and uniformed men all made such a splendid sight. Everyone who saw it said it was quite unforgettable.

When they got across it was clear the Russians had all withdrawn without firing a shot. What an anti-climax. Victor also received the order to march us back to our camp outside Danzig. This was to remain our base for some time.

The next target for the Army then became Vilna, (Vilnius) the Lithuanian city where the Russian HQ and the Tsar was based. It was a four day march. A detachment of our cavalry went with them to bring back orders for us from Napoleon and to report back to our generals. A week later they did so. They reported that on the journey the weather was hot, there was no food or forage to be found and as only some troops had been issued with the four days of rice rations Napoleon had ordered, many were very hungry.

They also described how the weather had suddenly turned, and how an extreme storm broke with driving rain and freezing water. The rain continued right through the night turning the roads into a quagmire. Many horses could not take it and soon the road was filled with the pitiful sight of horses struggling in deep mud, giving up and dying in harness.

When they reached Vilna they again found the Russians had withdrawn leaving it completely undefended and Napoleon moved into the palace where the Tsar and his staff had been only two days before. The Russians had, it appeared, taken off for the east. They also discovered there was very little food and no forage for the horses in Vilna for the Russians had taken it all, so there was no choice it seemed but to set off for the Russian city of Smolensk a further 320 miles east. Napoleon let it be known he was sure the Russians would at last face our Army in battle there.

Napoleon's initial plan of drawing the Russians into a major battle on their border had not worked and we were now faced with the Herculean task of trying to provide logistical support to the Army over ever more extended and hostile distances. Orders were immediately given by our generals for more horses and supplies to be sent to Danzig from the German states, the Polish areas and as far away as France, but receiving them was of course a slow business. In the meantime we lived in comparative comfort in our Danzig camp. Boye, Victor and the other senior officers were kept very busy planning and ordering supplies while the junior officers and NCOs organised training exercises to get our soldiers fit and combat ready after the long march from France.

Once the horses and supplies started to arrive we received messengers from Napoleon with orders that our whole corps bring as much in the way of food, particularly grain, together with ammunition, other supplies and of course horses and accompany them to Smolensk. He wanted it to be our main army depot once it had been captured. The news those same messengers brought back about what we could expect was not encouraging.

*****

The road from Danzig to Vilna and then to Smolensk is 660 miles long and we were warned it was a horrible march. We were going over a road which our army and the Russians had already used. As a result it was cluttered with the remains of dead horses, human corpses, discarded carts and coaches. The land was very difficult being crossed by rivers and ravines which made each day's progress agonisingly slow. Again the population was sparse and decimated for the most ruthless foraging of the locals by our Army had produced almost nothing but their hatred. As a result if anyone fell behind we discovered for the first time that bands of irregular Cossacks were following us ready to fall on any stragglers. These they would rob, strip naked and then turn over to the locals to torture as we could see from the wretched bodies they left behind. At night clouds of mosquitos tormented everyone and the extreme heat of most days also came with freezing cold at night.

It was half way to Smolensk that we first lost several of our horses and had to abandon Boye's coach for then very quickly our young coachman fell ill and died. Keeping the horses going and seeing them starve for lack of fodder and then collapse was too much for him for he really loved horses. Physically it had also been extremely demanding as every day and often several times we found ourselves trying to dig the coach wheels out of ruts and get the horses going again. It left him open to typhus for he was young and comparatively weak. He had never been away from home before and he was only 18 when he died. It seemed such a sad waste of such a kind and enthusiastic young man so keen to serve his Emperor. We were left with our saddle horses and a couple of pack horses, still much better off than the infantry.

As regards infantry on the move there were as usual no tents provided, the men being expected to bivouac under branches. Fine in France or Italy but not here after a long hard day's march. I had taken advice and provided Boye and myself with canvas sleeping bags. As I had suspected would happen we were also told that the shoes of many of the men in the leading corps had broken up and as there were no replacements they had to get used to walking barefoot. At least the men of our corps set off from Danzig with fresh shoes. Finally we were told that many men in the Army that had preceded us had contracted diarrhoea and dysentery and had died. This now happened to our men also. At least since we were bringing supplies, we were not as hungry as it seems they had been.

*****

Near the end of August we received new despatches from the front. On the 17th the Russians had put up a fight at Smolensk. It had involved our leading Army corps attacking the city with men, artillery and cavalry. The bombardment resulted in the city catching fire within its walls and few were left alive. The despatch reported this battle as a victory. It also estimated we had lost 7,000 dead or wounded. The next day the Russian General Tuchkov defended the road to Moscow where his men "fought like tigers." This time around 8,000 French died or were wounded. In the two engagements the Russians may have lost more than we did, but as Boye said to me, "Nothing has been achieved by either side strategically." If that was a "victory" I wondered what defeat would look like. Again the Russian army withdrew so the great battle Napoleon sought still lay ahead.

We arrived in Smolensk a few days later and were faced with devastation. The fire had carbonised and shrunk many of the bodies of those who had died, the only food left was what could be found in a few houses, there was no fodder for horses and the condition of the remaining population was pitiful. There were also a large number of wounded, both Russian and French. We housed them as best we could, but since there were very few surgeons and they could do little anyway, all that could be done was give them some shelter where they could die.

Our main army under Napoleon had set off straight away on the road to Moscow in the belief that surely that would provoke the Russians into a final stand - and it did. After they had covered 137 miles on another tough march they came to the village of Borodino some 75 miles outside Moscow and there General Katuzov faced Napoleon in battle on the 7th of September. When the report came through to us in Smolensk several days later we were told it was a great victory though we had lost around 35,000 men while the Russians had lost many more and had now withdrawn from the field. This was an enormous loss, yet this too Napoleon called a victory which had covered our men in "glory." There was also no mention of a Russian surrender. Instead Napoleon announced he was now off to Moscow where he was sure either Katuzov would again do battle or if he did not the Tsar would capitulate before he took the city.

We then waited in Smolensk until our next despatches arrived. It appeared neither had done what Napoleon expected. Kutuzov and his army had slipped away somewhere south and the Tsar refused to have any dealings with Napoleon so he was about to march into Moscow. This he did on 14th of September. We attempted to tidy up Smolensk and to implement Napoleon's order that we stockpile as much food and forage as we could raise from the area while we waited to hear what would happen next. In fact we raised little food and forage and we were starting to use what we had brought with us.

A few French expatriates who had been living for years in Moscow then arrived in their coaches. They described how for the first three days of the French occupation the city had descended into an orgy of looting, rape and violence as the city had by both accident and design, gone up in flames destroying they thought about two thirds of the buildings. They had heard the mayor of Moscow had removed all fire-fighting equipment and had released convicts with the promise of a pardon if they took part in setting the city on fire.

They said the wealthy and the nobility had retreated to their country houses and estates before the French arrived leaving the "lower orders" and the non-Russians like themselves in a totally lawless city. They now found themselves targets for looting by French soldiers and objects of local Russian anti-French hatred. They now wished to return to France. They were not alone and every day more civilian and military stragglers came limping into the city in increasing numbers. Soon they were all starving on the city outskirts for what food we had was for the Army. Their condition was pitiful.

Chapter 45
In the Arms of Mother Russia

As September ended the weather turned really cold and we wondered if Napoleon would plan to winter in Moscow. We also wondered how negotiations were going with the Tsar. Our next despatch announced that the "victorious French Army" would be marching out of Moscow on October the 19th aiming for us in Smolensk 215 miles away. There was no mention of the Tsar and on the 6th of November we encountered our first snowfall. The temperature plummeted and by the time he arrived in Smolensk on the 9th of November everything was iced up. We soon learnt that only about 40,000 men were left and around 60,000 had been lost since they had left Moscow.

By this time we learnt the Russian Army and Katuzov were in pursuit and several punishing engagements had taken place, each with the loss of more men, and each compounded by the marauding and vicious Cossacks, but it was lack of food and the cold and particularly the snow which was showing itself to be the greatest killer. Horses were dying everywhere and they froze up so quickly it was hard to cut them up to eat. Napoleon and his men had entered Smolensk under the illusion that it was a safe haven with ample food, only to find it was not. Morale all around us plummeted, though somehow a small minority kept order. Many now also were suffering from frostbite and coming from warm climes did not know how to handle it. Again the sergeant – major in Paris had given good advice about what to wear and how to cover up which we took while around us soldiers lost noses, fingers, ears and toes. On the 14th November Napoleon left the city and we all followed at one hour intervals. On the 17th Marshal Ney ordered the blowing up of the defences of Smolensk and the wounded in the hospitals were told we were leaving. His force of around 6,000 was followed by around 12,000 civilian stragglers.

Off then we marched through the snow. Each night we huddled in circles, feet first around camp fires. Stragglers crept in between us or were consigned to the outer edges. Each morning we found many around us lying stiff, frozen through. Boye and I tramped together, encouraging each other, our horses gone. As the younger and stronger I carried the heaviest back pack and we watched each other's backs for there were those around who would steal given the chance. A sad reflection on what was happening to us.

*****

Borisov was 154 miles on towards Vilna and it was the next town we had to go through and cross the bridge there over the River Berezina. The problem was the Russians had blown up the bridge and it appeared they had us trapped, their armies encircling us. A brave and desperate plan was hatched by our engineers to build two bridges across the river and get the whole army across. To divert attention to what was happening 4,000 of us from Victor's corps, including Boye and me and including the 29th Regiment of the Line who was mainly made up of those who had served in Haiti, were placed under the command of a General Partouneaux who we hardly knew.

Our role was to draw attention to ourselves with the objective of drawing Russian fire while the main body escaped over the river. At first things went well for when faced by Russian cavalry about to charge us, we formed classic squares and drove them off. This was the only time Boye or I saw action in the whole campaign. Then, while marching away, we got tied up with all the stragglers clogging the road and Partouneaux, seeing marching uniforms and thinking Victor's men were ahead, signalled for us to follow him. We soon found that the troops that were marching along on either side were not Victor's men but Russians. Partouneaux realising his mistake and seeing that we were hopelessly out-numbered and ripe for massacre, surrendered to the Russian general. When we realised what had happened we did not expect to survive.

Immediately we were all driven to the back of their army and placed under guard by regular Cossack troops. They disarmed us and roughly beat us up in the process before leaving us to stand for over an hour in the snow.

"Alberto, if we are to stay alive, we must stick together." Boye said. "They will separate us into officers and men and then we could both be finished."

"I agree sir, but you will then have a much better chance than me." I replied.

"No, Alberto, I don't think so and after all we have been through together I am sure our best bet is to stick together. If we work as a team we will have a much better chance of both coming through this alive. I have an idea. Just play along with it." With that he affected injury and leant on me until a Cossack officer appeared to look us over. When addressed in French he simply shook his head so Boye gestured frantically indicating his rank and that I was his servant and was desperately needed by him. He then handed over his fine handsome pocket watch while we were regarded with steely contempt by the officer. He took the watch, said nothing and did nothing, but when a group of Cossacks turned up with riding crops we were kept apart while our men were ordered to strip and run the gauntlet between the Cossacks. They were then allowed to dress, but some collapsed and did not get up.

"The officer pointed at them, pointed at us and wagged a finger and said in broken and accented French, "That is what happens if you do not obey. We do that to our own men also. Welcome to the care of Mother Russia." Again he did not smile.

That was the introduction to the toughest time in our lives. These Cossacks with their distinctive uniforms were Russian Army regulars unlike the sadistic bandits we had learnt to fear. They came from the same Don area and prided themselves on their toughness, discipline and horsemanship riding small tough horses which like the Polish cavalry, but not the French, were properly shod so they could be ridden on ice. We also soon found that compared to us the Russians were better fed, though the buckwheat gruel or *kasha* and hard bread they gave us was less than they had which was evidently not much.

We were formed into a company of about one hundred, part of

a column far longer, and were marched off to retrace our steps back from Borisov to Smolensk. The nights were now far longer and colder than anything we had known and following the example of the Cossacks we lay down together as close as possible. Still each day we awoke to find some had died and if during the day one fell or faltered they could expect a musket butt to the head.

All sense of time was lost as each day consisted of plodding through the ice and snow one step at a time. The mind wandered and I imagined being with Mary, little Jacques and Cecillia and relived glimpses of our lives in Crediton and Paris only to come back to the repetitive crunch of my boots in the snow. Sometimes I thought I heard Rochambeau laughing and the screams of his victims. Boye and I kept almost in step, seldom speaking as we trudged along.

On two occasions we came across groups of peasants scavenging on the road, going through abandoned carts and carriages and trying to cut meat off the frozen bodies of the dead horses. When they saw the Cossacks they begged for food and as we passed them they shouted and screamed in anger and sought to beat us. To our surprise and relief the Cossack officer ordered his men to drive them off. If he had not we would no doubt have met the fate of the mutilated corpses we had seen. That truly terrified, though their hatred was hardly surprising.

On we tramped until the burnt out and shattered remains of Smolensk appeared out of the snow. The city now contained a Russian regiment and a few inhabitants, but they welcomed our guards and the news they brought of our defeat at Berezina. That night we were given a bit more food and a taste of the vodka that seemed to be a daily part of the Cossack ration.

The cold seemed to drop to new depths. Fine powdery snow now stung our eyes. To meet the need to follow the calls of nature became frightening for to expose the lower body to that cold for more than the shortest time could, as we saw, prove fatal. More of us would have died except that for the few days we were there we could take shelter in the so called hospital buildings where the bodies of the wounded, now frozen solid, were moved to make room for us. Everywhere in the city the frozen bodies of men and horses lay, sat or in some cases stood like scare-crows, untouched, unburied and rigid.

Boye was called out to speak to the Russian commander of the regiment and our Cossack officer. They explained that this winter with its extreme cold was worse than anything they had ever seen.

"It is not just our Army you French have been up against, but the power of God. Your Napoleon invaded us thinking he was in charge, but our Tsar knew the deeper you came into our lands the worse it would be for you. And in this winter the Almighty has shown his hand." they said.

He told me how he had complained about the cruelty our men had received at first and the execution of stragglers. They had replied that without the toughest discipline none of us would have survived and it was more humane to finish off those who dropped behind quickly than leave them to the tender mercies of others who might find them. They also pointed out that while we were losing men on this march, they were also. He found this sobering.

On we went towards Moscow until we reached Borodino. There again the sight was of frozen, unburied bodies, but this time in numbers that just went on and on as far as the eye could see. Cossack irregulars were still to be seen picking over the battlefield. Some walked past us exchanging jokes with our guards. They were weirdly festooned in the uniformed jackets and headgear they had found and had collections of watches and medals draped around their necks.

Now the last few days of our march to Moscow faced us. Of our company of 100 we were down to 35. Our guards had also lost several.

Chapter 46
Back to Moscow;
on to Kazan

Approaching Moscow we were dreading the reception we might find from the locals, bearing in mind what we had heard of the fate of their city and the uncontrolled behaviour of our troops. Approaching it however our first reaction was one of wonder and awe. Silhouetted against a clear sky the snow topped outline of the remaining city buildings and their ruins was deeply moving. The multi-domed churches and cathedrals and the damaged fortress they called the Kremlin signalled a culture, a religion and a way of life quite unlike that of any Western city in its Orthodox strangeness.

Surprising and equally unforgettable was the kindness and sympathy we were shown by many of the inhabitants as they saw us stumbling in, a filthy column of ragged prisoners who had, if they had known it, just completed a 400 mile march through the snow. When we stopped we were brought soup, bread and some even gave us bowls of stewed meat. Our Cossack guards paused long enough for all of us, them included, to eat.

We were then marched on to a barrack building that had escaped the fire and was attached to the headquarters in Moscow of the Russian Army. Here we had the first opportunity to wash ourselves in warm water for many weeks. It was the best bath of my life. Somehow both Boye and I had come through without injury or sickness and with all our fingers and toes intact. We wondered how long our luck would hold out.

It was announced we would be staying there for about a week

while the headquarters staff decided where we were to be sent. Again Boye emphasised that he wished to be accompanied by me. This clearly caused some irritation and annoyance to the impeccably dressed young officer he spoke to for the gap between Russian officers and men was that between landed nobility and serf. Still he listened and agreed we would be posted together.

We were then all ordered to attend a parade where our situation was explained. Inevitably we thought of Norman Cross and how the English had treated us. We were told that the Tsar had given much thought to our condition and treatment. We should expect fairness and to be provided with suitable necessities. We should not be mistreated or robbed of our clothes or possessions and we should not be compelled to work. We were to be paid a daily subsistence allowance based on rank and housed with local citizens under the supervision of the provincial police. All this would be dependent on our good behaviour. If we did not behave well we could expect swift and severe punishment.

Over the next few days we were all interviewed, particularly to find out the nationality of our army unit, so I was put down as French, not Italian for my unit was French. It was also clear that the Russian attitude to us was quite different from the British, though both, it seemed, aimed to treat prisoners of war decently. While the British showed no interest in keeping us for a day longer in their country than they had to, the Russians were keen to attract those with the skills they needed to stay in Russia. No one was to be locked up and those with skills received Russian civilian rates of pay or in many cases were encouraged to enter Russian careers or Russian regiments, though there, conditions being so harsh for the "other ranks", few in fact did.

The group who it seemed were worst treated were the Poles, for they were treated as Russian rebels. Others were treated well, particularly Swedes, but the most wanted, it turned out were the French for the Russians clearly still saw the French language, literature, art and culture as the height of civilisation. They also knew French soldiers were conscripts, and had skills developed in their civilian lives.

Of course it turned out to be much longer than a week that we were kept there and the numbers they had to deal with continued to straggle in, still when our call came it was a shock. We were being sent to Kazan. We had never heard of it.

"It is the Capital of the Tatar region!" we were told by the enthusiastic young officer sent to inform us. "It is a thriving city with a mixed Orthodox and Muslim population. Impressive if you believe in religious freedom. It also has a new university founded by Tsar Alexander himself specialising in Mathematics, Science and Oriental Studies. I am sure Frenchmen like yourselves will be very welcome there."

The snag was that Kazan is 475 miles from Moscow and it was still winter. Boye very politely asked if he could see the senior officer in charge to discuss this posting and the next day was called in to see the general.

Half an hour later he was back looking glum. "Well he was perfectly polite and I can see his problem. He pointed out that those of us taken prisoner around the Berezina are almost the last group of prisoners of war to arrive in Moscow and that those of us who have survived that terrible journey here now total some 40,000 including 37 generals, 190 staff officers and over 3,000 junior officers. Settling us all in suitable accommodation is a huge logistical problem. The Tsar and Russia never expected to have to deal with so many. As they have already explained, their plan is to billet all the men and settle all the officers in suitable accommodation. This is why they have to send us so far for all their more local placements are now taken."

*****

We had just enough time to get properly kitted out. I procured long fleece-lined fur coats, strong high Russian boots, fur hats and gloves for we learnt most if not all the journey would be through snow. As an officer Boye would be provided with a horse and there was one pack horse for every 12 men and an army wagon with food and forage. We were told that though we should be provided with accommodation in homes on the way, there would be times when we could expect to have to use the wagon and tents and camp out in remote parts. This all added up to a long, tough journey of probably more than a month.

We were to set off as 36 men supervised by 12 members of the Internal Guard Corps led by Sodnik (captain) Verenich. He and the dozen men under him were all retired soldiers, dour, tough and used to a hard life. Verenich could only speak a few phrases of French so Boye and I decided it would show willing if we did all we could to pick up some Russian from them.

So early in February 1813 our little convoy left Moscow. Our guards were decent enough and all of us were happy to keep moving steadily for the countryside, be it wooded or open, was sparsely populated and snow covered. The farms that put us up for the night were glad to see us for the custom we brought and there was often late singing and much drinking of vodka before we set off again. The only major city we passed through was Nizhny Novgorod, complete with its own Kremlin and Cathedral which we all attended on the Sunday morning. Why did we do this? Curiosity I suppose after seeing all ranks of society flock to Church in Moscow.

This then was my first experience of the Orthodox liturgy. I found. as did Boye, the rich, unaccompanied polyphonic chanting, the incense, the icons, the elaborate vestments, the bearded priests, the obvious and enthusiastic piety of the large congregation and the solemn and complex ceremony deeply moving. Of course we did not understand a word of it and doubted if many of those present did either for as we learnt later the language used is an archaic form of early Russian called Church Slavonic. Somehow it touched eternity and rang on in the head as we set off across the snow on the following days.

*****

Our exalted mystical mood was however tested when Boye's horse went lame soon after Novgorod and he had to join us walking. He managed well for a couple of weeks until we reached the broad banks of the Volga. There we encountered a particularly violent storm and trudging through it Boye became ill. A rasping throat turned to pain in the lungs and he started to cough up blood and puss. Verenich ordered that a space be made for him in our wagon where he could lie wrapped up and out of the cold, but trundling along like that was not comfortable. He soon became delirious and clearly was very weak. Verenich made it plain his only hope of survival was to get him to Kazan as soon as possible and he sent a rider ahead to tell the local police chief he had a dangerously sick French general to care for. He could then prepare the "host" family to have a bed and care available while we pushed on to get to Kazan as fast as possible.

Chapter 47
Tolstoy's Guests

We tramped into Kazan to find a very smart three horse sledge-coach which they call a troika waiting for us. Out of it came an impressive older man with an air of authority and a striking young woman in a long fur coat and fur hat. The chief of police introduced Verenich to him and Verenich explained that I was the general's special army servant. I was then told that this was Count Nicolai Alexsandrovich Tolstoy and the young woman was his daughter Anna. Helped by the count's liveried coachman I got Boye onto the troika and jumped up on the back of it.

The Tolstoy house on the edge of the town was spacious and grand and they immediately placed Boye in a fire-warmed guest room. I was housed in the servant's wing where I was found a small but comfortable room with my own fire-place by the butler who to my surprise spoke to me in quite good French.

"The Count and his family have always spoken to each other in French, so to rise in service here you need to learn French." he later told me. "Of course your Napoleon invading has made them all so patriotic and they now speak and read Russian more often."

I will never forget that first evening and the days that followed when Boye was just clinging to life. There was no shortage of servants in the house and much rushing around by them as Anna took control of his care and after about an hour a doctor arrived. He diagnosed an infection of the chest, something he called pneumonia. He said it could easily be fatal, but with warmth, clean air and extended rest he might recover.

I asked if I could stay by him and help as much as possible and this was readily agreed, though the doctor suggested I had a bath and was given clean clothes before going near him. The next days merged into each other. I sat by him all through the night and for much of the day tending to his needs as appropriate. Things were clearly touch and go with him asleep or delirious most of the time. He did however become lucid for short periods when I was able to explain to him where we were and what was happening and get him to have something to drink.

After a few days the Count left, off to Moscow and then on to St Petersburg where he attended upon the Tsar. "He has a very important post at Court." the butler told me, "And you were lucky to meet him before he left for he only comes home once a year."

Anna also spent hours sitting in the room with us or sending me off to take a rest or sending in Tatiana, her maid to take her place.

With the Count away the resident family consisted of Anna and an elderly aunt who I hardly saw. Anna, in her mid-twenties was the youngest daughter, her two sisters and her brother I was told were married. A serious young woman, she came across as completely self-confident and at ease in her position. She was also well liked and respected by the servants. "Best mistress I could have." said Tatiana, "Sharp, kind, and runs this household very efficiently. Just what her father the Count wants. Guess he would be happy if she never married."

*****

In the hours we spent alone with Boye asleep Anna was keen to find out from me as much as she could about this French general who had ended up in her home. Naturally she wanted to hear about the Russian campaign, how we had been captured and about our journey across Russia. Then she wanted to know when and how we had met and was utterly amazed to hear about Saint Domingue, of our being sunk and picked up by the *Bellerephon,* of our many years together in England, of my marriage to Mary and of our time in Paris before the Russian campaign.

"What an amazing, exotic life you have lived." she said, "It makes my trip to Novgorod which is the furthest I have yet been from Kazan sound quite mundane."

Soon Boye was fully himself, but exceedingly weak. The doctor said this was the most critical time for if he did too much too soon the sickness could return and there might be no second chance. Rest, warmth, good food, and gentle exercise were prescribed.

Inevitably he and Anna spent hours talking together in his room, usually with either Tatiana or me present, but sometimes I suspected, she visited him on her own. I was however slow to pick up on what this might mean, but Tatiana was not.

"I think we've got something happening there." She said to me, "I've never seen her take such trouble over her appearance, or look so happy. You're sure your French general isn't married?"

"No. I can assure you he's not" I replied.

"Better be right. I've heard about you French lot and women. He'd better not try and take advantage of her." she said. "Next you'll be telling me you're not married either?"

"No I won't, because I am." I replied, "To a lovely English girl, Mary, and we have two children."

"I know. I was just testing. The mistress told me." said Tatiana.

Boye continued to improve to the point where Anna and I agreed he no longer needed someone to be sitting through the night with him as I had been doing and that I could keep normal hours. It was a couple of nights after this when I had taken to my bed for the night when I was woken in the early hours to find Tatiana sitting at the end of my bed.

"Alright Alberto, I know what you said, and I respect you for your honesty broadcasting that you are married, but before you have to go away we could keep each other warm. I'm not asking for anything more. We're only young once and I promise you I don't prattle and no one will ever know."

I asked if she had been bold like this before and she told me about Anna's handsome brother and how they had met secretly in the summer before he left to get married. I asked if she had not met anyone she wanted to marry and she pointed out, "You forget Alberto, I'm a serf. This is where I come from. Someday soon you will leave this place a free man to go where you want. I belong to the Count and will live and die here on this estate and will pleasure him and his sons if they want me. The only man I can ever marry would be one of his serfs, and I can tell you the rough life they would give me is not one I wish to choose after living here in this grand house." That really brought home to me just what serfdom meant for a young woman in her position.

She was a lively, spirited, good-looking girl with a great sense of humour and I will not pretend that I did not find her and her offer attractive, but it also brought me up short.

"Tatiana," I said, "I really appreciate your offer and I certainly find you attractive. I think you know that or you would not have done this. Still I am sure it would not be a good idea. Every night I think of Mary. I have been so lucky to have such a wonderful and beautiful wife and I just hate to think what she has been going through, particularly since the news came back to France of our defeat and of the huge and overwhelming losses we have had. She must be in widow's weeds by now, thinking I am almost certainly dead. Still, knowing her as I do I think she will wait years and refuse the offers I am sure she will have. Getting back to her as soon as I can is the most important thing in my life and when I do I want her to know that I have been faithful. Your coming here to my room tonight just helps me see that even more clearly."

"Thank you Alberto. I do understand." she said, gave me a hug, paused and looked at me. "Yes. I really do." she said, smiled and left.

*****

Time flew by as winter was replaced by spring and Tatiana was right. Boye and Anna had fallen for each other and when the Count next returned Boye asked him for her hand in marriage. At first the Count was not overjoyed, but after spending time with Boye he - in my opinion rightly - appreciated that his daughter had chosen in this Frenchman of forty-six rather an exceptional and admirable man. He thought however, there might be a snag.

The Count pointed out that the Russian regulations regarding the marriage of a parolee such us Boye to a Russian could only take place if he was prepared to convert to the Orthodox Church. This turned out to be no snag at all particularly when the local priest was only too eager to sign any certificate the Count placed in front of him.

Anna, like Mary, took her faith very seriously, but being thoughtful and well-read she was very happy with Boye's rather open, inclusive and ill-defined belief in God, which was something I shared with him. Probably on account of his rank he was not expected to attend classes, but regular attendance on Sunday at Kazan cathedral was expected.

Set in the city's kremlin the brilliantly painted, multi-domed Orthodox cathedral had nearby it an unusual neighbour which stood, complete with minarets to call the faithful to prayer, an equally large and impressive mosque. "Yes," Anna told me when I asked her about it, "Half the population of Kazan are Tatar Muslims and for a long time they ruled us. On our conquering them their mosques were destroyed and mosque building suppressed, but Catherine the Great let them build this one and we now seem to get on quite well."

Boye told me he found the singing in the cathedral inspirational as I did and we observed that for the Russian Orthodox it seemed that how you bowed and made the sign of the cross was considered more important than what you thought, so long as you kept critical thoughts to yourself. Again as Anna told me, "An attempt to introduce slight changes in traditional ceremony caused a dangerous schism here about a century ago by a group called the Old Believers who were stubbornly resistant to change."

*****

As Boye got well he would go off with me for a day's hunting on the estate. This was really a chance for a good walk and for the two of us to talk alone for though Anna was straightforward and considerate, fundamentally she saw me as part of the "lower orders" and treating me as Boye did was not possible for her. As in Paris he too had to fit in with the social expectations of those around him.

Out on a walk alone he could relax. We now could talk about the war and about Napoleon. "I think we have both come to the same conclusion about our beloved Emperor." he said. "For me Saint Domingue and now Russia. Both a total betrayal of what I believe are the values worth fighting for, such as the ending of slavery and the development of democracy. Yes his Code Napoleon is good for France and some other countries that have had bad legal systems, but is it as good as the system of Common Law they have evolved in England? And the cost of it all in human lives is just appalling. Napoleon continues to use conscription to call up thousands and thousands to die for his grandiose, selfish and ultimately futile plans. Really Alberto, I feel I can never serve him again."

I explained I felt much the same. We discussed how I had seen the Italian Campaign do nothing to "liberate" Italians or the Egyptian campaign to "liberate" Egyptians. As for Saint Domingue to send out a huge military expedition with the secret aim of re-enslaving the black population there, that was nothing less than a total betrayal of the population of those islands and of all of us who had seen the French Revolution as a step towards a better world.

Both of us agreed that as the years had gone by since we were out in Saint Domingue, our sense of guilt over what we had been implicated in as members of that Army had not faded, but had grown, though both of us felt powerless to ever do anything about it.

"You remember I told you I thought fighting for France in a proper campaign and risking our lives would somehow wipe out that sense of guilt. Well, it has not. " he said. I simply nodded.

"The upshot of all this is Alberto," he said to me on a subsequent walk, "Meeting and falling in love with Anna has changed everything. I have decided to stay here with her in Russia and see what opportunities there are for me. I am sure Napoleon will sooner or later be defeated and then I will not be going home. You of course need to get back to Mary and the children in Paris as soon as our time as prisoners of war is over."

*****

On one of our walks we also got to talking about serfdom and I told him that in conversation with Tatiana and other servants I had learnt that they were in fact all house-hold serfs, bound to work for the Count as did the farming serfs, for the rest of their lives. I told him I was shocked to discover how little freedom they had.

"Yes, Alberto, I have asked Anna about the servants and serfdom and we have discussed it at length. She emphasises the responsibilities of the landowner to see that all serfs are treated well and even fed in times of famine. She is sure the security they have in a good, well run house and estate keeps them all much happier than if they were simply wage-earners."

"It doesn't seem to me to be that much better than the slavery we saw in Saint Domingue." I suggested. That did not go down too well.

"Sorry, Alberto, I don't know how you could say such a thing. These people have been living, working and dying on this and similar estates for generations. They all know each other, respect each other and, as I am sure you have seen, often have much affection for each other. Did you know if there is a dispute down in the farm workers village, they call in the Count to sort it out and even ask him to impose penalties. That can't be compared to capturing blacks from Africa, exploiting them and cruelly treating them as we have seen."

I quietened down after that, though I did not really buy his picture of upstairs downstairs harmony. I had heard a good deal of grumbling and irritation among the house servants who felt that in some ways they were worse off than the farming serfs for they had no access to what amounted to their own land.

An element of how it all worked then came as a surprise to me. The head coachman was getting on in years and he asked if he could retire to the workmen's village where the agricultural serfs and his relations lived. It fell to Anna to set about finding a replacement. What she did was enquire of the other noble families if they had an extra young man who was well trained in keeping carriages and horses. The name Gregor Vasileyvich came up and he was delivered by the family who owned him and put through his paces by taking Anna and Boye out for a coach ride. They then went into negotiations with the Tolstoy family, a price was agreed and ownership transferred.

For young Gregor this was a step up and promotion and he was very proud when his previous family told him how much they had sold him for. He then moved into the Tolstoy servant's wing and occupied the room next to mine. There he showed himself exceptionally hardworking, dedicated to carriages and the upkeep of horses, and full of all the arrogance and self-assurance of youth. We did not get on. Tall, young and handsome his impact on Tatiana was obvious and immediate and it did not take very long before late-night sounds kept me awake and aware of what a good time they were having.

*****

The wedding of Anna and Boye took place that summer. All the family, local landowners and nobility were invited to the ceremony in the cathedral. This started with the exchange of rings seen by them as linked to their betrothal, marriage vows followed and then the couple wearing elaborate crowns and bearing candles led a procession around the Church while the choir chanted a litany. That evening there was a splendid reception with a great dinner followed by dancing. As servants we were kept on the run serving all the guests, but rewarded later by a special dinner in the servants' hall. At this the Count and the happy couple came in to thank us, but not of course to sit down and eat with us.

Meanwhile the whole situation was changing far away in Europe. As parole prisoners we were strictly forbidden to have any communication with France, so I could not write to Mary and Boye could not write to his parents. The Count however brought news from the capital of the war with Napoleon. After his Russian defeat a Sixth Coalition consisting of Russia, Austria, the United Kingdom, Portugal, Sweden, Spain, small German states and Prussia had formed. These had together taken on France resulting in a series of huge battles in Germany that resulted in a great loss of life on both sides. The results however were inconclusive. He also told us that the British led by Wellington had driven the French out of Spain with some Portuguese and Spanish help and were about to invade South West France.

Chapter 48
Off to St Petersburg

Towards the end of 1813 we heard that in October Napoleon had been decisively beaten in a huge battle at Leipzig by Russia, Prussia, Austria and Sweden. At last it seemed his days as Emperor were numbered and the Count agreed that we should move to share his St Petersburg residence until a suitable property could be found for Anna and Boye.

The Count, Boye and Anna had come to the conclusion that Boye could start his new life by setting up as a tutor to teach French and Military Science to young Russian Army officers. These young men, all of noble family, looked very pretty in their elaborate uniforms, but had received no proper military training, something the Russian Army had become only too aware of in its conflict with Napoleon. Boye told me it appeared the Russian Army was basically drilled and trained – notoriously harshly – by its NCOs. while the officer corps looked on and was generally ineffective, so he felt he had much to impart.

By this time Anna was clearly pregnant and they were keen to make the move which involved us all in packing up into two coaches and three carts and setting off on the 900 mile journey to St. Petersburg via Moscow. The Count, Anna and Boye were in the front coach with Tatiana and I in the back and with Gregor as lead coachman. Being hyper-jealous he was not keen on leaving her alone in a coach with me and kept on getting her to come and sit by him outside, something I was also able to do at times with Boye. Tatiana and I did however have opportunities to chat and she assured me she was happy with him and thought that given time Anna and Boye would probably agree to the two of them getting married. It looked like a union made in heaven.

We stopped on the way at a series of grand country houses where we were always hospitably received for the Count clearly had considerable prestige. Both Anna and Tatiana were very excited at the thought of seeing Moscow for the first time and for the Count, Boye and me it was impressive to see how far the rebuilding of the city had already gone, no doubt helped by the fact that so many of the buildings were made of wood.

Anna and Tatiana were particularly keen to visit Kazan Cathedral which stands by St Basil's Cathedral on the edge of the Moscow Kremlin. They wished to see and pray for a safe birth for Anna before the much revered and sacred icon of the Virgin called Our Lady of Kazan which the cathedral was built to house. It had originally come from Kazan and was also referred to as the *Theotokos*, birth-giver of God.

The final stage of our journey ended with our arrival in St Petersburg where we found as a high official at the Court the Count had a large and grand apartment in a huge building. It stood by the side of one of the canals that runs through this truly beautiful, classical, European style city. It was, Boye told me, essentially the expression of the formidable will and vision of one man, Tsar Peter the Great. Perhaps appropriately when Anna gave birth soon after our arrival, the boy was named Pietr.

*****

St. Petersburg was built to be the seat of government and the home for the Tsar and his court. He however was not there when we arrived, being with his Army which we heard was advancing on Paris. Soon after the news came through that the Tsar had been enthusiastically welcomed into Paris and that on the 11th of April 1814 Napoleon had abdicated and was being sent to Elba. This meant for Boye and me our time as prisoners was over and I would be able to return to Paris, Mary and the children.

The question then arose how? Boye and I examined maps and saw that the distance by land or by sea is around 1,300 miles. "You have done quite enough walking for Napoleon Alberto." he said, "Anna and I have thought about all this and I am going to pay for your return by sea, that means from here through the Baltic and on to Le Havre and then by coach to Paris. We would like you and Mary to continue living in the ground floor apartment for no rent on the understanding you keep an eye on the house. As you know, I left enough to cover her needs for six months, being twice as long as Napoleon said we would be away, but given our time here in Russia you may find she could have had a tough time this last year making ends meet. To cover that I am giving you an extra sum which I hope will be useful."

"That is generous of you sir," I replied, "Thank you. I just hope her dressmaking may have earned her enough to keep them comfortable."

"In a year or so we may visit Paris." he continued, "Who knows what we will find with Napoleon gone and the Bourbons back. One thing I do know. The Russians, like the British, are very keen on Paris and I think Anna would love to see it. I may also find I have business to attend to there."

That summer marked the end of my 13th year of working for General Jacques Boye. Again the best way we could be relaxed with each other and even have a meal together was for him to arrange a day of deerstalking on a friendly noble's estate followed by a meal at a country tavern, so off the two of us went.

He pointed out to me that he had found he was extremely lucky for through the Count and his family he had immediately become very well connected with the upper echelons of Russian Society including the Court. He had been amazed how many young nobles had signed up for his French and Military Science tutorials and he expected to be kept quite busy, particularly when they moved into their own home which was being prepared in Negin on the edge of the city in Grafskya Street.

I congratulated him on the fact that with the help of Anna he had got so far in his ability to speak and read Russian fluently.

"I have always loved languages Alberto." he replied, "You know how much I enjoyed Shakespeare and English writers when we were in Somerset and Devon and even at Norman Cross, but I just had no idea that Russia had produced such great writers. Anna has introduced me to the works of Pushkin and Gogol and there is a whole new school of Russian poets and novelists producing work which is being published almost daily."

"Have they been writing about this last campaign yet?" I asked.

"Not yet. I am sure they will." he replied, "There is this young relative of the Count, Lev Tolstoy and he is going around talking to veterans of the campaign, both officers and men and the women and families they left behind. He certainly has a book on the war in mind.

"He could call it *War and Peace*. I suggested.

"Perhaps," said Boye. "He actually spent time at the university in Kazan but never completed his degree and lived quite a wild life while he was there. I think he came to our wedding. Anna tells me his writing shows promise. No doubt he will be coming around to talk to us."

"That sounds very interesting. I hope he will not just tell the story from an upper-class point of view. The campaign was such a huge and terrible event. It should never be forgotten." I said.

"I don't think it will be." He replied quietly as we walked along. "In fact I think already it is being seen as a defining moment for Russia, as the time when all Russians stood together. I can tell you from the people I have been meeting, and particularly some of the young officer's I have been teaching, there is a great mood of optimism about the future, a feeling that defeating Napoleon has given the country a new start. Everyone, Tsar, nobility, middle classes and serfs have discovered they share a love for their country, their language and their faith. Many also see there is now a great need for change, and yes for the spread of the sort of liberal values we have stood for, but these must be shown in a Russian, not a French way. Oh yes Alberto, I am feeling really optimistic about this country and hopeful of what the Tsar might do and what I in a small way might do."

It was wonderful to hear him so enthusiastic. I was not so sure he was right however for from what I had heard the Tsar thought liberalism and democracy was good for Europeans, but not for Russians. I then asked him about something we had not really had a chance to discuss.

"Sir, I have often wondered why we had such good luck as you say to end up in the home of such an influential man as the Count and how, against their common practice, the Russians allowed you to keep me with you?

"Well Alberto I did not tell you for I had no idea how things would work out, but you will remember I had an interview with the general in charge in Moscow when I first heard about Kazan."

"Yes, sir. I remember."

"Well, you know how we masons are able to signal our membership to others.

"Of course sir."

"The Brotherhood has been almost as extensive in the Russian officer corps as it is in the French and British armies and as soon as we had recognised each other as masons and when I told him you were a brother mason he suggested placing us in the home of the highest ranking mason in Kazan, the Count."

"So why once you were better did we never go to a Lodge meeting in Kazan?" I asked.

"As you know the Tsar is a very religious and "spiritual" man Alberto, and he came to the conclusion that freemasonry was French, foreign and politically subversive and in this he has I am afraid been backed by the Orthodox hierarchy, so masons now have had to go underground or give up. Going off to lodge meetings in public places has ceased to be possible for us and of course for the Count."

Over the meal we then had together Boye said to me, "Alberto, there are a couple of tasks I would like you to do for me when you get to Paris. The first is obvious. Would you please post on a letter to my father telling him that our house in Paris is there for him and my relatives to use whenever they want to visit Paris and that you and Mary will be in the ground floor apartment keeping an eye on it. The other is a little delicate, but for me worth-while. We have just heard that as from April this year the Bourbon Louis 18 has been appointed King of France by the allies. Yes, the grandson of poor Louis 16, and when you get back I would like you to take a letter to him."

"How interesting sir. Can you tell me more? I asked.

"Well, yes. I do not wish to be in any sense financially dependent on the Count and I think I am entitled to two sources of income, my general's pension and my Legion of Honour pension. I think I have a good chance of King Louis granting them as I received both as a result of fighting against the British in Saint Domingue, not in fighting the allies of the Coalition. I am also going to make him an offer that just might come to something. I shall remind him that I served for years in Saint Domingue and am well known to those in authority in the new Republic of Haiti, in particular Dessalines and Boyer – you remember that young man we rescued from prison? I have been thinking that if Louis sent me out as an emissary I might be able to smooth things out between Haiti and France. Louis, though surrounded by some fanatical royalists, is apparently quite a reasonable man."

I was surprised and amazed, but also impressed. Certainly Haiti and its people deserved to be treated fairly by France and I could think of no-one who would try harder to see that done than Boye.

So ended our last day out together. As well as sharing a good meal it had also been a chance to indulge my tracking and shooting skills to bring down a fine deer for Gregor to butcher.

*****

Two weeks later Boye, Anna, Tatiana and the baby took me down in their coach driven by a liveried Gregor to the St Petersburg Harbour to see me off. This was soon after they had set up house in Grafskya Street. We did not know it, but it was the last time I would see any of them. What I did know was that it was goodbye to Mother Russia.

Chapter 49
Reunited

The Baltic voyage back to France on a merchant ship carrying a cargo of special timber was long, slow and boring. The captain was a Frenchman glad to be back trading with Russia after years of blockade of the Baltic by the Royal Navy. He said the blockade fleet was headed by a battleship called the *Bellerephon*. I could hardly believe it.

My fellow passengers consisted of five returning French officers who all made the unlikely declaration that they had never really supported Napoleon. Being in no mood to discuss my views and experiences with them, I took the opportunity to keep to myself and make notes and list dates of what I had been through.

Arriving at Le Havre I took one of the new public "omnibus" coaches to Paris. Excited and nervous I naturally could not wait to see Mary and the children. I had been away for over two years and Jacques would now be six and Cecillia four and in all that time there had been no way of communicating with Mary. How would she be? How had she managed after Boye's allowance ran out? What pressures, and yes I had to face it, what temptations might she have had to face as a beautiful young woman on her own with small children to support? There was nothing for it but to arrive in the city, take a *fiacre*, walk up the steps and knock on the door.

I waited in suspense while I heard the bolts being drawn back and the door was opened nervously, just a crack on a chain, then a gasp and rattling as she opened it. Mary stood there looking shocked as if she had seen a ghost with a hand over her mouth. Tugging at her skirt was a little girl - Cecillia. She beckoned me inside and threw her arms around me holding me tight while she broke into great choking sobs. "I had all but given up hope of ever seeing you again." she finally said. "It has been so long and the news about. Russia has been so terrible. I have visited your barracks several times for news, but there has been nothing except great lists put up months ago of those "missing in action." Yes, I read your name on one and the name of Boye."

We then turned our attention to the children who were naturally excited and bewildered. Clearly Cecillia hardly remembered me and Jacques was very reserved, but quickly full of questions and keen to show me things. They were both thrilled with the little presents I had brought them, a carved wooden egg-shaped doll with a series of other egg-shaped dolls inside for Cecillia and a model of a troika being pulled by three model horses for Jacques. I had also brought a fine necklace for Mary that Anna had helped me choose in St. Petersburg for I had not a clue when it came to such things.

As this was happening I was able to look at Mary and was shocked to see how thin she was. She also looked strained and exhausted. There was a pile of garments on the table. "Dresses you are making?" I asked.

"I wish they were." she replied. "No. Just needlework and repair jobs" And she quoted the ridiculously small amount she was paid for each garment completed. "It is just about all the work I can get now." She said.

It was not until after putting the children to bed that we were able to have a simple supper and be alone together. Of course there was so much to say and ask that neither of us knew where to start. I think we were also both covering up a fear that we might hear things from each other we did not want to. She went to the wardrobe and took out the black mourning dress she had worn after the news came through of our defeat at Berezina. I fingered it and saw how worn out it looked. "Yes," she said, "I wore nothing else for a year and when I stopped wearing it I had pretty well given up hope."

There was of course no bath in our apartment, a luxury I had become used to in Moscow living the grand life, so she boiled a kettle over the fire and filled a large bowl with hot water. She helped undress me and insisted I stand in front of the fire while she washed me, examining my body all over as if I were a child. "Let me look at you. I just can't believe you have come back to me in one piece Alberto." she said and shook her head. "Yes, and I have to say you look very fit and surprisingly well. You have been so lucky. Whenever I go out I see so many young men who have come back with broken bodies, terrible wounds, burns, scars and often a limb missing. With each one I see I imagine that could be you. Also often they have a wild, distracted look as if driven mad by what they have suffered and seen. Heaven knows what you have done and seen Alberto. I have been watching you with the children all day and you seem – well - to be yourself?"

"Yes Mary." I replied, "Some times have been very tough, but really, I am fine."

She then let me do the same for her. "Oh yes," she said with a sigh as she knelt on a rug before the fire and I washed her back. "Your Mary has become a bit of a scarecrow." and with that she took me to bed, a silent and rather awkward experience.

*****

So conditions and the mood had changed since the balmy days when we first came to Paris and had laid on fashionable dinner parties for Boye, and had gone out together to promenade, have a meal or see a show.

The next day we had a chance to talk when the children settled down to play and she was sitting at the table sewing. "Yes Alberto, at first it was all very good after you left." she said. "I had help with the children and as much work as I could handle. I really enjoyed making fashion gowns for my clients and even thought some of them had become friends. A mistake. Clients do not become friends. Then news started to come through about Russia."

"I suppose the papers said it was a wonderful victory and that the Russians had run off terrified." I suggested.

"Oh yes. At first there were attempts to hide what had happened, that it had all been some sort of victory and that the Army had covered itself in "glory." she said. "It was a very cold winter here too you know, so it was easy to imagine what it was like as bit by bit we learnt of the dreadful losses the Army had actually suffered as you all attempted to retreat from Moscow through all that snow and ice. Then Napoleon appeared here in Paris, but without you or his Army. He was back to raise yet more troops for yet another Army.

Next there was a flood of wounded and returning men. They were everywhere with their terrible stories of privation and defeat. That was when I started to give up hope. I'm sorry," she said, "I just couldn't help myself."

We sat in silence and I said, "And financially, how have you been?"

"At first that was fine." she said, "With an allowance in return for keeping Boye's apartment cleaned and what I was earning from dress-making I was even able to save, but after six months Boye's allowance ran out and you were not back. In the second year you were away I also had far fewer dressmaking orders. Times were getting tough and there was less money about to be spent on fashion, Also I think anti-English sentiment was growing as things were not going too well for the French. Finally in these last months I have had to start accepting seamstress work for a pittance like so many others. That has meant 12 or 14 hour days with the needle."

"And where is that nice girl, your child-care maid?" I asked.

"I had to pay her off four months ago. Just could not afford to keep her. It was awful. She needed the money so badly and the children really liked her, but without well paid dress-making coming in I just did not have enough to pay her and feed us."

"So now how have the children been?" I asked.

"As you can see it is hard for them. Jacques is a very bright boy and I have been able to teach him to read and now he gets lost in Boye's books. Oh yes he takes good care of them. He has often asked, "When is Papa coming home?" but not for months now. As for Cecillia as you can see she lives in the present and in her own fantasy world with her toys. Sometimes if the seamstress work does not come in I have to miss a meal to make sure they are not hungry."

"Have you made any local women friends?" I asked.

"Sadly no," she replied. "I have tried and they are polite, but I have had to wake up to the fact that the French do not mix much socially outside their own families, and hardly at all with foreigners. So with this war dragging on and money getting tight I have been very much on my own. Pretty bloody lonely in fact. Basically though I have to stick to working the needle if there is to be food on the table and the children have had to entertain themselves."

"So all these long hours are the reason you have lost so much weight?" I asked.

"Partly, I suppose Alberto, but I have more to tell you".

"I'm listening," I said, feeling slightly sick.

"It is the husband of one of my clients. He is the young owner of one of the biggest businesses in Le Halle with contracts to sell grain and provisions to the Army. He inherited the business and his wife loves to boast how rich and generous he is."

"So what has been going on with him?" I asked.

"It all started after he came around here to give his judgement on a gown I was making for his wife. She said she wanted him to see her in it and check that he liked it before I attached the trimmings. He was very complementary about the gown and how well it was made and I thought he seemed quite charming and amusing.

Next thing a week later he was knocking at the door asking if I could do some adjustments quickly to one of his waist-coats before he went out to an important dinner. Not feeling happy about it I let him in on his own and did what he asked, not wanting to lose his wife's custom if he complained for she was spending a lot."

"So then what happened?" I asked.

"Of course he turned on the charm, complimenting me on my skills and on the dress I was wearing and made a real meal of getting adjustments to the waistcoat just right while quizzing me about my life and English background. A week later he turned up with a jacket he said needed adjusting. I'd had a long and boring day on my own so I let him in and he was again so witty and easy to talk to. We discussed art and fashion and politics, just like I might with you."

"Charming. So you had a laugh together. And then?" I said.

"He paid me very handsomely for the alteration and left."

"And that was it?" I asked.

"No Alberto. Of course it wasn't. You are making this very difficult for me with your barbed remarks, but I am determined to be honest and tell you what happened. Well, nothing happened for two weeks, then he turned up on my doorstep after the children were in bed and said that his wife had gone to visit her mother in the country and he was on his own and what with me being on my own he had brought with him a hamper with some special charcuterie, a game pie and a good wine. Perhaps he said,

337

we could have a meal together."

"And did you?" I asked. "Invite him in, drink his wine and eat his charcuterie?

"Alberto! Of course I did not. I told him I was waiting for my husband to come home and it was thoughtless and hurtful of him to make such a suggestion without thinking it through and he had to stop turning up at my door alone and that if he did not stop doing it I would have to tell his wife."

"And his response?"

"He said did I not realise he had fallen madly and deeply in love with me and that I should think about that and left."

We sat in silence and she continued. "Of course he was back the next day. He said I shouldn't be so prudish. He said I didn't understand the French way of doing things. He said he did not expect me to be in love with him but if only I was happy to see him so I could get to know him, he would make it well worth my while. He said I should be realistic and face the truth. You must be dead and I had children and a future to think about."

"So that has not been the end of the matter? Have you been seeing him?" I asked.

"No. I have not. I told him to go and leave me alone and I was sure you would come back, but Alberto it has not been easy, particularly since, as you have already seen, I have been getting fewer and fewer clients and have been spending my days on my own with the children sewing for a pittance."

"So if you have not been seeing him, has he been pestering you?" I said.

"Sort of, but in quite a subtle way. About once a week when I open the door in the morning there will be a box or basket of carefully chosen provisions, a fine chicken, eggs, fresh milk, meat.

"Is there a note?" I asked.

"No, nothing, and the contents have been just what the children have needed. I couldn't throw them away, so we have been eating them. He has kept this up once a week for two months now without my seeing him, then a couple of days ago, yes just before you turned up, there was an extra big basket with wine, fine food and a letter from him saying that sadly I must realise you are dead and are never coming back and that he really loves me and if I agreed to see him once a week all my money worries would be over."

"Why does he keep this up? The bastard could easily find someone else if he has money like that?" I said angrily.

"I think he considers himself to be madly in love with me." she said, "Yes. It's dreadful."

"And you Mary, you sound as if you have been just a bit in love with him." I said.

"That's an easy, cheap thing to say Alberto. Can't you recognise that just seeing you and knowing you are alive again has changed everything for me? You have been gone for a very long time when I have had more and more reason to believe that you would never be coming back, but now I know you are alive and here. Now I know you are the only one I love – next to my children of course. Until you came back I was facing what? Along with thousands of others I was just another single woman with two small children, foreign, alone and abandoned in Paris with no family, no money, no prospects and what every day seemed more likely, that I was the widow of a husband who had died in Napoleon's war."

"So what do you want me to do now?" I asked.

"What do you think I was worrying about last night? She said. I think you should go and see him. Let him see you are alive and well and help him realise that he must just let me go and forget me. Last night I thought about little else. Don't get all aggressive and threaten to beat him up, please. I know you are tough and could take him apart, but for what? So you could end up in a French prison for he has a powerful well-connected family. No, just calmly tell him you are home and he should not try to see me again. I think that will bring it all to an end far better."

I said nothing, put on my coat, slammed the front door, caught a *fiacre* to the edge of the Seine and walked along it for hours feeling sick, angry and yes, terribly jealous. The more I thought about it all however, the less I could blame her and the more I thought what she had suggested was right and sensible. I went back and told her I agreed and asked for his address.

That evening I confronted him in the street after I saw him come out of his grand house on his own. He looked very dashing, dressed in the height of fashion with a shiny top hat and a long cloak. I stopped him and politely introduced myself as Mary's husband, He went white. I explained that she had told me just what had happened, making it clear that I was not looking for any sort of fight or to blackmail him and that now I was home we both simply expected him to leave us alone. I think I behaved with exemplary if scary civility and restraint and left it at that. He looked utterly surprised and remained almost speechless.

It worked and he never did turn up again, except that a few days later there was a magnum of the most expensive champagne left with no note on our doorstep. At first I was tempted to smash it or return it, but we put it to a better use.

*****

I was also tempted to tell her about Tatiana and my heroic stand in Kazan, but since Mary had not asked me about any temptations I might have had, and it was always possible that she might have difficulty believing me, I decided it was more sensible to leave it and say nothing.

Having told me and having seen how I had handled it, Mary quickly relaxed, regained her self-confidence, her quick tongue and slowly put on some weight. We soon found we still had lots to laugh about and enjoy. She also became pregnant which made us both very happy.

We never discussed what I would have found if I had turned up a week later, or what she would have done if I had never turned up at all.

This incident made me aware how ever since Kazan and the Tolstoys I had never had to give a thought about where the next meal was coming from and had been living quite an easy life. By contrast her life had become miserable as poverty and loneliness began to bite affecting not only her but the children. She could have seen no end in sight except to cling to the increasingly forlorn hope that I would be back, or to succumb to an offer that would have become increasingly difficult to refuse.

For my part despite looking and feeling physically well the horrors of that Russian campaign were not so easily forgotten and as with Saint Domingue I was plagued with dreams and nightmares of what I had felt, seen and imagined on the road, at Borodino, Smolensk and Berezina. Mary then had to put up with me waking her up with my cries and thrashing around and sometimes with my distant and black moods. This meant for both of us it was a case of getting to know the other on a new level. In fact coming back to Paris became a sort of new start for both of us.

Financially the money Boye had given me gave us a few months breathing space as it was enough for us to eat decently and have the odd family trip out on a *fiacre* and visit some of our former haunts.

Chapter 50
The End of His Empire

Interestingly there was a great fuss going on about the "appropriated" art in the Louvre. The victorious allies wanted it to be returned to Italy. Surprisingly the royalist Bourbon supporters wanted to keep it. More seriously though I had to explore how I might make a living. The options, as in Wincanton, were being involved in clock or watch making and repair, or in working as a barber. In the end I tried both, each for a few months.

The first involved working for long hours in the workshop of a fine master clockmaker who paid assistants like me, however skilled, very badly. The second involved working in the salon of a fine and pretentious hairdresser who did a great carry on with his well-healed clients while I swept the floor. I was then able, as a stylist, to earn good tips, for again the pay was derisory. Neither job however looked like a long-term career.

Getting to know the children and learning how to play and talk to them became easier, more fun and thoroughly rewarding. I found it intriguing to see the way they slipped from English to French and back again and I was very impressed with the way Jacques was reading.

It was as well we were so happy as a family for the Paris of 1814 was a very different place from the self-confident, vibrant Paris we had shared with Boye.

Despite the loss of so many young men in the wars the population had grown. The poor areas in particular were more crowded than anything I had ever seen as the indigent, the wounded, the starving and the young unemployed came to Paris to find what work they could - such as in the new factories that were starting up. At the same time the mood of war wariness was palpable. Everyone was saying that they had been through enough.

The side streets around us were as dirty and odorous as before, and two of the three basic food staples, meat and wine were markedly more expensive. Bread, the third staple, was however good and cheap to buy as a result of strict government regulation. The Revolution had seen food riots and they were determined not to have them again.

Most people just wanted to get on with their lives in peace after all that Napoleon had imposed in two decades of fighting. Into this mix came the supporters of the Bourbons, dispossessed aristocrats and property owners, lusting to take back what they felt was theirs and eager for revenge against the Revolution. The property next door to us was repossessed and the family that lived there thrown out. It was an ugly scene.

Still, there were many around who to a greater or lesser extent supported Napoleon, thought he had done good things for Paris and France, and were proud of the victories of his Army.

Mary told me of the Tsar's visit to Paris in March 1814 after the defeat of Napoleon at Leipzig, an event which she had gone out to witness. "The Tsar looked so handsome, smiled in such a kind and friendly way and said he had come to free the French, not take revenge, but work for reconciliation." she told me. Very touching I thought. I asked about King Louis, the 18th.

"We all knew he has been placed on the throne by the victorious allies," she said "And last year he was still accepted with some enthusiasm for everyone just wanted peace. I have to say though already a lot of people are turning against him. He has such a reactionary bunch of "royalists" around him. All they can think about it seems is their own lost properties and generally turning the clock back and changing back the names of every boulevard and square."

*****

With these thoughts in mind I set out for the king's palace at the Tuileries. The building was looking a bit shabby and I was of course stopped by a guard at the gate. When I explained why I had come I was allowed in and saw an official who accepted Boye's letter and assured me it would sooner or later be seen by the king. More than that I could not do. Post at that time was obviously erratic and slow, particularly to and from Russia, so I guessed it could be a long time before Boye received any reply.

Mary and I enjoyed visiting the cafes that had sprung up in great numbers, where one could drink coffee, read the papers and chat to those around. Some even welcomed the children. There I learnt that while King Louis accepted many of Napoleon's administrative and legal changes, he also claimed to be running a "constitutional monarchy", but this was no democracy. Power was centralised. He could pass laws as he liked and the vote for the advisory assemblies was restricted to nobility and the very wealthy.

This ruling "elite" and it seemed the king also, ignored the fact that for many, particularly those in the Army, Napoleon remained very popular. Each month new decrees were announced and Louis abolished the tricolour, brought back the old royal white flag, introduced celebrations of the Old Regime and backed the Catholic Church with a new and intolerant zeal, all at a time when more and more people were feeling the pinch and had given up church long ago. As a result by mid-February 1815 Louis and the royalists were beginning to look increasingly insecure.

This it appears was not lost on Napoleon in exile on the island of Elba (where it was reported he was being financially supported by Pauline - alone among his family members ready to still back him with cash) and he saw an opportunity for a comeback.

*****

In March 1815 we heard Napoleon had escaped from Elba and had no difficulty getting members of the Army to change sides, ignore King Louis and come over and back him. In fact Mary and I saw him come marching in triumph through Paris to take up his place in the Tuileries as King Louis was forced to flee for Ghent. I noted how fat he had become compared to the dashing young general of Nice and Alexandria.

During the next few months I was careful not to draw attention to myself in public or to my Army background. I had not reported my return to the Army for I had no intention of getting called up to go off to fight for Napoleon again even if this meant loosing back pay. At this time the atmosphere in the bars, cafes and bistros became more and more frenetic and hysterical as his supporters did all they could to recruit yet another army. This time Napoleon had stirred up a real hornets nest. The main powers, again Britain, Prussia, Austria and Russia, thought in putting him on Elba they had dealt with him decently and decisively. They thought they had removed him as a threat to Europe for ever, only to discover he was again determined to take over France and then who knew what?

In May we saw his Army marching off from Paris to face Wellington and the Prussian Blucher and on the 18th of June 1815 his last terrible battle took place at Waterloo. It was apparently a close run thing, but the end was decisive when after a steely defence led by Wellington and crucially supported by Blucher, the British routed Napoleon's Old Guard in a final charge after a day of mayhem. The carnage on both sides was devastating.

In Paris we waited to hear the result. First Napoleon came rushing back, to abdicate three days later, then the wounded and stragglers filled the streets and the crushing nature of his defeat became clear. Wellington and Blucher then marched in with King Louis who they placed on his throne again. The remnants of the French Army withdrew from Paris and an Army of Occupation took over. The British troops were camped in the Champs-Élysées where they behaved extremely well after Wellington, unlike Blucher, advertised and carried out the immediate flogging of the few of his men who were involved in pillage, theft or rape.

I walked down and chatted to the English and Scottish troops and found them exhausted, proud and feeling lucky to be alive. For many of them I heard Waterloo was their first experience of battle for Wellington's seasoned troops, who had fought and won with him in Spain, had been sent off to fight against the United States. Wellington was then in charge of Paris for some time.

Next we heard that Napoleon had tried to make a run for it to the US, but was caught by the Royal Navy blockade and so surrendered to Captain Maitland of the leading ship of the line which was, yet again, the *Bellerephon*.

Unbelievably I thought, when later I read it, Napoleon then asked if he could retire as "a country gentleman" and live out his days in England. This was turned down by the British Cabinet and he was sent off to St Helena to write his memoirs in July without having placed a foot on English soil. Blucher let it be known if he had been given his way he would have had Napoleon shot immediately.

*****

In August Mary gave birth to little Albert. The birth was straightforward enough and there was a kind midwife in attendance, but Mary was very weak for the first month. We could just afford the part-time support of her former maid which we needed for taking care of two small children and a baby is quite demanding as I rapidly discovered. It was something I had never really thought about.

On making enquiries about getting a birth certificate I came up against French bureaucracy and Catholic practice. I discovered that our marriage, as the vicar in Wincanton had pointed out years before, was not recognised in France, so Mary was considered an unmarried mother. Birth certificates for unmarried mothers were only issued to the children of "repentant" Catholics who had been to confession. When I told Mary this she was angrier than I had ever seen her and she declared that she had now had enough of the French and their Church and she wanted to go home to England.

"Let's go back to Wincanton where that kind vicar Mr. Radford who married us will baptise little Albert properly and give him a Baptism Certificate. I know my brother John and dear Jane will help us to get started." she said.

Quite suddenly that all made sense to me. Under the Bourbons France seemed to be more repressive and unstable and I was in no mood to see our family go through another revolution with violence in the streets for the Bourbons were clearly not popular. In comparison England looked rich, powerful, more stable and even more democratic than France. They had evolution, not revolution.

I also agreed with Mary that it would be a much happier place for our children to grow up in for they would soon feel they belonged in England while in France they would always be foreigners.

We found we had just enough money to pay for a coach to Calais, a channel ferry and a stage-coach back to Wincanton. I wrote to Boye and his family explaining our decision and thanking him again for the money which had tied us over and which made our decision to return to England possible.

So it was we got back to Wincanton in late 1815 where we

moved into a small thatched cottage in South Street. There I first set up as a barber also ready to pull teeth. I was 38, Mary 30 and on 30th June 1816 Albert Henry was baptised in Wincanton Parish Church. We had well and truly survived Napoleon.

Chapter 51
Cecillia Speaks

So by the end of 1815 the five of us had arrived in Wincanton. I was six years old, just old enough to know we were very short of money, pretty well penniless. Still the trip remains one of my earliest happy memories. I found it all strange and exciting, but I can now see feeding and looking after a baby with two other young children on a rough Channel crossing and in bumpy carriages on rough roads was not easy for my mother. Papa did what he could to keep us entertained, wiped up after us when we were sick, told us jokes and stories, and pointed interesting things out to us. He was very good at that.

Starting from scratch with almost nothing was quite a challenge for them, though we children hardly noticed. It all seemed fun. My uncle and aunt, John and Jane Feltham, faced with us arriving unannounced and out of the blue, squeezed us into their home and did all they could to help us settle when we arrived. They later told me they had never expected to see us again.

Almost three years earlier in 1812 all the French prisoners from Wincanton had suddenly been deported back to France without warning. This was after George Messiter had told the Transport Board he feared they were increasingly breaking parole and with so many across the country the government feared a widespread revolt so they were simply shipped back to France. This meant however that when we arrived there were still quite a few properties available at a low rent or for sale in the town and so we were able to move into a cottage in South Street quite quickly.

Being a market town meant market day brought in many men who needed a shave, a haircut or a tooth pulled, so Papa, quickly known as "the Italian Barber" attracted enough custom to keep us all fed, even if what he really wanted to do was get established as a clock, barometer maker and watch repairer.

We may have had little but it was good for us all to find ourselves in a little town that was friendly and welcoming. The Vicar, the Rev. Mr. Radford who had married Mother and Papa, the Church which we all attended, William Doney and the local clockmakers, his masonic lodge and of course my Uncle John and Aunt Jane were all glad to see us and I remember soon feeling at home as I never had in Paris.

The Duchemins my mother had hoped to see had gone to Birmingham, but Papa and my mother made a point of visiting Mr Messiter and telling him about their lives from the time they left Wincanton as a newly married couple, thanks to his decision to speed up their marriage and send them on to live in Crediton in 1807.

Both our parents were keen that we went to school and learnt to read, write and do Arithmetic. The National School in North Street was not yet open and there were no free schools then, but several small fee paying schools and we were duly sent off to them, one for boys, one for girls. Mine was run by a rather fierce lady who hammered precise copybook handwriting, spelling, reading aloud, grammar and our times tables into us, often with the liberal use of the ruler across our palms. Somehow the money for school fees was found. Despite the ruler I enjoyed school for it was the one thing I did which was just for me and was a real break from helping my mother with the children, cooking and housework for it was some time before we could afford any hired help.

It also opened the world of books to me and I became an avid reader of anything I could lay my hands on when we joined the subscription library. Jacques showed himself cleverer than me and was soon top of his class at the boys' school. That was something I have to say I envied.

In 1816 my little brother Charles Henry was born and in April 1817 Joseph Theodore. This put our numbers up to five children, Jacques, me Cecillia, Albert, Charles Henry, and Joseph Theodore. Three pregnancies in a row must have been very tough for my mother, though not exceptional. As things turned out I was also to have five. We were however, all healthy and thriving.

For Jacques and I memories of France soon seemed remote and for those around us it seemed the time when there had been hundreds of French prisoners on parole in the town was quickly set aside or forgotten, except that without them the town was poorer. There were a couple of other former prisoners in the town who had come back after the war as we had. One was Mr Gosue Soldini. Short and stout he was like Papa a trained clockmaker. Unlike Papa he was an ardent Roman Catholic. He was unmarried, never really settled and finally returned to Italy.

Into this atmosphere of general disinterest in "foreign politics" or in anything that did not immediately effect life in Somerset, the occasional letter arrived for Papa from Russia. It was from General Boye. Papa always spoke of him as his hero and with great affection. He was always thrilled to receive such letters and he wrote back immediately, even though sending a letter to Russia was expensive. Years later, after he had shown me all his notes and the account he had written of his life, he told me what was in those letters and carefully explained to me just what they meant. Sadly the actual letters were destroyed by mistake. Here though, as well as I can remember, is what he told me.

General Boye, had as a result of the letter my father had delivered successfully in Paris, received his pensions from the Bourbon French King Louis XVIII and in 1822 he was asked by him to visit Haiti on behalf of the French Government. By this time General Boye had done very well for himself in Russia and was being used by Tsar Alexander as an advisor on foreign policy.

General Boye's old friend Jean Pierre Boyer who my father had once met, dressed and fed when the general had freed him from prison, had become President of Haiti in 1818. He now wanted to normalise relations with France and get France to acknowledge Haiti as an independent republic. King Louis' supporters however wanted "compensation" for the slave owners for the "property", that is slaves and land, that they had lost. This meant when General Boye went to Haiti to negotiate, he found that the division between France and Haiti was so deep that no agreement could be made.

President Jean Pierre Boyer however, knowing and trusting General Boye, asked him while he was there, to negotiate on *his* behalf and try and establish a separate trade treaty and diplomatic recognition between Russia and Haiti. Unfortunately the Head of Russia's Ministry of Foreign Affairs said on his return, Russia should not upset France by recognising Haiti which the USA,

Spain, Britain and France would not recognise either. When I asked my father why they were all so against Haiti, Papa said Boye had explained that this was because they were all still slave owning states and were not prepared to accept a republic formed by rebel slaves in case it encouraged their own slaves to revolt. Instead they all banned trade with Haiti.

That, General Boye went on, was not the end of this sad story. King Louis died to be replaced by his brother Charles 10, an extreme and vengeful reactionary. In 1825 he sent a French fleet out to Haiti to force President Boyer to accept, in return for recognition of its independence, a £150 million franc indemnity or risk a total blockade. President Boyer had no choice but to accept, so consigning Haiti to a crippling debt it could never pay off.

General Boye said, when he heard about this despicable act of the French Government, that it was the end of any allegiance he felt for France. He said that when he had visited Haiti for King Louis he had seen how pitifully poor the country was and he could see the debt France had imposed would devastate the country completely. He now had taken out Russian citizenship and changed his name to Yakov (Jacques) Petrovich (son of Pierre) Boyko (Close to Boye).

He also said that Pietr had been joined by a daughter, Eugenia and another son, Yakov and that Anna was well and sent best wishes.

He also added that he had heard that General Rochambeau had left his maps and chateaux to fight for France in 1813 at the Battle of the Nations, had been mortally wounded and had died three days later at Leipzig at the age of 58. Incredibly his name was then inscribed on the Arc de Triomphe in Paris. How he would have loved that.

Papa's reaction to General Boye's letters was to be amazed and impressed that he had been able to put the case for Haiti's recognition to the Tsar when he had gone out as representative of France, and to hear that Jean Pierre Boyer had ended up president of Haiti. As regards the subsequent behaviour of King Charles X of France and his party, Papa felt vindicated in his decision to get us all out of France before such a reactionary group had got into power.

Turning again to our family story in 1829 Felix was born after a long and painful birth for my mother. He was never well and neither was my mother after that. She died in 1834 when I was 24. She was only 48. Poor Felix died a year later. He was six years old.

Of course my time from childhood was very much taken up with looking after my brothers and helping my mother run the home while Papa cut hair and pulled teeth. It was certainly not an easy life having a handicapped brother and a much weakened mother. This made those last years of Mother's life pretty tough for all of us and though Papa was kind and loving, he often retreated to his workshop where he could immerse himself in the world of clocks and I guess write up his notes - though he never mentioned that.

There were also times when it was difficult to get the boys to help with what they described as "women's work." Papa pointed out that in the French Army there had been no such thing, "There you cook, clean, wash and polish your own clothes and take care of each other. If you don't the Army would fall apart. It's the same for us as a family." Still Mother and Papa thought this was a good time for them to employ a young friend of Mother's, Martha Ewens, to work full time for us as housekeeper.

The result was we all got on pretty well together. Papa had a quick wit and a cheerful personality and I think he felt having already had such an extraordinary life in "the service of Napoleon," he could face anything.

He was also extremely good at working as a barber. A quick look as they came in and he could judge exactly what the right cut would be to suit a farmer, a labourer or a lawyer and know just what to say to them. He remembered the names of all his customers and they obviously enjoyed talking to him, so there was not much going on in the town he did not know about.

His hairdressing parlour was always immaculate with two high leather-backed barber chairs and comfortable seating for those who were waiting. His barber-shop was of course one of the few places in the town where men of different social classes and occupations rubbed shoulders and could be seen smoking and gossiping.

By acting as assistants, sweeping up hair from the floor and bringing in bowls of hot water and fresh towels, sharpening the cut-throat razors and watching their father, three of my brothers grew up to be well-trained barbers and hairdressers. Papa emphasised that it was a trade where you could make a fair living if you were self-confident, skilled and enjoyed working with people. You could also be your own boss. After his time in the French Army he never again wanted to be anything else.

Freedom for him meant being fully in charge of your own life, looking after your family and running your own business and that was something he did very well, so when his sons were ready and old enough he encouraged them to leave home with their skills to explore opportunities in new places.

Jacques preferred to be known as James and he set off for the expanding port of Liverpool where he successfully set up a large "salon" of his own. His brother Joseph Theodore went off to Brighton where high society and royalty spent part of the year. There he also trained as a specialist women's hairdresser and earned Queen Victoria's Royal Warrant for doing her hair and that of her ladies. The third was poor Albert. He set up in Mere a few miles away from Wincanton but was dogged by ill health. He died young at 35.

None of them showed any interest in becoming clockmakers or watch repairers which was a bit of a disappointment to Papa though he never said so.

Both Papa and I mourned the death of my mother Mary deeply. Mama and he were very close and she was always my closest friend. She often talked to me about our life in Paris and what a beautiful and exciting city it was and made sure that Papa and I continued to speak French to each other. She was very proud of the work she had done as a dressmaker in Wincanton, Crediton and Paris. With so many children however, it was not something she could continue doing. Papa felt sad about that.

At the time it came as a surprise, but later I recognised I should have seen it coming, my father being the man he was. Two years after Mama died he married Martha Ewens in 1836. At 33 she was closer to me in age than my mother and already a friend. Papa of course was 58 but looked and behaved like someone much younger. He seemed to have the secret of eternal youth.

Already used to her being around the children took to Martha as stepmother, something that does not always work out, but which in our case did. We were a big family and growing up we rather enjoyed that. John and Jane Feltham also liked Martha and were the witnesses to her wedding to Papa in Wincanton Parish Church.

I had been seeing Sydney Hayward for some time so now I felt free to marry. We than continued to live in Wincanton for several years before moving to Portsea with our growing family.

When he married Martha Papa was able to afford buying 31 High Street and with his boys doing much of the hairdressing, he was able to get fully established as a clock and barometer maker and watch repairer. Clock making was the craft he had loved most all his life as he told me and which never ceased to fascinate him.

Selling a clock movement was also much more profitable than hairdressing and he regularly sold the mechanical movements he had made to top clockmaker's in London who then put their names on them and sold them at premium prices, a practice widely used in the trade. He also sold several clocks and barometers under his own name as did the other clockmakers in the town.

I will never forget one in particular which he proudly showed me and explained was his masterpiece. With its handsome face and beautiful wooden case it stood over six foot high. It told one the year, the month, the day of the week, the hour, the minute and the second and behind that face ticked the most complex movement he had ever built.

It was at this time, before we moved, that Papa showed me the sheets of notes and dates he had been accumulating ever since his time at Norman Cross. I think it went with his clock making that time itself fascinated him as did history. He was always an avid reader and had the most remarkable memory for facts, dates and figures of anyone I have ever met. It left us all amazed.

His notes, dates and jottings covered his whole life from Turin to us leaving Paris. He was determined to write them up and did so originally in French, but he got me to translate what he wrote into what he called "ordinary English" which he then checked and corrected to his liking. He did this for only the two eldest of us had any French and he said he wanted the others to know his story.

"I can see sons are far too interested trying to make something of their own lives to be much interested in mine before I settled here in Wincanton." he said, "But one day when they get old they might be, and perhaps some of your children will be curious about their Italian ancestor."

If you wonder if he talked much about his life as we were

growing up, the answer is no. While my mother happily talked about Paris he said nothing about his amazing military career except for two incidents that every now and then he repeated, saying he just could not forget them. These were being fired on by the *Bellerephon* and lying in freezing circles around a fire in Russia. As for all the other things he saw and experienced, I only learnt about them when he showed me his manuscript and we discussed them together and once we had completed the work of translation he never wanted to talk about them again. He said he still dreamt about and remembered them all and I am sure they were just too painful.

Business was good enough for them to move to 71 High Street, a larger, better house with a fair sized strip of land behind. 31 High St was kept as his barber shop and workshop for he continued to do both, and Martha gave birth to three sons, Edwin Charles, Louis Alberto and Alvin George. In 1858 Martha died at 55 by which time Papa was 80. By then Sidney and I had moved to Portsea where he ran his own business. We liked it and both Martha's sons Edwin Charles and Alvin George joined us there with families of their own.

In 1861 the Somerset and Dorset Railway opened in Wincanton and I suggested to Papa that at 83 he might retire and come and live with us in Portsea. That he did despite being remarkably fit and well and as sharp as ever. He sold his properties and left Wincanton by train after 45 years. He remained healthy, active and much loved until he died quite suddenly on the 14th of March 1869 aged 91. We could not have been prouder of him.

Note and Sources

I have written Alberto's story as an historical novel in the first person because this seems to me the best way to bring his voice and experiences to life. Starting with Phil Stevens' carefully researched paper which gives an outline of the key events and dates I explored as many of the historical studies that relate to him and the Napoleonic era as I could find. Putting these together it became clear to me just what an incredible survivor Alberto Bioletti was. More than that, what emerges is an amazing story about a remarkable and admirable man.

I believe that Alberto has been underestimated. because from the time of his arrival in England his military role of ordonnance was translated as servant so he could remain with his general and not be sent off to the hulks and because when he settled penniless in Wincanton he needed to start work as a barber when actually he was a highly skilled clockmaker. The "servant" label I think has demeaned him when in fact to be recruited for the role of ordonnance while on active war-time service demanded considerable personal qualities and military skills, making him more a trusted personal assistant than a valet. My reading is that he proved himself to be a brave and resourceful soldier, intelligent, mentally and physically strong, adaptable, skilful, loyal and as an ordonnance completely dedicated to supporting his general.

In writing all this in the form of an historical novel I have inevitably filled in the gaps with plausible fiction based on my research and where I have done this I draw your attention to it here. I do this well aware that his life, his character and the course of events he experienced could all have been interpreted differently.

Alberto Bioletti's life fits into six phases.

1. Growing up in Italy, joining the French Revolutionary Army and fighting in Napoleon's First Italian Campaign.
2. The Egyptian and Syrian Campaign.
3. The Haiti /Saint Domingue campaign
4. Parole Prisoner in England.
5. Paris and the Russian Campaign.
6. Return and Life in England

1. Turin, his Italian Background and the Italian Campaign

Based on discussions with her grandfather, Constance Linacre (a Bioletti family member) in her 1982 "History" reports that the Bioletti family were Waldensians from Pinerolo who settled in Turin. The Waldensians were a religious community whose thinking and practice aimed at Church reform and prefigured the Protestant Reformation by more than a century. As directed by the Papacy they were brutally suppressed and massacred by Victor Amadeus 1, Duke of Savoy

Since the family moved to Turin we can assume that Alberto's parents would have had to practice their religion (which involved studying the bible in a French vernacular translation) either secretly or very discreetly and that he was not brought up a Catholic in a piously Catholic city – keeper of The Shroud.

Since after his military career Bioldetti proved to be an accomplished clockmaker and barometer maker – the most technologically sophisticated occupation of his day - it seems reasonable to suppose that his father was a clockmaker and that he was apprenticed and trained to be one. It is also possible that he acquired the mathematical and general education this career needed as a student at the school the Duke Victor Emmanuel set up, the Collegio delle Province. Here 100 boys "of low social extraction" were provided with a free education

Clock-makers being such skilled craftsmen, we now know saw themselves as under-rewarded and under-valued. This means they were naturally susceptible to adopting the ideas of the French Revolution. What was happening in nearby France was closely watched in Turin and inspired many locals with revolutionary zeal.

Bioletti Joined the French Army of Italy when he was aged 18 in 1796. "for two years of fierce fighting." He never returned to

Turin so the novel assumes the death of his parents and alienation from his relatives because he allied himself with and joined the French Revolutionary Army. It assumes he is sent to Nice to train under Napoleon and becomes a skirmisher. (A scout and sharp-shooter later called voltiguers) and describes in fictional terms what could have been his experience.

With the Army of Italy, Bioletti was sent to Toulon Navy base in 1797, to prepare for a campaign in the "Orient."

2. 1798: The Egyptian Campaign
We know Alberto then went on to Egypt. We have no details about where he went or what he did. To survive was quite an achievement as few did. Since he later became an ordonnance to General Jacques Boye'. I think after his service in Italy and the bias against promoting Italians he was well placed to be chosen to be an ordonnance to a general in Egypt. This would have increased his chances of survival and would have given him a greater understanding of the whole campaign. That he did so is however just a plausible guess. In my novel I place him with General Kleber, Napoleon's highly critical second in command.

3. The Haiti/Saint Domingue Campaign
Three confusing names, all tied in with each other and Bioletti need to be explained.

1. *Pierre Francois Joseph Boyer: 1772-1851.*
Boyer served as Brigade General and first Adjutant General (chief administrative officer) under Leclerc. Like Bioletti he fought in Italy and in Egypt and he was adjutant general to General Kleber. After Kleber's assassination he was accused of corruption and sent to France for Court Martial, but was vindicated before being appointed to be Adjutant General with Leclerc in 1801. He left Saint Domingue to report to Napoleon on the death of Leclerc. .

2. *Jacques Boye': 1766-1838*
From 1791 Boye' served in Saint Domingue with Commissioner Sonthonax and Governor General Louverture. He successfully defeated the British attempt to invade the island and supported giving freedom to the slaves. He chose Bioletti to be his ordonnance . He was not a part of Leclerc's invasion party but on the death

of Leclerc and the departure of PFJ Boyer, he had to take over his post to become adjutant general to General Rochambeau. He freed Jean-Pierre Boyer from imprisonment and signed the French surrender to Captain John Loring on the Bellerephon. He was held prisoner on parole in England with Bioletti and Rochambeau. In 1811 he returned to France with Bioletti and his family to fight in the Russian campaign where he was taken prisoner with Bioletti at Berezina. They walked 900 miles to Kazan. He married Anna Tolstoy, and later in St Petersburg he represented J.P. Boyer to Tsar Alexander. He became a Russian citizen changing his name to Yakov Yakovitch Boyko.

3. Jean-Pierre Boyer: 1776-1850

A French educated 'mulatto' and the friend and 'cousin' of Jacques Boye', he rose to become President of Haiti 1818-1843 and asked Boye' to represent him to get Haiti recognised by Russia.

In Haiti we know Alberto was captured as the ordonnance of General Jacque Boye' and that he experienced being attacked, sunk and saved by the Bellerephon. Nothing is said in his accounts about what this campaign must have meant and about the war on the island. Given its appalling nature that is not surprising.

Truth here is stranger than fiction and it took some disentangling and research to separate Jacques Boye' from Pierre Francois Joseph Boyer for they were similar in name and rank – but very different in experience and character. In the novel I have Boye' recruiting Bioletti in France. It may have been in Saint Domingue, but having them share the voyage provides a good opportunity to explain the complex local politics to Alberto. The slave ship described and its captain is genuine.

During his time on the island while assisting General Boye', Bioletti would have been around Rochambeau, P.F.J. Boyer, Courpon, Boye's friend the mulatto J.P. Boyer, Leclerc and his wife Pauline, and probably the "rebel" generals Christophe and Louverture. What he saw and heard at this time must have been horrific in the extreme. This is all explored in the novel. While the story is fiction, all the details and events described are not.

4. Eight and a half years as a parole prisoner in England.

This is all relatively well documented. It seems to me likely Boye' must have loathed Rochambeau, as they were political opposites, but there is no absolute proof of this. Courpon's romance with Doney's daughter is fiction as is her part in the actual event with gunpowder in Wincanton.

5. Paris and the Russian Campaign

The novel assumes that as was usual, Bioletti remained ordonnance to General Boye' throughout his time in Paris and Russia after their amicable life together in Crediton. It assumes Mary and the children remained in Boye's home in Paris. It assumes Boye' and Bioletti are captured together at Berezina and are marched 900 miles together to Kazan, not Siberia, and it assumes that Bioletti does not escape on his own to walk back to Paris from Siberia as James Albert Bioletti 1914 and Constance Linacre 1982 suggest, a walk of over 3,000 miles through hostile territory by a penniless soldier on his own. Instead the novel has a more plausible story, that he stays with Boye' in Kazan and, goes with him to St Petersburg and finally sails back to Paris.

The Tolstoy and Anna who saved Boye' in Kazan could not have been Leo, author of War and Peace as that was only published in 1869, but an older relative. Again if they took on Boye' they would surely have taken on Alberto as well. Both Boye' and Alberto could however have been interviewed by Leo when he was making notes for War and Peace for he did interview veterans. It is possible that on capture Alberto and Boye' were separated but I think it more likely they stayed together, supporting each other as the novel assumes.

Constance Linacre reports that Alberto always referred to Boye' as his hero – impressive for a 13 year working relationship.

6. Return to Wincanton

There is no doubt that he got back to Mary and the children in Paris, had another baby and after more than a year returned to England and Wincanton where he lived for 45years having six children by Mary and after her death another three with Martha Ewings and he worked as a barber, clockmaker, watchmaker and barometer maker. He died at 91 in Portsea staying with Cecillia who had married and had five children.

The novel has the final chapter as if written by Cecillia. This was how she spelled her name as a child of seven in a sampler now owned by Phil Stevens. A single photo of her exists taken as a young woman in an elaborate narrow-waisted long-sleeved dress holding a book – proof she was literate. All the details about Alberto's children and second marriage are taken from Phil Stevens. Constance Linacre thinks Cecillia never married but the Ancestry site says she married Sydney Hayward and lists her as having five children.

Letters mentioned in the novel as sent by Boye' to Bioletti in Wincanton are my creation. He probably never heard what Boye' did to try and help Haiti and of his visit to President Jean-Pierre Boyer in 1820. He may though have read in the press about the French blockade of Haiti in 1825. Again he would not have known about the death of Rochambeau in battle at Leipzig in 1813.

Sources

Phil Stevens. *The Life and Times of Alberto Bioletti 1999.* The document that set me off to research Alberto was Phil Stevens' paper. The result of visits to Wincanton, contacting relatives of Alberto together with work on his descendants.

James Albert Bioletti to Fred Bioletti, Berkley, University of California. A letter sent in 1914 and passed to me by Phil Stevens. This type-written letter is the work of James Albert, Alberto's grandson. This consists of 4 pages of text and a page of dates which Alberto left. Phil also has Cecillia's sampler, embroidered when she was 7 with her spelling of her name, a copy of which he shared with me.

Charles James and Susi Bioletti. For clocks and clockmakers Charles James, of Ottery Antiques, gave me names, dates and details about the group of clock and barometer makers in Wincanton – a surprisingly large number. He also alerted Susi Bioletti who he knew had one of Alberto's clocks.

Andrew Forster of the Clock Shop, Castle Cary, showed me Bioletti's name in a register of clock makers and showed me a Wincaunton (note spelling) clock.

Susie Bioletti, the proud owner of one of the clocks Alberto made, and who lives in Dublin, sent me a photo of Alberto's clock. She also shared a photo showing her visiting Turin to meet contemporary Biolettis.

Constance Linacre. *A History of My Great-Great-Grandfather, Alberto Bioletti* (1982). Sent to me by Susie Bioletti. Constance was a Bioletti who was at some stage interviewed by Radio 4 about Alberto.

George Sweetman. *The History of Wincanton, Somerset, from Earliest Times to the Year 1903* and his booklet *The French in Wincanton* (1904). These describe Alberto Bioletti as the servant of General Boye and also acknowledge that he was a clockmaker. Sweetman recognises the comparatively high status and surprising number of clockmakers in Wincanton including William Doney by devoting two chapters of his book to them.

Clive L Lloyd. *A History of Napoleonic and American Prisoners of War 1756-1816,* Antique Collectors Club (2007).

Philip Dwyer. *The Path to Power* (2007) and *Citizen Emperor* (2013).

Andrew Roberts. *Napoleon the Great,* Allen Lane, 2014.

Jenny Uglow. *Living in Britain Through Napoleon's Wars: In These Times,* Faber and Faber 2014.

Roy Adkins. *Trafalgar,* Abacus, 2004.

C.L.R. James. *The Black Jacobins*, Penguin, 1983.

Philippe R. Girard. *The Slaves Who Defeated Napoleon*, University of Alabama Press, 2011.

Paul Strathern. *Napoleon in Egypt,* Vintage, 2008.

Adam Zamoyski. *1812 Napoleon's Fatal March on Moscow'*, Harper Perennial, 2005.

Flora Fraser. V*enus of Empire - The life of Pauline Bonaparte,* John Murray, 2009.

L.M.Bray. *The Duchemin Family History,* Lantern Tower, 2009. Louis Duchemin was a French prisoner in Wincanton who married Elizabeth Clewett. This also reports the Rochambeau incident in Wincanton.

Articles

Haiti, Saint Domingue

Kona Shen. Brown University Dec 9 2008.

Philippe R. Girard. War Unleashed: The Use of War Dogs During the Haitian War of Independence. Napoleonica. La Revue 2012/3. A careful analysis of Rochambeau's use of dogs in executions, he blames Leclerc for ordering their purchase and initiating mass killings.

Prof Jeremy Popkin, The Haitian Revolution 1791 – 1804, University of Kentucky.

Anthony Phillips. Haiti, France and the Independence Debt of 1825.

Russia and the Fall of Napoleon

Alexander Mikaberidze. Napoleon's Lost Legions. The Grande Armee Prisoners of War in Russia.
Reports the surprisingly good treatment of French POW's.

Beryl Williams. Reader in History at Sussex U. Serfdom in Early Nineteenth Century Russia.

Lightning Source UK Ltd.
Milton Keynes UK
UKHW020951260919
350504UK00009B/304/P

9 780956 065551